ACETYLENIC COMPOUNDS

Preparation and Substitution Reactions

THOMAS F. RUTLEDGE
Chemical Research Department
Atlas Chemical Industries, Inc.
Wilmington, Delaware

REINHOLD BOOK CORPORATION
A subsidiary of Chapman–Reinhold, Inc.

NEW YORK   AMSTERDAM   LONDON

PREFACE

When the editors of the Reinhold Book Corporation first invited me to compose two books on the recent chemistry of acetylenic compounds, I agreed only that such books would be timely. The most modern book is R. A. Raphael's "Acetylenic Compounds in Organic Synthesis," published in 1955. The chemistry of acetylenic compounds has received so much attention during the last ten to fifteen years that I hesitated to tackle the task of assembling, organizing, and presenting even a part of the results. The timeliness argument finally prevailed. This book is the first of two. In this first book, the preparation, substitution reactions, and some uses of acetylenic compounds are discussed. In the second book, to be published shortly, preparation of allenic compounds and the addition reactions involving acetylenic and allenic bonds are covered.

Comprehensive coverage of the recent progress in acetylene chemistry is obviously impossible in two books of reasonable size. I have not attempted to assemble all the data and list all of the reactions and properties of acetylenes. My approach finally evolved into an effort to include enough details of the most important reactions of all kinds of acetylenic compounds to furnish interested chemists with a good background and with leads into the pertinent literature. In order to cover the maximum number of facts in the least number of words, I adopted a form of "informative writing" which is certainly not fascinating prose. I feel that this is a reasonable sacrifice.

Where possible, the subject matter is organized by kind of reaction. Mechanisms are emphasized because they furnish ideas for new reactions. Long chapters are divided into smaller parts, and literature references are listed at the end of each part in the order in which they appear in the text. This minimizes the annoyance of thumbing through page after page of references.

My employer, Atlas Chemical Industries, Inc., permitted me to write this book as a private venture. I am grateful for this cooperation. My boss, Dr. J. W. LeMaistre, read the text and made many appropriate suggestions, for which I am also grateful. Miss Alma Seekford's expert typing was a great help. My sons, Mark and Tom, and daughter Lee Anna, helped me with filing and some of the line drawings, and did an excellent job. Most authors conclude their prefaces by acknowledging the understanding of their families, and particularly of their wives. I now understand why they do this. I am very happy to dedicate this book to Betty Rutledge, my wife.

April 1968   THOMAS F. RUTLEDGE

INTRODUCTION

Where is the chemistry of acetylenic compounds going? What are the most important recent developments? Do these developments point the way to significant future areas for research and exploitation? The answers to these questions depend on one's point of view.

From a detached viewpoint, several facts are apparent. The only reactions of acetylene which have achieved important commercial stature are those involving highly efficient, low-pressure catalytic processes. Apparently the only pressure reactions now practiced commercially are the ethynylation of formaldehyde to form butynediol and propargyl alcohol, and the vinylation of alcohols to form vinyl ethers. Thus it can be said that research concerned with large-scale industrial reactions of acetylenes should emphasize catalytic processes under mild conditions. This compounds the research difficulties but offers a better chance of economic success. Commercial development of acetylenic chemicals has been hampered by the high cost of most acetylenic compounds. Only acetylene itself can be classified as a low-cost acetylenic reagent. New catalytic ethynylation, addition, and substitution systems will be necessary if this disadvantage is to be overcome. Some progress has already been made. Without the new systems and processes, the major utility of acetylenic compounds will be as specialty chemicals, as monomers for certain polymers, and as drugs.

From a technical point of view, progress is fast and exciting. As in other areas, progress in acetylene chemistry has been accelerated by the adoption of instrumental methods of analysis, especially GLC, infrared and ultraviolet spectroscopy and, more recently, NMR.

A few of the most significant developments in the synthesis and substitution reactions of acetylenic compounds illustrate the scope of the research now being carried on:

• Lithium metal reacts with 1-olefins to form lithium alkynylides and lithium hydride. This new dehydrogenation-substitution reaction indicates that other alkali metal alkynylides might be made at a lower cost than now possible. Calcium carbide has been used directly in a few reactions, serving both as a base and as a source of an acetylene unit. Copper acetylides react with aryl bromides to form arylacetylenes—an important new synthesis of a variety of valuable acetylenic compounds.

• Many new compounds have been made which contain a hetero atom attached directly to an acetylenic carbon. Among the hetero atoms are O, S, P, N, As, Sn, Sb, Si, Pb and Te. Compounds with a nitrogen attached to acetylenic carbon (alkyneamines) are especially interesting. Alkyneamines have such a great avidity for water that they can induce anhydrization reactions at room temperature. (Carboxylic acids form high yields of acid anhydrides.) The fascinating chemistry of 1-acetylenic ethers ($ROC\equiv CR'$) and thio-ethers has been explored in great detail, but unfortunately the ethers are still relatively expensive reagents.

• Several new systems have been developed for ethynylation of aldehydes and ketones. Aldehydes are ethynylated efficiently by a mixture of KOH, acetylene, diglyme and ethanol. Aldehydes and ketones can be ethynylated in a semicatalytic system which uses KOH and liquid ammonia. A detailed study of this reaction system has led to significant conclusions concerning the mechanism of ethynylation reactions. In another new system, acetone is ethynylated in the vapor phase over solid sodium hydroxide to form 3-methyl-1-butyn-3-ol. Such systems may be the forerunners of new commercially important systems.

• The known ethynylation and alkynylation systems have been applied to some unusual carbonyl compounds, including quinones and cyclic imides. Dialdehydes and other diketones have also been studied. In some cases, "ethynylation" of aromatic rings is a major reaction.

• Highly efficient oxidative coupling systems have been developed. Product conjugated diacetylenes are formed in high yield. In the newer Cadiot-Chodkiewicz coupling system, a 1-bromoacetylene reacts with a cuprous acetylide to form a conjugated diacetylene. The mechanism of oxidative coupling has been studied in some detail, but relatively little work has been done on the mechanism of the complementary Cadiot-Chodkiewicz system. Several variations of oxidative coupling have been applied to the synthesis of macrocyclic polyacetylenes. These interesting compounds can be converted to fully conjugated macrocyclic hydrocarbons ("annulenes"). Oxidative coupling reactions have also been applied to the synthesis of many naturally occurring polyacetylenic compounds. Progress in identification and synthesis of naturally occurring acetylenic and allenic compounds has been extremely fast. In fact, progress has been made so rapidly that the developments can be summarized only briefly in this book, much to my regret.

• Finally, recent literature indicates a resurgence of interest in acetylenic compounds as drugs. Acetylenic derivatives are widely used in oral contraceptives. Several new acetylenic carbamates are potential oncolytic agents. The presence of the acetylenic bond in the molecule seems to lower the toxicity and improve the rate of absorption and metabolism of some drugs. Since materials cost is not an overwhelming factor in drug research, the drug use promises to be even more significant in the future.

These few examples are covered in the text of this book, along with many others. I hope that the readers appetite is whetted, and that perusal of these pages will satisfy his appetite.

CONTENTS

Chapter One

ACETYLENIC COMPOUNDS: STRUCTURE
AND IMPORTANT PROPERTIES

1. PHYSICAL PROPERTIES

Physical properties, particularly melting point and boiling point, are important for identification purposes. Unfortunately, a complete listing of the physical properties of acetylenic and allenic compounds is impossible in this book. In addition to the standard references (Beilstein, *Chemical Abstracts*, etc.), the references given in connection with specific reactions can be used as sources of properties of most of the important acetylenic compounds. A few sources of less commonly used physical properties are:

	Reference
Bond parachors, bond refractions (alkynes)	3
Dipole moments	
Aromatic acetylenes	4,5
Enynes and silicoenynes	6
Propargyl halides	5
Alkynes	7
Ethynyl ethers	8, 9
Acetylenic phosphorus compounds	10

In his treatise on acetylene, Miller includes extensive lists of physical and thermodynamic data for acetylene.[11]

1.1. Bond Lengths and Arrangement of Electrons

Acetylene consists of *sp*-hybridized carbon atoms and two hydrogen atoms. One *sp*-hybrid orbital from each carbon overlaps the *s* orbital of its hydrogen atom, forming a σ bond. The other *sp* orbitals overlap each other endwise, and the unhybridized *p* orbitals form π bonds by lateral overlap. This forms the carbon-carbon triple bond.[1] All four atoms in acetylene are forced into a straight line.

The density distribution of the π electrons in the acetylenic bond can be represented as a cylindrical cloud of electrons which overlaps and extends past the carbon atoms.[2] In the ethylenic bond, on the other hand, the π electrons are not as delocalized. The density distribution of π electrons in the ethylenic bond can be pictured as two rods, one above and one below the carbon atoms. Figure 1-1 illustrates these representations.

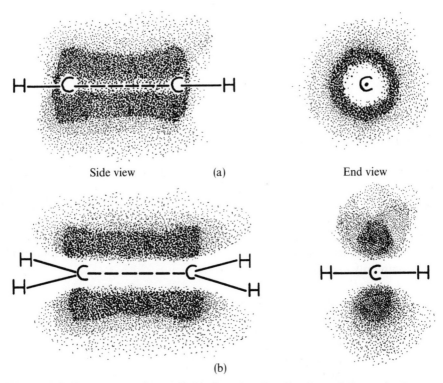

Side view   (a)   End view

(b)

Figure 1-1. Representations of the density distribution of the π electrons in (a) the acetylene molecule and (b) the ethylene molecule.

Acetylenic carbon atoms are more susceptible to nucleophilic attack and are less susceptible to electrophilic attack than ethylenic carbons. Acetylenic hydrogen atoms are more acidic than ethylenic hydrogens. The representations of Figure 1-1 explain these differences.

The high density of electrons about the triple bond causes the carbon atoms to be closer together than singly or doubly bonded carbons. The single bonds attached to acetylenic carbon are also shortened. Carbon double bond radii are usually about 0.105 Å less than the radii of single bonds, and triple bond radii are around 0.17 Å less. A few representative bond lengths are:

Bond Lengths for Conjugated Compounds (Å)[12,13]

Compound	C—C	C≡C	C≡N
$CH_3C≡C-C≡N$		1.157[14]	
$HC≡C-C≡N$	1.382	1.203	1.157
$HC≡C-C≡CH$	1.36	1.19	—
$N≡C-C≡N$	1.37	—	1.16
$N≡C-C≡C-C≡N$	1.37	1.19	1.14

Lengths of Unsaturated Bonds in Nonconjugated Compounds (Å)[14]

Compound	Bond Length
$H_2C=CH_2$	1.334
$HC≡CH$	1.204
$CH_3C≡CH$	1.207
$ClC≡CH$	1.211
$ClC≡CCH_3$	1.207

1.2. Molecular Radii

The *sp* bonds of an internal acetylene group cause a linear array of four atoms —the two acetylenic carbons and the carbons attached at each end. The acetylene group is unique in producing molecules having both a lesser (for conjugated polyynes) and greater (for alkynes) cross-sectional diameter than a paraffinic hydrocarbon:[15]

	Radius (Å)
n-Hydrocarbon in planar zigzag conformation:	4.66 (maximum)
Polyynes (Me(C≡C)$_n$Me)	3.7
Alkynes	4.30–5.23

Some alkynes form urea inclusion compounds if their radii are 4.65–5.23 Å.[15] The position of the triple bond is a factor. Of the nonynes, for example, only

4-nonyne does not form a urea inclusion compound, even though its radius is normal. In acetylenedicarboxylic acid esters, the cross-sectional diameter is 5.2 Å, and the shortest ester which forms an inclusion compound is di-n-propyl. Maleic acid has a cross-sectional diameter of 5.3 Å, and the lowest ester which forms a urea inclusion compound is di-n-butyl.

1.3. Solubility of Acetylenes

The amount of acetylene in solution is crucial for many reactions. Dimethylformamide is an excellent solvent for acetylenes. Acetylene, propyne and vinylacetylene do not associate with DMF. Solutions obey Henry's law.[16] Dissolution of these gases is exothermic in DMF (3.3–7.2 kcal/mole). The same acetylenes in N-methyl-2-pyrrolidone obey Henry's law up to a mole fraction of 0.1, and they have negative heats of solution.[17] Diacetylene forms a 1:1 complex with N-methylpyrrolidone, stable in solution in diacetylene.[18]

1.4. Solubility of Acetylene in Donor Solvents

McKinnis[19] developed a generally useful equation for predicting the solubility of acetylene in donor solvents:

$$S = kN^{1/2}(X_A - X_B)d^3$$

where S is grams of acetylene dissolved by a mole of solvent at 25° and atmospheric pressure; X_A is Pauling's electronegativity of the atom A, which forms the hydrogen bond with acetylene; X_B is the electronegativity of atom B, to which A is bonded; N is bond order (1 for C—Cl, 2 for C=O, 3 for C≡N); d is the bond distance as determined by the summation of atomic radii of the electronegative atom and the atom to which it is bonded, according to Pauling; k is a factor assigned to substituent groups comprising the remainder of the molecule.

The relative hydrogen-bonding powers of donor groups for acetylene are listed in Table 1-1.

TABLE 1-1
Relative Hydrogen-bonding Power of
Donor Groups with Acetylene

Donor Center	$N^{1/2}(X_A - X_B)d^3$	Donor Center	$N^{1/2}(X_A - X_B)d^3$
P=O	7.66	C—Br	2.09
P—O—P	7.64	C—N	1.59
S=O	4.97	C≡N	1.32
C—F	4.21	C—S	0
C—O—	2.93	C—I	<0
C—Cl	2.73	C—H	<0
C=O	2.70	—	—

The k values for some substituent groups are listed in Table 1-2. The calculated solubilities of acetylene in a large number of solvents fall within 10% of the observed values. Hexamethylphosphoramide is the best solvent for acetylene. Dimethylformamide is next best, with tetramethylenephosphorus-diamide, dimethyl sulfoxide and tetramethylurea following in that order.

TABLE 1-2
k Values of Substituent Groups in Acetylene Solvents

Substituent	k	Substituent	k
$-N(CH_3)_2$	1.24	$-C_6H_5$	0.43
$-P(OCH_3)_2$	1.15	$-Si(OC_2H_5)_3$	0.41
$-\overline{N-C_4H_8}$	1.08	$\overset{O}{\overset{\|}{-C}}-C_6H_5$	0.39
$-CH_2OCH_3$	0.94	$-CHO$	0.37
$-C_2H_5$	0.68	$-C_2H_4O\overset{O}{\overset{\|}{C}}CH_3$	0.36
$-C(CH_3)(OCH_3)_2$	0.64	$-C_2H_4$	0.29
$-CH_3$	0.63	$-SCH_3$	0.28
$-\overset{O}{\overset{\|}{C}}CH_3$	0.60	$-CH_2O\overset{O}{\overset{\|}{C}}CH_3$	0.22
$-H$	0.53	$-\overset{O}{\overset{\|}{C}}C_3F_7$	0.14
$-OC_2H_5$	0.48	$-Cl$	-0.07
$-B(OCH_3)_2$	0.46	$-F$	-1.43

Solubility in hexamethylphosphoramide is calculated to be 9.50 grams of acetylene per mole of solvent:

$S = k \times N^{1/2}(X_A - X_B)d^3$ $\begin{cases} k = 1.24 \text{ (from Table 1-2)} \\ N^{1/2}(X_A - X_B)d^3 = 7.66 \text{ (from Table 1-1)} \end{cases}$

$S = 1.24 \times 7.66$

$S = 9.50$

(observed = 8.8 g/mole)

2. CHEMICAL PROPERTIES OF ACETYLENIC COMPOUNDS

2.1. Acetylenes as Hydrogen-bonding Acids

West reviewed the evidence for hydrogen bonding in acetylenes.[20] The high solubility of acetylene in basic solvents[19] and deviations from Raoult's law in such solutions[21] are indicative of hydrogen bonds from the acetylenic proton to basic sites in the solvent molecule. Phenylacetylene dissolves exothermically in ethers and amines, perhaps due to hydrogen-bond formation.[21] In 1941, the first direct evidence for this hydrogen bonding was reported.[22] The acetylenic C—H stretching absorption band of phenylacetylene at 3315 cm^{-1} was observed to be shifted to lower frequency by ethers and amines. More recently, such shifts have been reported for other acetylenes and for acetylene itself.[23-25] The acetylenic C—H stretching frequency also changes in N,N-dimethyl-acetamide and dimethylformamide. Electronegative substituents in the acetylenic compound increase the C—H frequency shifts (e.g., halomethyl, phenyl).

Acetylenes associate with the oxygen atom in ethers. Such association would change the frequency and shape of the two hydrogen fundamentals (in infrared spectra) of the ethynyl group.[29] Other evidence for association with ether groups is noted in the retention times in gas-liquid chromatography (GLC) of acetylenes. With basic substrates such as "Carbitol" or tritolyl phosphate, the retention times relative to n-pentane increase for 1-butyne, diacetylene and isopropenylacetylene. Brand[29] obtained the absorptions of some acetylenic compounds in solutions and recorded the absorption at 3300 cm^{-1}. The changes in peak absorption between n-hexane solutions and ether solutions indicate association with the ether, and the fraction associated can be estimated in some cases. Alkynes were about 0.3 (mole fraction) associated. As more electronegative substituents were added to the molecule, association increased to 0.6–0.7. An arrangement in increasing order of "acidity" obtained by this method roughly parallels the activity of the acetylenic C—H bond in reactions which remove the ethynyl hydrogen as a proton.

Benzoylacetylene is especially suitable for studies of association because the acetylenic hydrogen is more acidic than in most other acetylenes. Brand[30] determined the association of benzoylacetylene with aromatic hydrocarbons and with butyl ether by both infrared and proton magnetic resonance spectroscopy (PMR; see Table 1-3). The structures of the hydrogen-bonded complexes were assumed to be:

Some of the inconsistencies may be due to the fact that the aromatic ring in the complex is in the same plane as the benzoylacetylene, instead of perpendicular as assumed, and also perhaps because of some association through the carbonyl group instead of exclusively through the ethynyl hydrogen.

2.2. Acetylenes as Hydrogen-bonding Bases

The basic properties of the C≡C bond in hydrogen-bond formation have not been studied as much as the acidic ones. Intramolecular hydrogen bonding of

TABLE 1-3
Association of Benzoylacetylene with
Aromatic Hydrocarbons and with
n-Butyl Ether

Complexing Molecule	% Association by	
	IR	PMR
Benzene	38	41
Toluene	58	52
p-Xylene	71	—
Mesitylene	75	—
n-Butyl ether	64	68
n-Butyl ether	43[a]	—

the —OH group to the C≡C group in aliphatic acetylenic alcohols[26] and in o-ethynylphenols[27] has been noted.

The shift of the phenol O—H stretching frequency which results from OH···H bonds is used to measure the extent of hydrogen bonding. 1-Alkynes shift the frequency 90 cm^{-1}, while 1-alkenes shift the frequency only 70 cm^{-1}.[28] Acetylenes are also stronger bases toward phenol hydroxyl groups than aromatic hydrocarbons are. When the terminal hydrogen in 1-alkynes is replaced by a methyl group, electron availability at the C≡C bond is increased and the frequency shift increases to about 132 cm^{-1}. A further small increase is caused by larger alkyl substituents. The same effect is noted in aryl acetylenes.

2.3. Intermolecular Association of Ethynyl Groups

Terminal acetylenes have both proton-donating and proton-accepting properties, so intermolecular hydrogen bonding is expected. West[20] investigated intermolecular association thoroughly. He measured the C—H stretching bands of phenylacetylene, 1-heptyne, 1-hexyne, and propargyl bromide and chloride at several concentrations in CCl$_4$ and in the neat liquids. As the concentration of the acetylenic compound increased, a new absorption band appeared on the low-frequency side of the C—H fundamental at concentrations above 1M. The differences in frequency between the new band and the fundamental were small: 12–14 cm^{-1} for 1-alkynes, 14–17 cm^{-1} for the propargyl halides, and 22 cm^{-1} for phenylacetylene. This indicates weak intermolecular hydrogen bonding. The association is small even in the neat liquids. Intermolecular hydrogen bonding has only a small effect on the gross physical properties of 1-alkynes.

2.4. Donor Capacity of Acetylenes

HCl is a convenient small acceptor molecule for investigating the donor capacity of ethylenic and acetylenic compounds. Molecules with lone pair orbitals usually form strong hydrogen bonds because the electron cloud is localized and projects far out from the end of the molecule. Molecules with π electrons can also form hydrogen bonds, but these are usually weaker because the π electron is not so localized, and its effect does not project very far out of the molecule. The same effects are noted in other molecular complexes. Cook[31] determined the freezing point diagram of binary mixtures of unsaturates and HCl, and from the curves could determine how many complexes formed as well as the HCl:unsaturate ratio. Simple olefins and butadiene formed 1:1 and 2:1 complexes. Acetylene formed only the 1:1 complex, while propyne, 2-butyne and 3-hexyne formed three complexes (1:1, 2:1 and 4:1) each.

The same addition complexes form with each member of a homologous series, suggesting that the complexes have little to do with crystal packing, but must form by specific forces between the HCl and hydrocarbon. The π orbital must be the donor center, and the H of the HCl molecule must be directed toward a lobe of the π orbital. Each π orbital can accommodate two HCl molecules. The π orbitals in butadiene and other conjugated diolefins are more delocalized than those of ordinary olefins, and they should form weaker bonds with acceptors. Acetylene is also a weak donor.

3. STRUCTURE AND ACIDITY

Cram[32] discussed the acidity and structure of acetylenic compounds. He compared the acetylenic hydrocarbons with other hydrocarbons which are weak acids. Data from several sources gave pK_a values, called the McEwen-Streitwieser-Applequist-Dessy (MSAD) pK_a scale. Some common hydrocarbons are listed in Table 1-4 according to the MSAD pK_a.

TABLE 1-4
MSAD pK_a Values of Some Common Hydrocarbons

Compound	pK_a	Compound	pK_a
Cyclopentadiene	15	Propylene (α-hydrogen)	35.5
Indene	18.5	Ethylene	36.5
Phenylacetylene	18.5	Cyclopropane	39
Fluorene	22.9	Ethane	42
Acetylene	25	Propane	44
Triphenylmethane	32.5	Cyclohexane	45
Toluene (α-hydrogen)	35		

The order of kinetic and thermodynamic acidity of simple hydrocarbons is: acetylene > ethylene > cyclopropane > ethane. There is nearly linear correlation between acid strength and per cent s character contributed by carbon to the C—H bond.[32] The greater the s character of the C—H bond, the greater is the acidity. The 2s electrons are closer to the nucleus than the 2p electrons,

Hydrocarbon	% Character	Estimated pK_a
HC≡CH	50	25
$H_2C=CH_2$	33	36.5
$CH_3—CH_3$	25	42

so the stability of carbanions should increase as the 2s character of the orbital they occupy increases.

Dessy[33] determined the rates of triethylamine-catalyzed isotopic exchange between monosubstituted acetylenes and 5M D_2O in dimethylformamide at 40°. The results are given in Table 1-5. Hydrogen and phenyl are comparable as substituents, showing that the electron-withdrawing inductive effect of the

TABLE 1-5[33]

$$RC≡CH + D_2O \xrightleftharpoons[\text{DMF, 40°}]{\text{Et}_3\text{N}} RC≡CD + H_2O$$

R	Relative Rate	R	Relative Rate
$C_6H_5—$	1.0	o-$CF_3C_6H_4—$	3.5
H—	0.73	m-$CF_3C_6H_4—$	5.2
$C_4H_9—$	0.058	p-$CF_3C_6H_4—$	3.3
$CH_3O—$	2.0	m-$ClC_6H_4—$	28
$(C_6H_5)_3Si—$	68	p-$ClC_6H_4—$	4.8
o-$FC_6H_4—$	4.7	p-$BrC_6H_4—$	2.1
m-$FC_6H_4—$	7.7	p-$CH_3OC_6H_4—$	1.0
p-$FC_6H_4—$	1.5	p-$HC≡CC_6H_4—$	13.8

phenyl group has little overall effect. Apparently a small conjugative effect in the opposite direction tends to distribute positive charge into the benzene ring. p-Methoxyphenyl is the same as phenyl, indicating that the electron-releasing effects of methoxy cancel any extra inductive effect from it. Relative rates of the m- and p-halophenylacetylenes also indicate that conjugative effects of the electron pairs on halogens are superimposed on their inductive effects, the inductive effects being more important. Data and theory show there are no conjugative effects between aryl groups and the negative charge of the acetylide ion.

The rate of exchange of acetylenic hydrogen in phenylacetylene with water in aqueous pyridine is first order on phenylacetylene and on hydroxyl ion.[34,35]

The rate-determining step is abstraction of a proton by the base. Rates were measured by observing the broadening of the acetylenic hydrogen nuclear magnetic resonance (NMR) peak caused by exchange.

Charton[7] correlated with the Hammett equation the ionization constants of 3-substituted propiolic acids, the rates of alkaline hydrolysis of 3-substituted ethyl propiolates, and the dipole moments of 1-hexyne and 1-heptyne. He used the σ,ρ-substituent constants. The transmission of the substituent effect through the *trans*-vinylene group is greater than through acetylene group, which in turn is much greater than transmission through the *p*-phenylene group.

4. SOURCES OF DATA ON OTHER PROPERTIES

Property	Reference
Bond energies and appearance potentials	36, 37, 38
Bonding, charge distribution and transmission, and electronegativity	39, 40, 41, 42
Anisotropic polarizability	5
Hybridization	43

References

1. Knox, B. E., and Palmer, H. B., *Chem. Rev.*, **61**, 247 (1961).
2. Ingold, C. K., "Structure and Mechanism in Organic Chemistry," p. 28, Ithaca, N.Y., Cornell University Press, 1953; Noller, C. R., "Chemistry of Organic Compounds," Third ed., pp. 87, 167, Philadelphia, Pa., W. B. Saunders Co., 1965.
3. Grzeskowiak, R., Jeffery, G. H., and Vogel, A. I., *J. Chem. Soc.*, 4719 (1960).
4. Lumbroso, H., Golse, R., and Liermain, A., *Bull. Soc. Chim. France*, 1608 (1956).
5. LeFevre, R. J. W., Orr, B. J., and Ritchie, G. L. D., *J. Chem. Soc.* (B), 281 (1966).
6. Petrov, A. A., *et. al.*, *Zh. Obshch. Khim.*, **31**, 352, 3525 (1961); *Chem. Abstr.*, **57**, 7295, 10988 (1962).
7. Charton, M., *J. Org. Chem.*, **26**, 735 (1961).
8. Drenth, W., Hekkert, G. L., and Zwanenburg, B. G., *Rec. Trav. Chim.*, **79**, 1056 (1960).
9. Drenth, W., and Hekkert, G. L., *Rec. Trav. Chim.*, **81**, 313 (1962).
10. Bogolyubov, G. M., Mingaleva, K. S., and Petrov, A. A., *Zh. Obshch. Khim.*, **35**, 1566 (1965); *Chem. Abstr.*, **63**, 17860 (1965).
11. Miller, S. A., "Acetylene. Its Properties, Manufacture and Uses," Vol. 1, Ch. 2, New York, Academic Press, 1965.
12. Hannan, R. B., and Collin, R. L., *Acta Cryst.*, **6**, 350 (1953).
13. Westenberg, A. A., and Wilson, E. B., Jr., *J. Am. Chem. Soc.*, **72**, 199 (1950).
14. Pauling, L., "The Nature of the Chemical Bond," p. 230, Ithaca, N.Y., Cornell University Press, 1960.
15. Radell, J., Connolly, J. W., and Yuhas, L. D., *J. Org. Chem.*, **26**, 2022 (1961).
16. Braude, G. E., Leites, I. L., and Dedova, I. V., *Khim. Prom.*, 232 (1961); *Chem. Abstr.*, **55**, 18265 (1961).

17. Backalov, I. M., *et al.*, *Tr. Z-go Vses. Soveshch. po Radiats. Khim.*, *Akad. Nauk SSSR, Otd. Khim. Nauk, Moscow*, 455 (1960); *Chem. Abstr.*, **58**, 4652 (1963).
18. Schachat, N., *J. Org. Chem.*, **27**, 2928 (1962).
19. McKinnis, A. C., *Ind. Eng. Chem.*, **47**, 850 (1955).
20. West, R., and Kraihanzel, C. S., *J. Am. Chem. Soc.*, **83**, 765 (1961).
21. Copley, M. J., and Holley, C. E., Jr., *J. Am. Chem. Soc.*, **61**, 1599 (1939).
22. Stanford, S. C., and Gordy, W., *J. Am. Chem. Soc.*, **63**, 1094 (1941).
23. Jacob, J., *Compt. Rend.*, **250**, 1624 (1960).
24. Sondheimer, F., and Ben-Efraim, D. A., *J. Am. Chem. Soc.*, **85**, 52 (1963).
25. Murahashi, S., Ryutani, B., and Hataka, K., *Bull. Chem. Soc. Japan*, **32**, 1001 (1959).
26. von R. Schleyer, P., Trifan, D. S., and Bacskai, R., *J. Am. Chem. Soc.*, **80**, 6691 (1958).
27. Prey, V., and Berbalk, H., *Monatsh.*, **82**, 990 (1951).
28. West, R., *J. Am. Chem. Soc.*, **81**, 1614 (1959).
29. Brand, J. C. D., Eglinton, G., and Morman, J. F., *J. Chem. Soc.*, 2525 (1960).
30. Brand, J. C. D., Eglinton, G., and Tyrrell, J., *J. Chem. Soc.*, 5914 (1965).
31. Cook, D., Lupien, Y., and Schneider, W. G., *Can. J. Chem.*, **34**, 957 (1956).
32. Cram, D. J., "Fundamentals of Carbanion Chemistry," pp. 19, 48, 54, 59, New York, Academic Press, 1965.
33. Dessy, R. E., Okuzimi, Y., and Chen, A., *J. Am. Chem. Soc.*, **84**, 2899 (1962).
34. Ballinger, P., and Long, F. A., *J. Am. Chem. Soc.*, **81**, 3148 (1959).
35. Charman, H. B., Tiers, G. V. D., and Kreevoy, M. M., *J. Am. Chem. Soc.*, **81**, 3149 (1959).
36. Coats, F. H., and Anderson, R. C., *J. Am. Chem. Soc.*, **79**, 1340 (1957).
37. Streitwieser, A., Jr., *J. Am. Chem. Soc.*, **82**, 4123 (1960).
38. Sinn, H., *Z. Elektrochem.*, **61**, 989 (1957); *Chem. Abstr.*, **52**, 4263 (1957).
39. Wilmhurst, J. K., *J. Chem. Phys.*, **28**, 733 (1958).
40. McLean, A. D., Ransil, B. J., and Mulliken, R. S., *J. Chem. Phys.*, **32**, 1873 (1960).
41. Fuchs, R., *J. Org. Chem.*, **28**, 3209 (1963).
42. Landgrebe, J. A., and Rynbrandt, R. H., *J. Org. Chem.*, **31**, 2585 (1966).
43. Bloor, J. E., and Gartside, S., *Nature*, **184** (Suppl. 17), 1313 (1959).

Chapter Two

EXPERIMENTAL AIDS

1. SAFE HANDLING OF ACETYLENE AND ACETYLENIC COMPOUNDS

1.1. Atmospheric Pressure

Acetylene can be used safely in the laboratory at atmospheric pressure. The only requirement is that sparks and other ignition sources be avoided, as with any other flammable gas. Reaction vessels should be placed in good, efficient hoods. Stirrers should be driven by induction or air motors, and not by brush-type motors. The "Cenco" cone-drive motor and the "Waco" two speed motor are typical induction stirrers. Transformers used to control voltage to heating mantles and motors should be placed outside the hood. Unreacted acetylene can be vented from usual laboratory scale reactions into the hood, preferably via a piece of tubing leading to the top of the hood near the outlet. Glass or stainless steel apparatus should be used. Copper and high-copper brasses must be avoided.

Acetylenic compounds and their reactions differ enormously in their stability and hazards. The vast majority of reactions of acetylenic and allenic compounds are as safe as other comparable organic reactions. The references given in discussions of reactions should be used as a guide to the relative hazards involved. If particularly careful conditions must be used to avoid difficulties, these are generally emphasized.

1.2. Elevated Pressure

The best way to handle acetylene explosions, as any other, is to prevent initiation. Acetylene explodes by deflagration, a relatively slow decomposition, or by detonation, a very fast decomposition. Frequently an explosion starts as a deflagration and develops into a detonation. The speed of development of detonation depends on the initial pressure and on the diameter of the vessel.

Sargent[1] described a method for calculating the predetonation distance for an acetylene system and, from this, how much force an explosion will produce. For example, the predetonation distance in a tube $1\frac{1}{2}$ inches in diameter or larger, for 40-psia acetylene, is 8–55 feet. Thus, acetylene, upon ignition, will detonate somewhere between 8 and 55 feet from the point of ignition. For a 100-foot tube, the final pressure from detonation will be 2200–4400 psia, a 55- to 110-fold increase. At 17.7°, acetylene deflagrates at 33 psia or above in a 1-inch tube, and detonates at 47 psia or above, once initiated. Tube diameters should be kept as small as possible, consistent with overall design, to minimize propagation of a deflagrative flame through the apparatus.

Goodwin[2] described an autoclave reactor and auxiliary equipment for pressure acetylene reactions, and gave detailed operating procedures. Low partial pressure of acetylene is necessary for safe operation. The stability of acetylene in mixtures with methanol, formaldehyde and acetaldehyde is known.[3] These are not as effective as methane in stabilizing acetylene.

Pure allene can decompose explosively at 2 atmospheres, while propyne requires 4.5–5.6 atmospheres pressure.[4] Diacetylene is even more explosive. The critical pressure for explosion of diacetylene is 30–33 mm. This can be raised to 700 mm by using 15–40 % of a diluent such as ammonia, acetylene, carbon dioxide or nitrogen.[5]

Divinylacetylene is a very hazardous chemical because it reacts rapidly with oxygen to form an explosive peroxidic polymer.[6] Divinylacetylene must be handled in an oxygen-free atmosphere. After experiments are finished, the equipment should be rinsed immediately with solvents containing a polymerization inhibitor to prevent formation of unstable films.

2. LABORATORY PURIFICATION OF CYLINDER ACETYLENE

The only reasonable source of laboratory acetylene is commercial cylinders, which are filled with acetone and a solid filler. Acetylene from cylinders must be purified before use. The traces of air in the cylinders can be removed by bleeding off a few pounds of pressure into a good hood. The acetone entrained by the gas is easily removed by a trap cooled in dry ice. The trace impurities (ammonia, arsine, stibine, etc.) can be removed in a number of purification systems, which also remove the last traces of acetone:

(1) Activated alumina, calcium chloride and sodium hydroxide pellets.[7]

(2) Aqueous KOH (50%), concentrated aqueous sodium bisulfite, acidified chromic acid, concentrated sulfuric acid, and then a column of soda lime and calcium chloride.[8]

(3) Concentrated H_2SO_4, solid KOH and then activated alumina. This system gives 99.96% pure acetylene (by mass spectral analysis).[9]

(4) Activated alumina, concentrated sulfuric acid and sodium hydroxide pellets.[10]

(5) Activated alumina alone.[11]

3. DETECTION, ANALYSIS AND IDENTIFICATION OF ACETYLENIC COMPOUNDS

Traces of acetylenic hydrocarbons containing four or five carbon atoms have been detected and determined by hydrating the triple bond to a ketone (sulfuric acid–mercuric sulfate) and measuring the ultraviolet absorption of the 2,4-dinitrophenylhydrazones.[12] Capillary GLC analysis can also detect trace quantities of acetylenic compounds. The acetylenic hydrogen is a handle for analysis. Conversion of terminal acetylenes to the silver acetylides by treatment with silver nitrate is the most common wet analytical method. The silver nitrate liberates nitric acid, which is titrated.[13,14]

3.1. Analysis by Gas-Liquid Chromatography

This method has been widely used in recent work. Hively[15] determined the retention times of 93 hydrocarbons, including acetylenes and allenes, on several columns: dimethylsulfolane, tritolyl phosphate, di-n-decyl phthalate, mineral oil and 2,2'-oxydipropionitrile. These columns are probably satisfactory for most separations of hydrocarbons with acetylene and/or allene groups.

3.2 Infrared Absorption

Infrared analysis of pure products was reviewed in 1952.[31] Most authors have used infrared as part of their product identification. Details of some analyses are given along with a discussion of specific reactions at appropriate places in the text. At the end of this chapter, references to infrared determinations on the following kinds of acetylenic compounds may be found:

(1) Alkynes,[32]
(2) α-Acetylenic acids and esters,[33]
(3) 1-Acetylenic ethers, thioethers and selenoethers,[34,35]
(4) Acetylenic phosphorus compounds,[36]
(5) Acetylenic germanium compounds,[37]
(6) Vinylethynylsilanes,[38]
(7) 1-Halo-1-alkynes,[39]
(8) 1-Amino-1-alkynes,[40]
(9) Haloacetylenes.[41]

TABLE 2-1
GLC Analysis of Acetylenic and Allenic Compounds

Compound(s)	Column Liquid	Column Temperature (°C)	Reference
Hydrocarbons			
C_2–C_3	Dimethylsulfolane	20	16
	"Apeizon" B + dibutyl maleate	—	17
	Dry deactivated alumina	25	18
C_2–C_5	Hexamethylphosphoramide	25	18
C_3–C_4	Formamide + 2,2'-oxydi-propionitrile	25	19
C_4–C_5	Dimethylformamide	0	18
C_4–C_6	"Apiezon" L,	20	
	"Carbowax" 600	20	20, 21
	Tritolyl phosphate	20	
Propyne, diacetylene, vinylacetylene	Dioctyl phthalate	25	22
Enynes, C_6	7-Ethoxylated laurol		23
C_7	"Carbowax" 1500	110	24
C_9–C_{11}, cyclic	NMPN	78, 110	25
Other compounds			
Enynols, C_9	Neopentyl glycol	150	26
Enynes, carbinols, β-chloroacetylenes	Silicone oil	134	30
1-Iodopropyne, 1-iodoallene	Dinonyl phthalate	40	28
Acids, C_{15}–C_{18}	Polyglycol succinate	200	27
1-Alkynylamines	"Carbowax" 20M + KOH	—	29

3.3. Nuclear Magnetic Resonance Spectra

NMR is the newest tool available in most laboratories, and considerable work has already been done on acetylenic and allenic compounds.

Spin-spin coupling constants between hydrogens in organic molecules depend mainly on the structure and the stereochemistry of the molecule, and only slightly on the nature of the substituents. Hatton [42] determined the spin-spin coupling constants in some acetylenic compounds. The chemical shift between the resonances of acetylenic hydrogen and the resonances of the methylene group is much larger than the coupling constant between $\equiv CH$ and $-CH_2-$, so the coupling constant can be obtained directly from the spacing of the triplet and doublet resonances. Table 2-2 lists some proton magnetic resonance data.

TABLE 2-2
PMR Data for Some Acetylenic Compounds[42]

Acetylene	J (cycles/sec)	Chemical Shift of $\equiv CH$ from Cyclohexane (ppm)	State
$HC\equiv C-CH_2Cl$	2.65	−1.19	Liquid
$HC\equiv C-CH_2Br$	2.70	−1.31	Liquid
$HC\equiv C-CH_2OH$	2.50	−1.32	Liquid
$HC\equiv CCH_2-N\overset{CO}{\underset{CO}{}}$	2.55	−0.375	Dilute solution in benzene
$HC\equiv C-CH_2-O-$	2.51	−1.19	Liquid
$HC\equiv C-CH_2-N(CH_3)_2$	2.51	−1.02	Liquid
$HC\equiv C-CH_2-N(C_2H_5)_2$	2.55	—	Liquid
$HC\equiv C-CH_2\overset{Me}{\underset{Et}{\overset{+}{N}}}-Me \quad I^-$	2.60	—	Solution in H_2O
$HC\equiv C-CH(OH)CH_3$	2.15	−1.23	Liquid
$HC\equiv C-CH(OH)C_6H_5$	2.20	−1.02	CCl_4 solution
$HC\equiv C-CH(CH_3)N(C_2H_5)_2$	2.20	—	Liquid
$HC\equiv C-CH(CH_3)N\underset{}{\bigcirc}O$	2.10	—	Liquid
$HC\equiv C-CH(CH_3)NHCH(CH_3)_2$	2.20	−1.21	Liquid
$HC\equiv C-CH(CH_3)NHn-C_4H_9$	2.10	—	Solution in CCl_4
$HC\equiv C-CH(CH_3)N(CH_3)_2$	2.00	—	Solution in CCl_4

The coupling constants are similar but can be divided into two groups. Coupling constants in the range of 2.0–2.2 cycle/sec are obtained for compounds $RR'CH\!-\!C\!\equiv\!CH$, while constants in the range 2.5–2.7 cycle/sec are found for propargyl compounds, $RCH_2C\!\equiv\!CH$. The smaller values for the first group may be caused by distortion of the bond angles by the two substituents R and R'. The chemical shift of the acetylenic proton is -1.02 to -1.32 ppm except in N-propargyl phthalimide. The shift to higher field is caused by π-donor association with the benzene solvent. The chemical shift is seen to be insensitive to substituents, and this indicates that acetylenic hydrogen can be easily characterized by PMR.

The chemical shift of a hydrogen atom is sensitive to the formation of hydrogen bonds, and for strong interactions, the shifts are usually dominated by this association. For weaker associations, however, the shifts are not a simple measure of such interaction. Acetylenic hydrogen has acidic properties and can form weak hydrogen bonds.[20]

The shifts observed when propargyl chloride, phenylacetylene and benzoylacetylene were dissolved in several solvents are listed in Table 2-3.[43] Positive shifts indicate solvent-solute interaction leading to increased shielding of the acetylenic compound, and negative shifts indicate decreased shielding. Solvents which cause acetylenic resonance to shift to lower applied fields contain strongly electronegative centers which can be proton acceptors, and the lower-

TABLE 2-3
Shifts (τ, ppm)[a][43]

Solvent	Propargyl Chloride CH	CH$_2$	Phenyl-acetylene	Benzoyl-acetylene[c]
Pure compound	7.41	5.87	6.91	6.42
Cyclohexane[b]	7.81	6.13	7.26	6.90
N,N-Dimethylacetamide	—	—	5.78	4.63
N,N-Dimethylformamide	6.38	5.61	5.65	4.89
Pyridine	—	—	5.90	4.80
Acetone	6.94	5.77	6.39	5.49
Dioxane	7.07	5.87	6.50	5.87
Acetonitrile	7.20	5.83	6.65	5.75
Nitrobenzene	7.10	5.79	6.56	6.05
Nitromethane	7.27	5.82	6.74	6.18
Fluorobenzene	7.75	6.26	7.08	6.99
Thiophene	7.92	6.38	7.22	7.28
Benzene	8.12	6.58	7.29	7.42
Toluene	8.16	6.62	7.36	7.43

[a] $\tau = 10.00 - \dfrac{H_{SiMe_4} - H}{H_{SiMe_4}}$
[b] Reference compound.
[c] Saturated solution in CCl_4.

field shift may be caused by weak hydrogen bonds: $>C{=}O{\cdots}H{-}C{\equiv}C{-}$. When the hydrogen bond forms, the acetylenic hydrogen experiences a strong electric field from the electronegative center. Diamagnetic circulations around the hydrogen are inhibited, and the resonance shifts to lower applied field.

Kreevoy[44] determined the NMR spectra of some monosubstituted acetylenes. He used carbon tetrachloride or pyridine as the solvent and tetramethylsilane as an internal standard. Most of the acetylenic protons gave closely spaced doublets or triplets, so measurements were to the central line of a triplet or the center of a doublet (Table 2-4).

TABLE 2-4
Solvent Shifts and Long-range Spin-Spin
Couplings in $RC{\equiv}CH$[44]

R	τ CCl$_4$ (ppm)	$\Delta\tau$ (ppm)	J (cycles/sec)
H	8.20	—	<0.5
n-C$_3$H$_7$	8.21	—	2.7
n-C$_9$H$_9$	8.27	—	2.4
n-C$_5$H$_{11}$	8.25	0.95[a]	2.1
ClCH$_2$	7.60	—	2.7
BrCH$_2$	7.67	—	2.7
ICH$_2$	7.81	—	2.8
HOCH$_2$	7.67	0.85	2.7
HOC(CH$_3$)$_2$	7.72	0.92	<0.5
CH$_3$OCH$_2$	7.63	0.92	2.5
CH$_3$OC(CH$_3$)$_2$	7.67	0.92	<0.5
C$_6$H$_5$OCH$_2$	7.99	1.39	2.35
(C$_2$H$_5$O)$_2$CH	7.61	1.21	1.61
O=CH	8.11	—	<0.5
C$_6$H$_5$	7.07	1.04	<0.5
CH$_2$=CH	7.08	—	<0.5
HOCH$_2$CH$_2$	8.08[b]	—	2.4

[a] 10 % aqueous pyridine, not pure pyridine.
[b] Pure liquid.

The acetylenic functional group is hard to identify because the τ values for the acetylenic hydrogen are close to those of methylene and methine hydrogen. This difficulty is avoided by using pyridine as solvent. This removes the acetylenic proton spectrum from the area of the methylene or methine protons. The magnitude of the shift is indicative of an acetylenic proton, and the coupling constant is determined from the spectra obtained in pyridine.

Other sources of NMR data on acetylenic compounds are:

Compounds	References
1-Alkynes	45, 46, 47, 48, 49, 50
Vinylacetylene	51
Conjugated polyacetylenes	52
Tin, germanium and arsenic compounds	53
Silylacetylenes	54
Ethers and thioethers	55, 53
Enynes, dienynes, and their Si-, Sn- and Pb-containing analogs	56
α-Acetylenic carbinols	57
α-Carbonyl acetylenes	52
Mono-, di- and triacetylenes and their phosphorus compounds	36, 53
Allenes and polyacetylenes	58
Allenes	59
$Ph_3MC\equiv CH$ (M = C, Si, Ge, Sn, Pb)	60

References

1. Sargent, H. B., *Chem. Eng.*, **64**, 250 (1957).
2. Goodwin, R. D., *Ind. Eng. Chem.*, **49**, 861 (1957).
3. Glikin, M. A., and Strizhevskii, I. I., *Zh. Prikl. Khim.*, **38**, 2879 (1965); *Chem. Abstr.*, **64**, 9575 (1966).
4. Bondar, A. M., *et al.*, *Khim. Prom.*, **41**, 923 (1965); *Chem. Abstr.*, **64**, 11020 (1966).
5. Mushii, R. Ya., *et al.*, *Khim. Prom.*, 109 (1963); *Chem. Abstr.*, **59**, 7309 (1963).
6. Handy, C. T., and Benson, R. E., *J. Org. Chem.*, **27**, 39 (1962).
7. Sauer, J. C., *J. Am. Chem. Soc.*, **79**, 5314 (1957).
8. Nesmeyanov, A. N., and Borisov, A. E., *Akad. Nauk. SSSR Inst. Organ. Khim. Sintezy Organ. Soedin. Sb.*, **1**, 128, 150 (1950); *Chem. Abstr.*, **47**, 8001, 8004 (1953).
9. Luttinger, L. B., *Chem. Ind.* (*London*), 1135 (1960); *J. Org. Chem.*, **27**, 1591 (1962); (to American Cyanamide) U.S. Patent 3,174,956 (Nov. 23, 1965).
10. Heying, T. L., *et al.*, *Inorg. Chem.*, **2**, 1089 (1963); *Chem. Abstr.*, **60**, 1782 (1964).
11. Rutledge, T. F., *J. Org. Chem.*, **22**, 649 (1957).
12. Scroggins, M. W., and Price, H. A., *Anal. Chem.*, **35**, 48 (1963).
13. Beumel, O. F., Jr., and Harris, R. F., *J. Org. Chem.*, **29**, 1872 (1964).
14. Barnes, L., Jr., and Molinini, L. J., *Anal. Chem.*, **27**, 1025 (1955).
15. Hively, B. A., *J. Chem. Eng. Data*, **5**, 237 (1960).
16. Kuivila, H. G., Rohman, W., and Fish, R. H., *J. Am. Chem. Soc.*, **87**, 2835 (1965).
17. Miyake, H., and Mitooka, M., *Nippon Kagaku Zasshi*, **84**, 593 (1963); *Chem. Abstr.*, **61**, 1275 (1964).
18. Dubrin, J., MacKay, C., and Wolfgang, R., *J. Am. Chem. Soc.*, **86**, 4747 (1964).
19. Tago, S., and Koudo, O., *Bull. Japan Petrol. Inst.*, **7**, 1 (1965); *Chem. Abstr.*, **63**, 17749 (1965).
20. Brand, J. C. D., Eglinton, G., and Morman, J. F., *J. Chem. Soc.*, 2526 (1960).

21. Shokhovskoi, B. G., Stadnichuk, M. D., and Petrov, A. A., *Zh. Obshch. Khim.*, **35**, 1031 (1965); *Chem. Abstr.*, **63**, 9978 (1965).
22. Gunesch, H., and Stadtmüller, H., *Rev. Chim.* (*Bucharest*), **9**, 35 (1958); *Chem. Abstr.*, **52**, 19712 (1958).
23. Boehm-Goessl, T., *et al.*, *Chem. Ber.*, **96**, 2504 (1963).
24. Smadja, W., *Ann. Chim.* (*Paris*), **10**, 105 (1965); *Chem. Abstr.*, **63**, 6834 (1965).
25. Moore, W. R., and Ward, H. R., *J. Am. Chem. Soc.*, **85**, 86 (1963).
26. Blanc-Guenee, J., d'Engenieres, M. P., and Miocque, M., *Bull. Soc. Chim. France*, 603 (1964).
27. Grimmer, G., and Hildebrandt, A., *Ann. Chem.*, **685**, 154 (1965).
28. Baker, C. S. L., Landor, P. D., Landor, S. R., and Patel, A. N., *J. Chem. Soc.*, 4348 (1965).
29. Marszak, I., Guermont, J. P., and Epsztein, R., *Bull. Soc. Chim. France*, 1807 (1960).
30. Hennion, G. F., and Lynch, C. A., Jr., *J. Org. Chem.*, **25**, 1330 (1960).
31. Sheppard, M. A., and Simpson, D. M., *Quart. Rev.* (*London*), **6**, 1 (1952).
32. Edgell, W. F., *et al.*, U.S. Atomic Energy Commission, TID-15201, 1962, 87pp.; *Chem. Abstr.*, **58**, 5161 (1963).
33. Märkl, G., *Chem. Ber.*, **94**, 3005 (1961).
34. Arens, J. F., *Advan. Org. Chem.*, **2**, 117 (1960).
35. Brandsma, L., and Arens, J. F., *Rec. Trav. Chim.*, **81**, 539 (1962).
36. Charrier, C., Chodkiewicz, W., and Cadiot, P., *Bull. Soc. Chim. France*, 1002 (1966).
37. Mathis, R., Mazerolles, P., and Mathis, F., *Bull. Soc. Chim. France*, 1955 (1961).
38. Yakovleva, T. V., Petrov, A. A., and Standnichuk, M. D., *Opt. Spektroskopiya*, **11**, 588 (1961); *Chem. Abstr.*, **56**, 4266 (1962).
39. Wojtkwiak, B., *Ann. Chim.* (*Paris*), **9**, 5 (1964); *Chem. Abstr.*, **61**, 6895 (1964).
40. Montijn, P. P., Harryvan, E., and Brandsma, L., *Rec. Trav. Chim.*, **83**, 1211 (1964).
41. Hunt, G. R., and Wilson, M. K., *J. Chem. Phys.*, **34**, 1301 (1961).
42. Hatton, J. V., and Richards, R. E., *Trans. Faraday Soc.*, **56**, 315 (1960).
43. *Ibid*, **57**, 28 (1961).
44. Kreevoy, M. M., Charman, H. B., and Vinard, D. R., *J. Am. Chem. Soc.*, **83**, 1978 (1961).
45. Braillon, B., *J. Chim. Phys.*, **58**, 495 (1961); *Chem. Abstr.*, **55**, 26681 (1961).
46. Shigorin, D. N., *et al.*, *Dokl. Akad. Nauk SSSR*, **140**, 419 (1961); *Chem. Abstr.*, **56**, 13697 (1962).
47. Fixman, M., *J. Chem. Phys.*, **35**, 679 (1961).
48. Petrakis, L., and Sederholm, C. H., *J. Chem. Phys.*, **35**, 1174 (1961).
49. Jouve, P., *Compt. Rend.*, **256**, 1497 (1963); *Chem. Abstr.*, **58**, 10890 (1963).
50. Ebsworth, E. A. V., and Frankiss, S. G., *J. Chem. Soc.*, 661 (1963).
51. Hirst, R., and Grant, D. M., *J. Am. Chem. Soc.*, **84**, 2009 (1962).
52. Jouve, P., and Simonnin, M. P., *Compt. Rend.*, **257**, 121 (1963); *Chem. Abstr.*, **59**, 7094 (1963).
53. Simonnin, M. P., *Bull. Soc. Chim. France*, 1774 (1966).
54. Eglinton, G., and McCrae, W., *Advan. Org. Chem.*, **4**, 225 (1963).
55. Drenth, W., and Loewenstein, A., *Rec. Trav. Chim.*, **81**, 635 (1962).
56. Petrov, A. A., and Lebedev, V. B., *Zh. Obshch. Khim.*, **32**, 657 (1962); *Chem. Abstr.*, **57**, 14612 (1962).

57. Pittman, C. V., Jr., and Olah, G. A., *J. Am. Chem. Soc.*, **87**, 5632 (1965).
58. Snyder, E. I., and Roberts, J. D., *J. Am. Chem. Soc.*, **84**, 1582 (1962).
59. Matteson, D. R., *J. Org. Chem.*, **27**, 4293 (1962).
60. Masson, J. C., and Cadiot, P., *Bull. Soc. Chim. France*, 3518 (1965).

Chapter Three

PREPARATION OF ACETYLENIC COMPOUNDS BY ELIMINATION REACTIONS

Introduction

Some acetylenic compounds are most conveniently made by elimination reactions. Others such as *t*-alkylacetylenes and acetylenic ethers cannot be made by any other method. Several recent reviews cover elimination reactions thoroughly: Jacobs (1949) listed many acetylenes prepared by elimination reactions;[1] Arens (1960) reviewed preparation of ethynyl ethers and thioethers;[2] Franke (1963),[3] Ziegenbein (1963),[4] and Köbrich (1965)[5] discussed other compounds and preparations. The main purpose of this chapter is to present enough data and references to provide a convenient starting point for chemists interested in preparing certain acetylenes.

Dehydrohalogenation is the first and most widely used elimination reaction for making acetylenes. Dehydrohalogenation of haloolefins by an oxygen-containing base is the oldest elimination method: In 1861, Sawitsch[6] made the first known alkylacetylene, propyne, from bromopropene. In 1933, Rujicka[7] made the first cyclic acetylene, cyclo-heptadecyne, by dehydrobrominating 1-bromo-1-cycloheptadecene with KOH-EtOH at 180°. Franke has described a good laboratory synthesis for cyclodecyne. Oxygen-containing bases have some limitations: they cannot be used to make dihaloacetylenes in solvents, but dry KOH can be used; they isomerize terminal acetylenes to internal acetylenes; products sometimes add fragments from the reaction mixture (alcohol, for example, to form vinyl

22

ethers); oxygen-containing bases usually work well only if the eliminated H and X are *trans*.

Alkali metal amides are also widely used. They work well with both the *cis* and the *trans* compounds. A good laboratory preparation of sodium amide has been described.[7] Commercial sodamide can be used, but should not be ground because peroxides may be contaminants.

Alkali metal organic compounds, such as lithium alkyls, are strong bases but weak nucleophiles. They dehydrohalogenate haloolefins under very mild conditions. Metals such as zinc can dehalogenate dihaloolefins to acetylenes. Alkali metals cleave halovinyl ethers to form acetylenes.

Dehydrohalogenation reaction mechanisms are interesting but are not within the scope of this brief discussion. Köbrich[5] presented an excellent discussion of mechanisms in his review.

1. TERTIARY AND SECONDARY ALKYNES

Alkali metal acetylides dehydrohalogenate tertiary and secondary alkyl halides, so normal alkylation gives low yields. Elimination reactions are better. Dehydrohalogenation of *gem*-dichlorides by KOH[8] is usually slower than by sodium amide.[9] The starting dichlorides are easily made by the $AlCl_3$-catalyzed addition of secondary or tertiary alkyl chlorides to vinyl chloride at $-39°$. van Boom[9] made some acetylenes from alkyl chlorides and vinyl chloride, and the overall yields of alkynes were 30–55% based on alkyl chloride (using sodamide in ammonia). Dehydrohalogenation of similar dihalides by KOH-ROH at 150–200° gave tertiary alkyl-acetylenes in 33–70% yields.[8] Some tertiary alkylacetylenes and secondary alkylacetylenes made by dehydrohalogenation are listed in Table 3-1.

Pomerantz and co-workers[10] have done some of these reactions on a 50-mole scale. Their procedure for the alkyl halide-vinyl chloride reaction is:

To 50 moles of isopropyl chloride in a 5-gallon brass kettle was added 2.5 moles of anhydrous aluminium chloride. After a short time the darkening and effervescence stopped and the mixture was cooled to $-30°$. Vinyl chloride, 53 moles, was bubbled rapidly into the stirred mixture. Efficient heat removal was necessary to prevent the reaction from becoming violent. All of the vinyl chloride was added in 2 hours. The mix was stirred for another $1\frac{1}{2}$ hours and poured onto ice. The product layer was on the bottom; it was extracted by ligroin, washed and fractionated. The cut boiling at 127–130.5° amounted to 72% yield.

The starting dichlorides can also be made by reacting carbonyl compounds with PCl_5. Jacobs[1] lists some acetylenes made from dichlorides prepared by this reaction.

Cymerman-Craig[11] noted that phosphate anions are possible leaving groups in the biosynthesis of acetylenes. He found he could make acetylenes by treating diethyl vinyl phosphates with sodamide in ammonia:

$$\underset{\overset{\displaystyle |}{RC}=CHR'}{OPO(OEt)_2} \longrightarrow RC\equiv CR'$$

TABLE 3-1

Secondary and Tertiary Alkynes by Dehydrochlorination

$$RCl + CH_2=CHCl \longrightarrow RCH_2CHCl_2 \longrightarrow RC\equiv CH$$

R	Dehydrochlorination	% Yield of $RC\equiv CH$ from RCl	Reference
Me_2CH-	$NaNH_2$-mineral oil	62	10
	$NaNH_2$-NH_3	41	9
$EtMeCH-$	$NaNH_2$-mineral oil	59	10
	$NaNH_2$-NH_3	40	9
Me_3C-	$NaNH_2$-mineral oil	45	10
Me_3C-	$NaNH_2$-NH_3	56	9
Me_2EtC-	$NaNH_2$-NH_3	45–50	9
Et_2MeC-	$NaNH_2$-NH_3	30–35	9
Et_3C-	$NaNH_2$-NH_3	35–40	9
$BuMe_2C-$	$NaNH_2$–NH_3	40	9
i-$PrMe_2C-$	KOH-glycol-200	70	8
t-$BuMe_2C-$	KOH-170	33	8
$Me_3CCH_2C(Me)_2-$	KOH-glycol-200	50	8

2. ARYLACETYLENES

Arylacetylenes are usually made by elimination reactions, although a few have been prepared by reacting aryl iodides with cuprous acetylides (see Chapter 4).

In the *Organic Syntheses*[12] procedure for phenylacetylene, α,β-dibromoethylbenzene is treated with sodium amide in ammonia to give 50% yield of pure product. Good laboratory preparations of p-tolylacetylene and of p-bromophenylacetylene have been described. KOH-EtOH was used as the dehydrohalogenating reagent.[1] Drehfahl[13] prepared diarylacetylenes and some bis-(acetylenes) by brominating stilbenes and treating the bromides with KOH-butanol at 170° for 3 hours (Table 3-2).

α-Diketones react with 2 moles of triethyl phosphite at 215° to give disubstituted acetylenes in 24–60% yields.[14] The 1:1 diketone-triethyl phosphite adducts with excess phosphite at 215° give 74–81% yields. A cyclic phosphate may be the intermediate, and may decompose to a ketene:

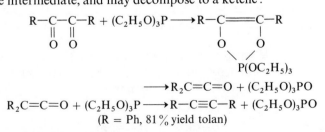

$$R_2C=C=O + (C_2H_5O)_3P \longrightarrow R-C\equiv C-R + (C_2H_5O)_3PO$$
(R = Ph, 81% yield tolan)

TABLE 3-2
Preparation of Tolan and Bis(tolans)[13]

Tolan[a]	m.p. (°C)	% Yield
PhC≡CPh	60	93
MeC$_6$H$_4$C≡CPh	78	90
MeC$_6$H$_4$C≡CC$_6$H$_4$Me	136	90
PhC≡CC$_6$H$_4$C≡CPh	185	—
PhC≡CC$_6$H$_4$C≡CC$_6$H$_4$Me	174	—
MeC$_6$H$_4$C≡CC$_6$H$_4$C≡CC$_6$H$_4$Me	216	—
PhC≡CC$_6$H$_4$CH≡CHPh	277	85

[a] Disubstitution in benzene rings is *para* in all cases. All of the solid products showed green to violet fluorescence.

Table 3-3 contains a list of arylacetylenes prepared by various dehydrohalogenation reactions. Several other elimination reactions are also included.

3. DIACETYLENES

Armitage[30] prepared free diacetylene by adding 1,4-dichloro-2-butyne to 10% NaOH plus a little dioxane at 100°. He collected free diacetylene at −25°, as much as 15 grams in a single experiment. No difficulties were experienced if the receiver for diacetylene was held below −25°. The reverse addition procedure has been used, with a stream of hydrogen to sweep out the diacetylene.[31] Pomerantz[10] worked on a larger scale, using KOH-EtOH-water as the dehydrohalogenating medium. The diacetylene was purified by fractionation. Pomerantz also made 1,5-hexadiyne by sodamide-ammonia dehydrobromination of 1,2,5,6-tetrabromohexane. The yield was 63% in a 50-mole reaction.

4. POLYFLUOROACETYLENES

4.1. 3,3,3-Trifluoropropyne

A novel method for making 3,3,3-trifluoropropyne is:[32]

$$CF_3CCl=CCl_2 + 2Zn \xrightarrow[ZnCl_2]{solvent} [(CF_3C≡C)_2Zn \text{ or } CF_3C≡CZnCl] + ZnCl_2$$
$$(dust)$$

$$\xrightarrow{H_2O} CF_3C≡CH$$
$$(75.3\%)$$

Dimethylformamide, dimethylacetamide and N-methyl-2-pyrollidone are good

TABLE 3-3
Arylacetylenes by Elimination Reactions

Starting Material	Reagents	Arylacetylene	% Yield	Reference
		(a) Monoarylacetylenes		
$PhCCl{=}CCl_2$	Mg-THF	$PhC{\equiv}CH$	68	15
$RPhCCl{=}CH_2$	$NaNH_2$-NH_3	$RPhC{\equiv}CH$	High	16, 17
$PhCH{=}C(SO_2Et)_2$	650°	$PhC{\equiv}CH$	40	18
$Ar(CCl_2CH_3)_n$	$NaNH_2$-NH_3	4-Ethynyldiphenyl, 4,4'-diethynyl-diphenyl, bis[4-(4'-ethynyldiphenyl)], diacetylene, 2-ethynylfluorene, 2,7-diethynylfluorene	70	19
α,α-Dichloroethyl-azo-benzene	$NaNH_2$-NH_3	4-Ethynyl-trans-azo-benzene		20
(Pyridine + CCl_2CH_3	KOH-EtOH, reflux	1-, 2- and 3-Ethynyl-pyridine	1–30	21
(Quinoline + CCl_2CH_3	KOH-EtOH, reflux	3-, 4-, 5-, 6-, 7- and 8-Ethynylquinoline		21
		(b) Diarylacetylenes		
$RR'CCl{-}{=}N$ $HN{\diagdown}_{N{\diagup}}{N}$	110–200°	$RC{\equiv}CR'$ (R = aliphatic, aromatic)	16–80	22
$ArCHBrCHBrAr'$	KOH-BuOH, 160°	$ArC{\equiv}CAr'$	90–93	13
$PhCHBrCHBrPh$-p-CHO	KOH-BuOH, reflux	$PhC{\equiv}CPh$-p-CHO + $PhC{\equiv}CPh$-p-CO_2H	15 46	23
β-Phenylphenacyl chloride	Ph_3P, benzene, reflux	$PhC{\equiv}CPh$	90	24
$(p$-$ROPh)_2C{=}CBr_2$ or $(p$-$ROPh)_2C{=}CHCl$	$NaOCH_2CH_2$-OH, glycol, reflux	p-$ROPhC{\equiv}CPh$-p-OR (note Ar migrates)	95 (R = Me)	25, 26
$Ph_2C{=}CHCl$	BuLi, Et_2O, $-35°$	$PhC{\equiv}CPh$ (Ph migrates)	80	27
$ArC{-}CAr'$ $\;\;{\Vert}\;\;{\Vert}$ $H_2NN\;\;NNH_2$	Silver trifluoro-acetate, Et_3N, 20°	$ArC{\equiv}Ar'$	60–80	28

TABLE 3-3-(continued)

Starting Material	Reagents	Arylacetylene	% Yield	Reference
(c) Aryl Polyacetylenes				

$HCC{\equiv}CCHClCH_3$ (Cl, aryl ring)	$NaHN_2$	$(C{\equiv}C)_2CH_3$ (aryl ring)	7	29
$HCC{\equiv}CCHClCH_3$ / Cl (aryl ring)		$(C{\equiv}C)_2CH_3$ (aryl ring)		
4,4'-Bis(phenylethynyl) desoxybenzoin	$Al(i\text{-}OPr)_3$, 180–280°	$(PhC{\equiv}CC_6H_4C{\not\equiv})_2$	82	23
$PhC{\equiv}CC_6H_4C{=}CH-$ / CO_2H / $C_6H_4C{\equiv}CPh$	250°	$(PhC{\equiv}CC_6H_4CH{\not\equiv})_2$	30	23

solvents. Trichlorotrifluoropropene reacts much faster than 1,2-dichloro-3,3,3-trifluoropropene, perhaps because the additional electron-withdrawing chloride accelerates the initial reaction with zinc.

4.2. Hexafluoro-2-butyne

Dehalogenation of 2,3-dichlorohexafluoro-2-butene is the most widely used method for making hexafluoro-2-butyne.[3,33] In a completely different synthesis, acetylenedicarboxylic acid reacts with SF_4 to form hexafluoro-2-butyne.[34]

4.3. Symmetrical Polyfluoroalkylacetylenes

Krespan[35] has developed two new syntheses for these products:

(1) $F_2C{=}CF_2 + CCl_4 \xrightarrow[25\ min]{275°} Cl(CF_2CF_2)_nCCl_3 \xrightarrow{Cu,\ 180°} [Cl(CF_2CF_2)_nC{\not\equiv}]_2$ (Cl)

$$\begin{pmatrix} n = 1,\ 30\%\ \text{yield} \\ n = 2,\ 14\%\ \text{yield} \\ n = 3,\ \ 7\%\ \text{yield} \end{pmatrix} \quad (65\%\ \text{yield})$$

$\xrightarrow{Zn\text{-}Ac_2O} [Cl(CF_2CF_2)_nC{\not\equiv}]_2$
(70%)

(2) $2R_FCOCl + Ni(CO)_4 + CF_2{=}CCl_2 \longrightarrow R_FCF_2CCl_2 \cdot \xrightarrow{\times 2} R_FCF_2CCl_2CCl_2CF_2R_F$

$\xrightarrow{Ni(CO)_4} R_FCF_2CCl{=}CClCF_2R_F \xrightarrow{Zn\text{-}Ac_2O} R_FCF_2C{\equiv}CCF_2R_F$

5. ENYNES

5.1. Vinylacetylene

1,4- or 1,2-Dichloro-2-butene with sodium amide in ammonia at $-35°$ gives sodium vinylacetylide. This is a convenient source of vinylacetylene in a safe form which can be alkylated or reacted with carbonyl compounds to form derivatives. In the *Organic Syntheses* preparation, 2,4-dichloro-2-butene is reacted with KOH-glycol at 170° to give 45 % yield of vinylacetylene.[36]

5.2. Isoalkenylacetylenes

The most general synthesis is dehydration of tertiary acetylenic carbinols over a sulfonated polystyrene resin at 70°:[38]

$$\underset{\underset{OH}{|}}{\overset{\overset{R'}{|}}{RCH_2C}}{-}C{\equiv}CH \longrightarrow \overset{\overset{R'}{|}}{RCH}{=}C{-}C{\equiv}CH$$

5.3. Other Enynes

1-Alkynyl or 2-alkynyl ethers in the presence of at least 2 equivalents of sodium amide or potassium amide in ammonia give 1,3-enynes, perhaps via cumulenes.[39] If the 2-alkynyl ethers are used, they must have at least one hydrogen atom in the 4-position.[40] Potassium amide, which is more soluble in ammonia than sodium amide, is required for ethers with a tertiary carbon at the 4-position: $RR'\overset{4}{C}H\overset{3}{C}{\equiv}\overset{2}{C}\overset{1}{C}H_2OEt$. Sodium amide isomerizes these ethers to allenyl ethers and enyne forms slowly.

Cyclic ethers also cleave to form enynes:

$$MeC{\equiv}C\overset{\overset{Me}{|}}{C}\underset{\diagdown \diagup}{\overset{}{\quad}}CH_2 \xrightarrow{2KNH_2} HC{\equiv}CCH{=}C(Me)CH_2OH$$

$$\underset{O}{\diagdown} C{\equiv}CMe \xrightarrow{2KNH_2} HC{\equiv}CCH{=}CH(CH_2)_4OH$$

Polyene systems can also be prepared by elimination:

$$MeC\equiv CC-CH=CH_2 \xrightarrow{2KNH_2} HC\equiv CCH=C-CH=CH_2$$

with Me substituent on the first structure (O—R below) and Me substituent on the product.

(R = 2-tetrahydropyranyl)

If the methyl group on carbon 1 is replaced by hydrogen, only tarry products form.

1-Alkynyl ethers give only 30–40% yields of enynes. The eliminated group can be O-alkyl, O-phenyl, O-propargylic or tetrahydropyranyloxy. S-Alkyl groups also eliminate well.[41] Halogen, acyloxy and hydroxy are not suitable leaving groups. The *cis-trans* ratio in the product enynes varies from 1 to 0.6. The *cis* isomer is lower boiling.

Table 3-4 summarizes some typical eliminations which form enynes.

6. ALCOHOLS

Acetylenic alcohols are usually made by ethynylation or alkynylation reactions, but some must be made by eliminations. 2-Chloromethylfuran treated with sodamide in ammonia gives 2-pentyn-1-ol in 80–85% yield.[47,48] Dihydropyran with *n*-amylsodium gives the same alcohol.[49]

The *Organic Syntheses* preparation of 2-butyn-1-ol is a two-step procedure:[50]

$$MeC=CHCH_2Cl + Na_2CO_3 \xrightarrow{H_2O} MeC=CHCH_2OH \xrightarrow[NH_3]{NaNH_2} MeC\equiv CCH_2OH$$
$$(63\%) \qquad\qquad (80\%)$$

with Cl substituents on the first two structures.

7. ALDEHYDES AND ACETALS

Dihaloacetals can be dehydrohalogenated to acetylenic acetals:[51]

$$CH_2BrCHBrCH(OEt)_2 \xrightarrow[NH_3]{NaNH_2} HC\equiv CCH(OEt)_2$$
$$(78\%)$$

An enyne aldehyde is formed by this unusual reaction:[52]

$$CH_2=C-CC\equiv CH + \text{2-nitropropane} \xrightarrow[H_2O,\ 5°]{KOH,\ MeOH,} O=C-C=CC\equiv CH$$

with CH$_3$ CH$_3$ substituents and Br substituent on the reactant, and H, CH$_3$, CH$_3$ substituents on the product.

TABLE 3-4

Formation of Enynes by Elimination Reactions

Starting Material	Reagent	Enyne	% Yield	Reference
$[Me_3N^+(CH_2)_nCH{=}]_2$	Heat, vacuum	Vinylacetylene	29	42
		2-Hexen-4-yne	85	43
$ClCH_2CH{=}CHCH_2Cl$	KOH-ethyl Cellosolve	Vinylacetylene (good lab prep.)	82	38
$RR'C(OH)C{\equiv}CCH{=}CH_2$	Sulfonated polystyrene, 70°	$RCH{=}CC{\equiv}CCH{=}CH_2$ (R′)	74–84	44
$ROCH_2C{\equiv}CCH_2OR$	KOH, 100°	$ROCH_2CH{=}CHC{\equiv}CH$	—	
$HCR''R'''C(R'){=}C{=}CHBr$	CuCN or CuI, DMF, 80°	$R''R''C{=}C(R')C{\equiv}CH$ all R = H	22	45
$BrCH_2CH(OEt)CH_2C{\equiv}CH$ (R)	Zn–t-BuO	Allylacetylene	78	46
$HC{\equiv}CCH{=}CCH_2CH_2OR'$ (R)	KNH_2–NH_3 (1,2-elimination)	$HC{\equiv}CCH{=}CCH{=}CH_2$ (R) (R = H, CH₃)	50	46a
$CH_3C{\equiv}CC{=}CHCH_2OR'$ (R)	KNH_2–NH_3 (1,6-elimination)	$HC{\equiv}CCH{=}CCH{=}CH_2$ (R) (R = H, CH₃)	15–70	46a

8. AMINOBUTYNES

These are usually made by the Mannich reaction or by reacting a propargylic halide with an amine. Elimination methods are illustrated by two reactions (see references 53 and 54, respectively):

$$\underset{\underset{\displaystyle Cl}{|}}{Me_2NCH_2C}=CHCH_2NMe_2 \xrightarrow{\text{KOH, EtOH}} Me_2NCH_2C\equiv CCH_2NMe_2$$
$$(68\%)$$

$$\alpha\text{-aminotetrahydropyrans} \xrightarrow{\text{Mg acetylides}} \underset{\underset{\displaystyle NRR'}{|}}{HO(CH_2)_4CHC}\equiv CR''$$
$$(70\text{–}89\%)$$

9. α-ACETYLENIC KETONES

In 1965, Chopard[55] reported a new synthesis of α-acetylenic ketones:

$$Ph_3P=CHCR + (R'C)_2O \longrightarrow Ph_3P=C \overset{\displaystyle CR}{\underset{\displaystyle CR'}{}} \xrightarrow[\text{0.01 mm, 1 hr}]{250\text{–}280°} RC\equiv CCR'$$

Starting Materials		Ketone	% Yield
R	R'		
Me	Me	MeC≡CCMe (O)	88
Me	Ph	PhC≡CCMe (O) + MeC≡CCPh (O)	90
Ph	Ph	PhC≡CCPh (O)	67

10. α-ACETYLENIC ACIDS

α-Acetylenic acids are frequently made by carbonating metal derivatives of terminal acetylenes, but some are best made by elimination reactions. Several new reactions give good yields.

In the *Organic Syntheses*[56] procedure for acetylenedicarboxylic acid, α,β-dibromosuccinic acid is refluxed for 15 minutes in KOH-MeOH. The yield is 75–85%. Detailed laboratory syntheses for phenylpropiolic acids are available.[3]

An intermolecular Wittig reaction was used to prepare precursors to acetylenic acids.[57] One mole of acyl chloride added to triphenylphosphinecarbomethoxymethylene in benzene gives instant precipitation of salt, leaving the product

$$Ph_3P=C-CO_2Me$$
$$|$$
$$O=C-R$$

in solution (75–100% yields). Heating the soluble adduct at 220–250° gives 65–80% yields of acid esters, $RC\equiv CCO_2Me$, where R can be aryl, furyl or methyl (see also reference 58).

Enol elimination reactions can also be used to prepare olefinic- or aromatic-acetylenic acids.[59,60]

$$
\underset{RCCH(CO_2Et)_2}{\overset{O}{\overset{\|}{}}} \xrightarrow[(2),\,p\text{-BrPhSO}_2\text{Cl}]{(1)\ \text{NaOEt}} \underset{RC=C(CO_2Et)_2}{\overset{OSO_2PhBr}{\overset{|}{}}} \xrightarrow[\text{aqueous dioxane}]{\text{NaOH}}
$$

$$RC\equiv CCO_2H + R\overset{O}{\overset{\|}{C}}CH(CO_2Et)_2$$

Note that the starting acylmalonic ester is regenerated in the hydrolysis step; this improves the overall yield. This method is general for enynoic acids, $X(CH=CH)_nC\equiv CCO_2H$, but R must be unsaturated and conjugated with the developing acetylenic bond.

R	$RC\equiv CCO_2H$ m.p. (°C)	% Yield
Ph	138	73
PhCH=CH—	151	52
MeCH=CH—	131	57
Me(CH=CH)$_2$—	120	30

The reaction also works when R is 2-furyl, 2-thienyl or cyclopropyl (an exception to the general rule that R must be unsaturated and conjugated).

Ketones can also be prepared:[61]

$$\underset{\overset{|}{\text{PhC}}}{\overset{\text{OSO}_2\text{R}}{}} = \underset{\overset{\|}{\text{C(CPh)}_2}}{\overset{\text{O}}{}} + \text{NaOH} \longrightarrow \text{PhC} \equiv \text{CCPh} + \text{benzoic acid} + \text{RSO}_3^-$$

Several other elimination reactions which form acetylenic acids are listed in Table 3-5.

TABLE 3-5
Preparation of Acetylenic Acids by Elimination Reactions

Starting Material	Reagent	Acid	% Yield	Reference
4,4-Dichloro-2-pyrazolin-5-ones (from β-ketoesters)	Aqueous NaOH, then acid	$RC \equiv CCO_2H$		
		R = Ph	89	62
		Me	76	63
		Et	72	
		Pr	71	
		t-Bu	57	
$\left[\underset{\overset{\|}{R-C}}{\overset{R'-SMe}{}} = CHCO_2Et \right]^+ MeSO_4^-$	NaOH	$RC \equiv CCO_2Et$		64
		R = p-NO$_2$Ph	70	
		Ph	80	
		m-NO$_2$Ph	50	
		p-ClPh	75	
		α-naphthyl	55	
		β-naphthyl	77	
		2-thienyl	25	
		p-Phenylene-di-propiolic ester	65	
		m-Phenylene-di-propiolic ester	70	

11. ACETYLENIC TIN COMPOUNDS

Tributyltin azide does not add to acetylenedicarboxylic acid to give triazoles as other azides do.[65] The tin-nitrogen bond cleaves (Table 3-6):

$$\text{Bu}_3\text{SnN}_3 + \text{HO}_2\text{CC} \equiv \text{CCO}_2\text{H} \longrightarrow 2\text{HN}_3 + \text{Bu}_3\text{Sn}\overset{\overset{\text{O}}{\|}}{\text{OCC}} \equiv \text{CC}\overset{\overset{\text{O}}{\|}}{\text{OSnBu}_3}$$

This product at its melting point evolves CO_2 and forms bis(tributylstannyl)-acetylene, $\text{Bu}_3\text{SnC} \equiv \text{CSnBu}_3$ (Table 3-7). This is the first known preparation of acetylenic tin compounds by decarboxylation.

TABLE 3-6
Organotin Acetylenedicarboxylates from
Acetylenic Acids and R_3SnN_3[65]

Product	% Yield	m.p. (°C)
$(CH_3)_3SnOOCC{\equiv}CCOOSn(CH_3)_3$	68	—
$(C_2H_5)_3SnOOCC{\equiv}CCOOSn(C_2H_5)_3$	48	161 (dec.)
$(n\text{-}C_3H_7)_3SnOOCC{\equiv}CCOOSn(n\text{-}C_3H_7)_3$	50	155–156 (dec.)
$(n\text{-}C_4H_9)_3SnOOCC{\equiv}CCOOSn(n\text{-}C_4H_9)_3$	83	176–177 (dec.)
$(C_6H_5)_3SnOOCC{\equiv}CCOOSn(C_6H_5)_3$	59	185 (dec.)
$(n\text{-}C_4H_9)_3SnOOCC{\equiv}CH$	quant.	53–55
$(C_6H_5)_3SnOOCC{\equiv}CH$	81	174–175.5 (dec.)
$(n\text{-}C_4H_9)_3SnOOCC{\equiv}CC_6H_5$	59	57–58
$(C_6H_5)_3SnOOCC{\equiv}CC_6H_5$	91	175–176 (dec.)

ᵃ dec. = decomposes.

When the organotin acetylenecarboxylates are heated to 170–180°, they form the organotin-substituted acetylenes listed in Table 3-7.

TABLE 3-7
Organotin-substituted Acetylenes

Product	% Yield	m.p. (°C)	b.p. (°C, @ mm Hg)
$(CH_3)_3SnC{\equiv}CSn(CH_3)_3$	78	57.5–59	97–98, @ 16
$(C_2H_5)_3SnC{\equiv}CSn(C_2H_5)_3$	52.5	—	114–115, @ 0.18–0.1
$(n\text{-}C_3H_7)_3SnC{\equiv}CSn(n\text{-}C_3H_7)_3$	94	—	136–137, @ 0.1–0.12
$(n\text{-}C_4H_9)_3SnC{\equiv}CSn(n\text{-}C_4H_9)_3$	92	—	158–159, @ 0.08
$(C_6H_5)_3SnC{\equiv}CSn(C_6H_5)_3$	37.5	140–142.5	—
$(n\text{-}C_4H_9)_3SnC{\equiv}CC_6H_5$	89.5	—	184, @ 1–2
$(C_6H_5)_3SnC{\equiv}CC_6H_5$	93	58–59	—

Tributyltin propiolate does not decarboxylate. Triphenyltin propiolate gives moderate yield of bis(triphenyltin)acetylene. This forms via triphenylstannyl-acetylene, which is thermally unstable and disproportionates to acetylene and the disubstituted acetylene.

Acetylenic acid esters, however, add tributyltin azide and form the expected triazoles:

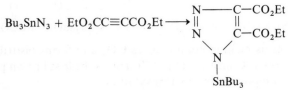

12. ACETYLENIC ETHERS

The usual laboratory procedure[66] for ethoxyethyne is

$$ClCH_2CH(OEt)_2 + 3NaNH_2 \xrightarrow{NH_3} NaC{\equiv}COEt \xrightarrow[N_2]{H^+} HC{\equiv}COEt$$
$$(60\%)$$

The sodium ethoxyacetylide intermediate is extremely pyrophoric, and the acidification step must be done under nitrogen. Variations of this dehydrohalogenation are used for many alkynyl ethers. In his comprehensive review in 1959, Arens[2] listed the physical properties of all the known ethynyl ethers and gave some detailed syntheses. Procedures reported since then are emphasized here.

Ethynyl ethers and 1-alkynyl ethers are colorless liquids. The lower ethers have "objectionable, musty" odors, but the higher ones smell sweeter.[2] Ethoxyethyne is toxic, and its vapors cause headaches. The Humphrey Chemical Company offers ethoxyethyne commercially. According to one of their recent bulletins, ethoxyethyne has only slight oral toxicity. Alkoxyethynes are more stable than phenoxyethyne and can be kept at $0°$ for considerable periods of time. Arens never had explosions with ethoxyethyne under normal conditions, but ethoxyethynylcarbinols did cause a few violent explosions.

1-Acetylenic ethers must be made by elimination procedures. One common method is dehydrohalogenation of halovinyl ethers by KOH, sodium amide or potassium alkoxides:

$$RCX{=}CHOR' + KOH \longrightarrow RC{\equiv}COR' + KX + H_2O$$
$$(30–90\%)$$

Another general synthesis starts with α,β-dihaloalkyl ethers. The first mole of HX is usually removed by diethylaniline, and the second by lithium amide or sodium amide in ammonia.

12.1. Alkyl 1-Ethynyl and 1-Alkynyl Ethers

In 1961, van Daalen reported the first t-butyl acetylenic ethers:[67]

$$H_2C{=}CH{-}O{-}t\text{-}Bu + Br_2 \longrightarrow H_2CBrCHBr{-}O{-}t\text{-}Bu \xrightarrow{PhNEt_2} BrCH{=}CH{-}O{-}t\text{-}Bu$$

$$\xrightarrow[NH_3]{LiNH_2} HC{\equiv}C{-}O{-}t\text{-}Bu \xrightarrow[(2)\ RBr]{(1)\ LiNH_2,\ NH_3} RC{\equiv}C{-}O{-}t\text{-}Bu$$

KOH cannot be used for removing the second HX.

The same procedure can be used to make isopropyl and neopentyl acetylenic ethers. Aldehydes are convenient starting materials for the α,β-dihaloalkyl ethers:

$$RCH_2CHO + i\text{-}PrOH + HCl \longrightarrow RCH_2CHCl{-}O{-}i\text{-}Pr \xrightarrow{Br_2}$$

$$RCHBrCHBr{-}O{-}i\text{-}Pr \xrightarrow{PhNEt_2} RCBr{=}CH{-}O{-}i\text{-}Pr \xrightarrow[NH_3]{NaNH_2} RC{\equiv}C{-}O{-}i\text{-}Pr$$

Sodium amide is much better than KOH for removing the second molecule of HBr. Sodium amide dehydrobrominates both the *cis* and *trans* forms of unsaturated bromoethers, but KOH will not remove HBr from the *cis* isomer. Sodium amide is not as good for 1-propynyl ethers because it isomerizes them to propargyl ethers.

12.2. Benzyl 1-Alkynyl Ethers

Again starting with the corresponding aldehydes, the first acetylenic benzyl ethers were made in 1964:[68]

$$RCH_2CHO + HCl + HOCHR'Ph \longrightarrow RCH_2CHCl-O-CHR'Ph \xrightarrow{Br_2}$$

$$RCHBrCHBr-O-CHR'Ph \xrightarrow[\text{(2) NaNH}_2, \text{ NH}_3]{\text{(1) PhNEt}_2, \text{ benzene}} RC\equiv C-O-CHR'Ph$$
$$(60-90\% \text{ yield})$$

The benzyl ethers are more sensitive to heat than the aliphatic acetylenic ethers. They can explode around 60°.

12.3. Bis(1-acetylenic) Ethers

Nooi and Arens in 1962 reported the first examples of bis(1-acetylenic) ethers.[69] Type (1): $ROC\equiv C(CH_2)_nC\equiv COR$; type (2): $RC\equiv CO(CH_2)_nOC\equiv CR$. They made type (1) ethers, $n = 3$ or 4, by reacting sodioethynyl ethyl ether with dihalides:

$$\begin{array}{c} ClCH=CHOEt + 2NaNH_2 \\ \text{or} \\ ClCH_2CH(OEt)_2 + 3NaNH_2 \end{array} \longrightarrow NaC\equiv COEt \xrightarrow{X(CH_2)_nX} EtOC\equiv C(CH_2)_nC\equiv COEt$$

They modified the aldehyde-alcohol-HCl reaction to make bis(α-chloroalkyl) glycol ethers as starting materials for type (2) bis(acetylenic) ethers:

$$2CH_3CHO + HOCH_2CH_2OH + HCl \longrightarrow CH_3CHCl-OCH_2CH_2O-CHClCH_3$$
$$(100\% \text{ yield})$$

$$CH_2BrCHBr-OCH_2CH_2O-CHBrCH_2Br \xleftarrow{Br_2} CH_2=CH-OCH_2CH_2O-CH=CH_2$$
$$(100\% \text{ yield}) \qquad\qquad\qquad (55\% \text{ yield})$$

(Br₂, diethylaniline)

$$CHBr=CH-OCH_2CH_2O-CH=CHBr \xrightarrow[\text{HN}_3]{4LiNH_2} LiC\equiv C-OCH_2CH_2O-C\equiv CLi$$
$$(52\% \text{ yield})$$

(2MeI)

$$MeC\equiv C-OCH_2CH_2O-C\equiv CMe$$
$$(80\% \text{ yield})$$

They prepared numerous examples and determined physical properties. Yields of type (2) ethers are sometimes low: the bis(bromovinyl) ether reacts at one end only, and products contain allenes which polymerize.

12.4. Dialkynyl Ethers

A good synthesis for dialkynyl ethers is:[70]

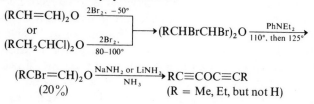

$$(RCBr{=}CH)_2O \xrightarrow[\text{NH}_3]{\text{NaNH}_2 \text{ or LiNH}_2} RC{\equiv}COC{\equiv}CR$$
$$(20\%) \qquad\qquad (R = Me, Et, but not H)$$

13. ETHYNYL AND 1-ALKYNYL THIOETHERS AND SELENOETHERS

Ethynyl and 1-alkynyl thioethers are frequently made by dehydrohalogenation procedures similar to those used for the oxygen ethers.[2,3] Thioethers can also be made by nucleophilic displacement reactions between thiolate anions and 1-haloacetylenes (see Chapter 4). Aromatic thioethers are not very stable even at 0°. The aliphatic thioethers are more stable and can be kept for some time in sealed tubes. Ethynyl thioethers are not very explosive. In 1959, only one acetylenic selenoether existed: phenylselenoethyne. Since then, other selenium ethers and a few tellurium ethers have been made, usually by nucleophilic displacement reactions. For example, sodioalkynes react with S, Se or Te, and then with RX to form $R'C{\equiv}C{-}S(Se \text{ or } Te){-}R$.[71]

13.1. Ethynyl and 1-Alkynyl Thioethers

Dehydrobromination is the most common elimination reaction. Aromatic and aliphatic thioethers are also prepared from *cis*- or *trans*-ethenylene 1,2-bis-(thioethers) by elimination of thiol. Butyllithium is an efficient reagent:

$$RSCH{=}CHSR + 2BuLi \longrightarrow 2BuH + LiC{\equiv}CSR + RSLi$$

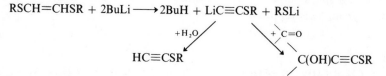

When the unfiltered unhydrolyzed mixture reacts with a ketone, carbinols form. Equally good results are obtained starting with 1-alkoxy-2-(alkyl or arylthio)-ethylenes, $ROCH{=}CHSR$. ROH is eliminated.

A simpler and more general synthesis uses sodium amide or lithium amide in ammonia instead of butyllithium:

$$RSCH=CHSR + 2NaNH_2 \longrightarrow 2NH_3 + RSNa + NaC{\equiv}CSR \xrightarrow{\overset{\diagdown}{C=O} \diagdown} \underset{/}{C(OH)C{\equiv}CSR}$$

With ethylthioethyne, acetone, methyl hexyl ketone, and cyclohexanone gave carbinol in 80, 68 and 63% yields, respectively.[72]

RSNa must be removed if the ethynyl thioether is to be recovered from the mixture. This is done most simply by adding organic halide, RX. 1-Acetylenic thioethers were isolated in 23–47% yields by this procedure.[72] Side reactions are possible because many ions are present in the reaction mixture. The ion $RSC{\equiv}C^-$ can react with the alkyl halide to form $R'C{\equiv}CSR$; if two moles of alkyl halide are added, alkylated ethers are obtained in 20–60% yields. *cis*-Ethenylene 1,2-bis(thioethers) are prepared easily: If 1 equivalent each of commercial *cis*, *trans*-dichloroethylene and thiol are added to 2 equivalents of sodium amide in ammonia, the bis(thioethers) form in 55–60% yield. If another 2 moles of sodium amide are added without isolating the ethenylene bis(thioether), and then 2 moles of alkyl halide are added, $RC{\equiv}CSR'$ is made directly.

13.2. RSC≡CSR

In 1961, Nooi and Arens[73] reported compounds which have one acetylene group between two sulfur atoms:

$$ClCH=CHCl \xrightarrow{LiNH_2,\ NH_3} Li^+\ C{\equiv}CCl^- \xrightarrow{+RSSR} RSC{\equiv}CCl \xrightarrow{+RS^-} [RS\overset{|}{\underset{Cl}{C}}{=}CSR]$$

$$\longrightarrow RSC{\equiv}CSR + Cl^-$$
$$(82\%)$$

This is a more convenient synthesis of 1,2-bis(ethylthio)ethyne than the one described by Boganz and Triebsch.[74] Bis(trifluoromethylthio)acetylene is formed in 67% yield when the corresponding dibromoethane is heated with KOH.[74a]

13.3. Alkenyl Alkynyl Thio- and Selenoethers

In 1961, the first compound with a sulfur atom between a vinyl group and an ethynyl group was reported:[76]

$$2CH_3CHO + 2HCl + H_2S \xrightarrow{0°} CH_3CHCl{-}S{-}CHClCH_3 \xrightarrow[45°]{Br_2}$$
$$(50–70\%)$$

$$CH_2BrCHBr{-}S{-}CHClCH_3 \xrightarrow[80–95°]{PhNEt_2} CHBr=CH{-}S{-}CH=CH_2 \xrightarrow{KOH}$$
$$(30\% \text{ on dichloro ether})$$

$$HC{\equiv}C{-}S{-}CH=CH_2$$
$$(50\% \text{ in last step})$$

This scheme has been modified to prepare a series of alkenyl alkynyl ethers, thioethers and selenoethers.[75] An example of a selenoether preparation is:

$$(CH_2{=}CH)_2Se + Br_2 \xrightarrow{20°} CH_2BrCHBr{-}Se{-}CH{=}CH_2 \xrightarrow[100°]{PhNEt_2}$$

$$CHBr{=}CH{-}Se{-}CH{=}CH_2 \xrightarrow[NH_3]{2LiNH_2} LiC{\equiv}C{-}Se{-}CH{-}CH_2 \xrightarrow{MeI}$$

$$\underset{(50\%)}{MeC{\equiv}C{-}Se{-}CH{=}CH_2}$$

Modifications of this sequence gave other ethers in 20–70% yields:

$$LiC{\equiv}C{-}X{-}CH{=}CH_2 \underset{(X\,=\,O,S,Se)}{\Big\langle}$$

$$\xrightarrow{H_2O} \text{free ethers (X = Se, 40\% yield)}$$

$$\xrightarrow{RX} RC{\equiv}C{-}X{-}CH{=}CH_2$$

$$\xrightarrow{C=O} C(OH)C{\equiv}C{-}X{-}CH{=}CH_2$$

Vinylselenoethyne could not be purified. An attempt to distill it at atmospheric pressure resulted in explosive decomposition. The crude product boiled at 30–40° at 60 mm.

Alkenyl alkynyl ethers can be prepared by this sequence also:[75]

$$(RCH_2CHCl)_2X \xrightarrow{Br_2,\ 80°} RCHBrCHBr{-}X{-}CHClCH_2R \xrightarrow{PhNEt_2}$$

$$\underset{(30\%)}{RCBr{=}CH{-}X{-}CH{=}CHR} \xrightarrow[NH_3]{LiNH_2} \underset{(80\%\ yield)}{RC{\equiv}C{-}X{-}CH{=}CHR}$$

R	X	b.p. (°C, @ mm Hg)
Me	O	110
Et	O	42, @ 9
Me	S	51, @ 10

The alkenyl alkynyl ethers are fairly stable at reflux.

13.4. Dialkynyl Thioethers

Brandsma and Arens[77] in 1961 described the first compounds with sulfur between two acetylene groups:

$$RC{\equiv}CH + SCl_2 \longrightarrow \underset{(80\%)}{RCCl{=}CH{-}S{-}CH{=}CClR} \xrightarrow{LiNH_2,\ NH_3} RC{\equiv}C{-}S{-}C{\equiv}CR$$

R	% Yield	b.p. (°C, @ mm Hg)
Et	40	95, @ 15
Me	35	64, @ 12

A series of di(1-alkynyl) thioethers was prepared by another dehydrohalogenation method.[70] The parent compound diethynyl sulfide is unstable and decomposes after a few days at room temperature. The substituted acetylenic thioethers are more stable.

$$(CH_2{=}CH)_2S + 2Br_2 \xrightarrow{-50°} (CH_2BrCHBr)_2S \xrightarrow{PhNEt_2} (CHBr{=}CH)_2S \xrightarrow[NH_3]{4NaNH_2}$$
$$(45\% \text{ on divinyl sulfide})$$

$$(NaC{\equiv}C)_2S
\begin{cases}
\xrightarrow{\text{ice}} (HC{\equiv}C)_2S \xrightarrow[(2)\ EtBr]{(1)\ NaNH_2} (EtC{\equiv}C)_2S \\
\xrightarrow{\text{acetone}} (Me_2\underset{\underset{OH}{|}}{C}{-}C{\equiv}C)_2S \\
\xrightarrow{\text{RBr or RI}} (RC{\equiv}C)_2S \ (R = Me, Et, Pr, Bu; 60{-}70\% \text{ yield on bromovinyl sulfide})
\end{cases}$$

An improved synthesis was described in 1963,[78] starting with 2,2'-dichlorodivinyl thioether prepared from vinyl chloride and sulfur dichloride:

$$2CH_2{=}CHCl + SCl_2 \xrightarrow[6\ hr,\ 20-25°]{CH_2Cl_2} (CHCl_2CH_2)_2S \xrightarrow[2\frac{1}{4}\ hr,\ 20-30°]{KOH,\ MeOH}$$

$$(CHCl{=}CH)_2S \xrightarrow[NH_3]{4NaNH_2} (NaC{\equiv}C)_2S \xrightarrow{2RX} (RC{\equiv}C)_2S$$
(*cis* and *trans*:   R = Et, 72–75%
65–75% yield)   R = Pr, 81–85%

If only 1 equivalent of RX is added, ethynyl alkynyl thioethers $RC{\equiv}C{-}S{-}C{\equiv}CH$ are the products. Moderate yields of dialkynyl thioethers can be obtained directly in one step:

$$(CHCl_2CH_2)_2S \xrightarrow[(2)\ 2RX]{(1)\ 6NaNH_2} (RC{\equiv}C)_2S$$

Several other acetylenic thioethers have been made recently by elimination procedures: phenylthioethyne[79,80], *p*-tolylthioethyne,[81] and phenyl thiophenylethyne.[81] Yields were 50–100%.

14. 1-AMINOACETYLENES

Wolf and Kowiz[82] prepared the first alkynylamine, $RC{\equiv}CNR_2'$, in 1960; they reacted $LiC{\equiv}CPh$ with $ClNEt_2$ to give a 2.3% yield of $PhC{\equiv}CNEt_2$. Other alkynylamines have been made since by substitution reactions (see Chapter 4). In 1963, Viehe[83] reported that lithium diethylamide reacts with $PhCH{=}CHCl$ to give $PhC{\equiv}CNEt_2$. In 1964, Ficini and Barbara[84] reported a fairly general synthesis of acetylenic amines, using butyllithium to dehydrochlorinate the chloroolefinic starting materials:

$$PhCCl=CClNEt_2 \longrightarrow PhC\equiv CNEt_2$$
$$(70\%)$$

$$CHCl=CClNPh_2 \longrightarrow HC\equiv CNPh_2$$
$$(65\%)$$

$$CCl_2=CClNEt_2 \longrightarrow ClC\equiv CNEt_2$$

Tsmur and Ivanik[85] carried out similar reactions:

$$\overset{\overset{\textstyle O}{\|}}{CH_2BrCNEt_2} + PCl_5 \longrightarrow CH_2BrC(Cl)_2NEt_2 \longrightarrow BrC\equiv CNEt_2$$

Montijn[86] observed that acetylenic ethers react with lithium dialkylamides to give good yields of acetylenic amines. This may be an addition-elimination reaction (Table 3-8):

$$RC\equiv COEt + \;:NR_2' \longrightarrow \left[RC=C\underset{NR_2'}{\overset{OEt}{\diagup}} \right] \longrightarrow RC\equiv CNR_2' + \;^-OEt$$

TABLE 3-8
$RC\equiv C-NR_2'$ from Acetylenic Ethers[86]

R	R'	% Yield	b.p. (°C) @ 15 mm Hg
Me	n-Pr	14	57–58
Et	n-Pr	67	71–72
Et	(CH$_2$)$_5$	55	78–79
n-Pr	Et	68	60–61
n-Bu	Et	65	75–76

15. ETHYNYLIMIDAZOLES

A recently reported synthesis of ethynylimidazoles is this ring cleavage-dehydrohalogenation reaction:[87]

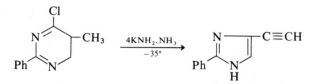

4-ethynyl-2-phenylimidazole

References

1. Jacobs, T. L., *Org. Reactions*, **5**, 1 (1949).
2. Arens, J. F., *Advan. Org. Chem.*, **2**, 117 (1960).
3. Franke, W., Zeigenbein, W., and Meister, H., in "Newer Methods of Preparative Organic Chemistry," Vol. 3, p. 425, New York, Academic Press, 1964.
4. Ziegenbein, W., "Einführung der Äthinyl- und Alkinyl-Gruppe in organische Verbindungen," Weinheim/Bergstr., Germany, Verlag Chemie, 1963.
5. Köbrich, G., *Angew. Chem. Intern. Ed.*, **4**, 49 (1965).
6. Sawitsch, V., *Compt. Rend.*, **52**, 399 (1861).
7. Rujicka, L., Hürbin, M., and Boeckenoogen, H. A., *Helv. Chim. Acta*, **16**, 498 (1933).
8. Mersheryakov, A. P., and Petrova, L. V., *Izv. Akad. Nauk SSSR, Ser. Khim.*, 1488 (1964); *Chem. Abstr.*, **64**, 19386 (1966).
9. van Boom, J. H., *et. al.*, *Rec. Trav. Chim.*, **84**, 31 (1965).
10. Pomerantz, P., *et al.*, *J. Res. Natl. Bur. Std.*, **52**, 51 (1954).
11. Cymerman-Craig, J., and Moyle, M., *Proc. Chem. Soc.*, 149 (1962).
12. Campbell, K. N., and Campbell, B. K., *Org. Syn.*, **3**, 763 (1963).
13. Drehfahl, G., and Plotner, G., *Chem. Ber.*, **91**, 1280 (1958).
14. Mukaiyama, T., Nambu, H., and Kumamoto, T., *J. Org. Chem.*, **29**, 2243 (1964).
15. Coe, P. L., Plevey, R. G., and Tatlow, J. C., *J. Chem. Soc.* (C), 597 (1966).
16. Yen, V.-Q., *Ann. Chim.* (*Paris*), **7**, 785 (1962); *Chem. Abstr.*, **59**, 5043 (1963).
17. Yen, V.-Q., *Ann. Chim.* (*Paris*), **7**, 799 (1962); *Chem. Abstr.*, **59**, 5044 (1963).
18. Leonard, E. C., *J. Org. Chem.*, **30**, 3258 (1965).
19. Tani, H., Toda, F., and Matsumiya, K., *Bull. Chem. Soc. Japan*, **36**, 391 (1963); *Chem. Abstr.*, **59**, 5092 (1963).
20. Tani, H., Tanaki, S., and Toda, F., *Bull. Chem. Soc. Japan*, **36**, 1267 (1963); *Chem. Abstr.*, **60**, 437 (1964).
21. Haug, V., and Fürst, H., *Chem. Ber.*, **93**, 593 (1960).
22. Behringer, H., and Matner, M., *Tetrahedron Letters*, 1663 (1966).
23. Drehfahl, G., and Plötner, G., *Chem. Ber.*, **93**, 990, 998 (1960).
24. Trippett, S., and Walker, D. M., *J. Chem. Soc.*, 2676 (1960).
25. Tadros, W., *et. al.*, *J. Chem. Soc.*, 3994 (1965).
26. Tadros, W., Sakla, A. B., and Ishak, M. S., *J. Chem. Soc.*, 4210 (1958).
27. Curtin, D. Y., *et al.*, *Chem. Ind.* (*London*), 1453 (1957).
28. Newman, M. S., and Reid, D. E., *J. Org. Chem.*, **23**, 665 (1958).
29. Bohlmann, F., and Politt, J., *Chem. Ber.*, **90**, 130 (1957).
30. Armitage, J. B., Jones, E. R. H., and Whiting, M. C., *J. Chem. Soc.*, 44 (1951).
31. Georgieff, K. K., and Richard, Y., *Can. J. Chem.*, **36**, 1280 (1958).
32. Finnegan, W. G., and Norris, W. P., *J. Org. Chem.*, **28**, 1139 (1963).
33. Haszeldine, R. N., *J. Chem. Soc.*, 2504 (1952).
34. Hasek, W. R., Smith, W. C., and Engelhardt, V. A., *J. Am. Chem. Soc.*, **82**, 543 (1960).
35. Krespan, C. G., Harder, R. J., and Drysdale, J. J., *J. Am. Chem. Soc.*, **83**, 3424 (1961).
36. Hennion, G. F., Price, C. C., and McKeon, T. F., Jr., *Org. Syn.*, **3**, 683 (1963).
37. Croxall, W. J., and Van Hoock, J. O., *J. Am. Chem. Soc.*, **76**, 1700 (1954).
38. Vartanyan, S. A., Pirenyan, S. K., and Tokmadzhyan, B. V., *Dokl. Akad. Nauk Arm. SSSR, Khim. Nauk*, **17**, 513 (1965); *Chem. Abstr.*, **62**, 11672 (1965).
39. Brandsma, L., Montijn, P. P., and Arens, J. F., *Rec. Trav. Chim.*, **82**, 1115 (1963).

40. Montijn, P. P., *et al.*, *Rec. Trav. Chim.*, **84**, 271 (1965).
41. Montijn, P. P., and Brandsma, L., *Rec. Trav. Chim.*, **83**, 456 (1964).
42. Slobodin, Ya. M., *Zh. Obshch. Khim.*, **27**, 2473 (1957); *Chem. Abstr.*, **52**, 7119 (1958).
43. Babayan, V. O., *Zh. Prikl. Khim.*, **38**, 448 (1965); *Chem. Abstr.*, **62**, 13025 (1965).
44. Mkryan, G. M., and Mndzhoyan, Sh. L., *Izv. Akad. Nauk Arm. SSR, Khim. Nauk*, **18**, 44 (1965); *Chem. Abstr.*, **63**, 6842 (1965).
45. Greaves, P. M., Landor, S. R., and Laws, D. R., *J. Chem. Soc.* (*C*), 1976 (1966).
46. Bertrand, M., *Compt. Rend.*, **244**, 619 (1957).
46a. van Boom, J. H., *et al.*, *Rec. Trav. Chim.*, **85**, 952 (1966).
47. Jones, E. R. H., Eglinton, G., and Whiting, M. C., *J. Chem. Soc.*, 2873 (1952).
48. Jones, E. R. H., *Org. Syn.*, **3**, 404 (1963).
49. Paul, R., and Tchelitcheff, S., *Bull. Soc. Chim. France*, 808 (1952).
50. Ashworth, P. J., Mansfield, G. H., and Whiting, M. C., *Org. Syn.*, **3**, 128 (1963).
51. Ward, J. P., and van Dorp, D. A., *Rec. Trav. Chim.*, **85**, 117 (1966).
52. Mavrov, M. V., and Kucherov, V. F., *Izv. Akad. Nauk SSSR, Ser. Khim.*, 546 (1965); *Chem. Abstr.*, **63**, 484 (1965).
53. Babayan, V. O., *Dokl. Akad. Nauk Arm. SSR*, **19**, 41 (1954); *Chem. Abstr.*, **50**, 160 (1956).
54. Glacet, C., and Kapka, E., *Compt. Rend.*, **261**, 5528 (1965).
55. Chopard, P. A., Searle, R. J. G., and Devitt, F. H., *J. Org. Chem.*, **30**, 1015 (1965).
56. Abbott, T. W., Arnold, R. T., and Thompson, R. B., *Org. Syn.*, **2**, 10 (1943).
57. Märkl, G., *Chem. Ber.*, **94**, 3005 (1961).
58. Gough, S. T. D., and Trippett, S., *J. Chem. Soc.*, 2333 (1962).
59. Fleming, I., and Harley-Mason, J., *Chem. Ind.* (*London*), 560, 561 (1962); *J. Chem. Soc.*, 4771, 4778 (1963).
60. Fleming, I., and Harley-Mason, J., *Proc. Chem. Soc.*, 245 (1961).
61. Brown, E. J. D., and Harley-Mason, J., *J. Chem. Soc.* (*C*), 1390 (1966).
62. Carpino, L. A., *Angew. Chem.*, **70**, 275 (1958).
63. Carpino, L. A., Terry, P. H., and Thatte, S. D., *J. Org. Chem.*, **31**, 2867 (1966).
64. Grosselck, J., *et al.*, *Angew. Chem., Intern. Ed. Engl.*, **4**, 1080 (1965).
65. Luijten, J. G. A., and van der Kerk, G. J. M., *Rec. Trav. Chim.*, **83**, 295 (1964).
66. Jones, E. R. H., *et al.*, *Org. Syn.*, **3**, 404 (1963).
67. van Daalen, J. J., Kraak, A., and Arens, J. F., *Rec. Trav. Chim.*, **80**, 810 (1961).
68. Olsman, H., Graveland, A., and Arens, J. F., *Rec. Trav. Chim.*, **83**, 301 (1964).
69. Nooi, J. R., and Arens, J. F., *Rec. Trav. Chim.*, **81**, 517 (1962).
70. Brandsma, L., and Arens, J. F., *Rec. Trav. Chim.*, **81**, 510 (1962).
71. Brandsma, L., Wijers, H. E., and Jonker, C., *Rec. Trav. Chim.*, **83**, 208 (1964).
72. Boonstra, H. J., and Arens, J. F., *Rec. Trav. Chim.*, **79**, 866 (1960).
73. Nooi, J. R., and Arens, J. F., *Rec. Trav. Chim.*, **80**, 244 (1961).
74. Boganz, H., and Triebsch, W., *Chem. Ber.*, **89**, 895 (1956).
74a. Harris, J. F., *J. Org. Chem.*, **32**, 2063 (1967).
75. Brandsma, L., and Arens, J. F., *Rec. Trav. Chim.*, **81**, 539 (1962).
76. *Ibid.*, **80**, 237 (1961).
77. *Ibid.*, **80**, 241 (1961).
78. *Ibid.*, **82**, 1119 (1963).
79. Montanari, F., and Negrini, A., *Ric. Sci.*, **27**, 467 (1957); *Chem. Abstr.*, **52**, 9985 (1958).
80. Parham, W. E., and Stright, P. L., *J. Am. Chem. Soc.*, **78**, 4783 (1956).

81. Truce, W. E., Hill, H. E., and Boudakian, *J. Am. Chem. Soc.*, **78**, 2760 (1956).

82. Wolf, V., and Kowiz, F., *Ann. Chem.*, **683**, 33 (1960).

83. Viehe, H. G., *Angew. Chem.*, **75**, 638 (1963).

84. Ficini, J., and Barbara, C., *Bull. Soc. Chim. France*, 871 (1964).

85. Tsmur, Yu. Yu., and Ivanik, V. I., *J. Gen. Chem. USSR Engl. Transl.*, **33**, 1653 (1963).

86. Montijn, P. P., Harryvan, E., and Brandsma, L., *Rec. Trav. Chim.*, **83**, 1211 (1964).

87. van Meeteren, H. W., and van der Plas, H. C., *Tetrahedron Letters*, 4517 (1966).

Chapter Four

SUBSTITUTION OF ACETYLENIC HYDROGEN BY OTHER ELEMENTS

Introduction

Ethynyl hydrogen undergoes many useful substitution reactions. It reacts with alkali metals and alkali metal amides and hydrides, with Grignard reagents, with compounds of Group IB metals, and with many other elements. The products of these reactions, in turn, undergo substitution reactions to form a wide variety of final products. The most important substitution reactions are collected in this chapter, with emphasis on recent work. Substitution reactions are numerous, so this chapter is arranged in parts. Each part deals with similar substituting reagents and products. The addition reactions of some of the products are logically included here.

PART ONE

Alkali Metal Acetylides and Acetylenic Grignard Reagents
—Preparation and Reactions

1. SODIUM ACETYLIDE

1.1. Preparation in Liquid Ammonia

The oldest and most widely used laboratory method for preparing alkali metal acetylides is the reaction of the metal amide with acetylene in liquid ammonia. Many detailed directions are available.[1,2] Pomerantz and co-workers have written an excellent description of their semi-pilot plant scale preparations of sodium acetylide, sodium carbide and alkylacetylenes derived from them.[3] Preparation of sodium acetylide in ammonia on this large scale has seldom been so thoroughly described. The procedure is summarized:

Sodium amide: Commercial anhydrous ammonia (10 kg) was added as liquid to a 10-gallon stainless steel autoclave equipped with a dry ice condenser. Ferric chloride, 15 grams, was added "deftly" in three portions, causing a violent reaction. After reflux subsided, 60 grams of sodium, in small pieces, was added. The sodium dissolved, and then dry air was passed through the solution for 1.5 minutes to form the catalyst. Sodium (60 moles), as $\frac{1}{2}$-inch cubes, was added next. A vigorous stream of hydrogen evolved.

Sodium acetylide: The solution of sodium amide was stirred for 2 hours; cylinder acetylene, scrubbed through sulfuric acid, was then bubbled in. Acetylene was not introduced until the blue color of dissolved sodium had changed to the characteristic black of sodium amide. Occasionally this required standing overnight or longer. Disodium acetylide (sodium carbide) formed first as a milky white dispersion. If sodium carbide was the desired product, reaction was stopped after 30 moles of acetylene had been added. As more acetylene reacted, the sodium carbide changed to black sodium acetylide.

Dimethyl sulfate reacted with the sodium acetylide to give a 65% yield of propyne, and with the sodium carbide to give a 42% yield of 2-butyne. Only one methyl group of the dimethyl sulfate reacted.

1.1.1. COMPOSITION OF SODIUM ACETYLIDE PREPARED IN AMMONIA

Sodium, potassium, rubidium and cesium acetylides prepared in ammonia are unsolvated $MC{\equiv}CH$.[4] Lithium, calcium, strontium and barium acetylides are ammoniates, $MC{\equiv}CH \cdot xNH_3$. Sodium acetylide in ammonia is ionized.

Metal	Acetylene:Metal (moles)	Ammonia:Metal (moles)
Ca	1.83	0.99–2.45
Sr	1.38–1.40	0.13
Ba	2.0	2.22
	(2.0)	(4)[5]
Li	(1.0)	(1.0)[5]

Sodium acetylide and lithium acetylide·NH$_3$ in ammonia electrolyze to deposit carbon on the anode and the metal on the cathode.[5]

1.2. Preparation in Inert Organic Diluents

Although sodium acetylide is easily prepared in liquid ammonia, handling liquid ammonia presents some problems for laboratory work, and these are magnified in large-scale preparations. In addition, the conversion of sodium to sodium amide is sometimes tricky and slow.[3] Sodium acetylide made in ammonia is usually hard to disperse in an organic diluent for subsequent reactions. The few literature references before 1957 indicate that the reaction of acetylene with sodium in organic diluents is very slow. For example, a 1926 German patent[6] described adding acetylene to a stirred mixture of sodium and xylene at reflux. The product was a yellowish-white powder; sodium acetylide content corresponded to 83% conversion. A time of more than 60 hours was apparently required. This is inferred from a later patent[7] which claimed that acetylene reacted faster (less than 60 hours) with sodium deposited on sand. In 1897, Matignon[8] described a procedure for making sodium acetylide which is almost identical to the one described in the later patent.[7]

The reaction of acetylene with 10- to 25-μ sodium dispersion in inert diluents gives sodium acetylide.[10] In xylene, the best reaction temperature was 100–110°. The complete reaction of 0.25 mole of sodium in 300 ml of xylene required 1.5–2.5 hours. The yield based on sodium was 100%; on acetylene, 75–85%. The reaction of sodium dispersion with acetylene in several diluents showed that there is an optimum temperature for each diluent (Table 4-1). Increasing the reaction temperature from 100–130° in xylene decreased the sodium acetylide yield rapidly. The same trend was less pronounced in di-n-butyl "Carbitol." Either solid or molten sodium particles reacted equally well. The excellent reaction in dioxane was obtained only at 65–70°. Outside this range, the results were very poor.

Sodium particles less than 25 μ in diameter were best. Reactions with sodium sand, about 100 μ, required times double those shown in Table 4-1, and the yields were only 50%. Commercial grade and C.P. grade sodium contains some impurities. Dispersions made from unpurified sodium gave sodium acetylide of

TABLE 4-1
Reaction of Sodium Dispersion with
Acetylene in Organic Diluents[10]

Diluent	Temperature (°C)	Time (hr)	Yield[a] of NaC_2H Based on Sodium (%)
Xylene	100	$2\frac{1}{2}$	99+
	120	$2\frac{3}{4}$	71.5
	130	3	7.3
Di-*n*-butyl "Carbitol"	65	$2\frac{1}{2}$	99+
	95	1	99+
	130	$3\frac{1}{3}$	59
	150	$1\frac{1}{2}$	49
	175	$1\frac{1}{4}$	31
Di-*n*-butyl ether	80	2	99+
	100	1	99+
Dioxane	65–70	2	99+

[a] Yield = moles of sodium acetylide formed per mole of sodium consumed × 100. All of the sodium reacted in every case.

only 95–96% purity. The major impurity was sodium carbonate. Melting under xylene and decanting the flotsam gave sodium pure enough to make 98–99% pure sodium acetylide.

Acetylene purity was especially critical, and the results indicated that the excessively long times reported in the earlier literature were caused partly by improper temperatures, but mainly by impurities in the acetylene. (This probably also applies to other reactions of acetylene.) When acetylene is taken from a commercial cylinder, the main impurity is acetone which is a poison for the sodium acetylide reaction. In addition, commercial acetylene contains traces of phosphine, vinyl sulfide, arsine and ammonia. The best purification system for the laboratory was very simple. Most of the acetone was removed by passing the cylinder gas through a dry ice trap. The rest of the acetone and nearly all of the trace impurities were removed by passing the gas upward through a column of commercial activated alumina, 8–14 mesh. One gram of alumina could purify about 2.4 liters of acetylene. Deactivation of the alumina was indicated by a yellow band which moved up the column.

Oxygen was a very potent poison. Oxygen, especially along with the trace impurities, caused either very long reactions or no reaction at all. The oxygen level had to be below 0.3 volume % for best reactions. The traces of oxygen in acetylene cylinders can be removed by bleeding off a few pounds of pressure. Sodium dispersions stabilized with cumene hydroperoxide did not react. The inhibition was removed by adding hydroquinone. Hydroquinone did not prevent the oxygen effect, however.

The sodium acetylide made in the inert diluents was easily isolated as a stable, dry powder.[10] The sodium acetylide adsorbed about 2.2 times its weight of xylene, twice its weight of butyl ether, and 1.6 times its weight of dioxane. Diluents were removed by filtering under nitrogen, and then pumping at 65° and 5 mm. Dried sodium acetylide was slightly yellow to gray-white, and was stable. It could be heated to about 300° in the absence of air; darkening indicated disproportionation. At 170–190° in air, slow ignition and quiet burning occurred. Poured into a large volume of water, the acetylide rapidly liberated acetylene. The dried sodium acetylide was not shock or abrasion sensitive.

In 1957, a patent[9] claimed that sodium, lithium or potassium in inert diluents, between 0° and the melting point of the metal, reacted slowly with acetylene to form the corresponding acetylide (Table 4-2).

TABLE 4-2
Reaction of Sodium with Acetylene in Organic Diluents[9]

Diluent	Time for 100% Reaction (hr)	Temperature (°C)
Diisopropyl ether	10–30	—
Tetrahydrofuran	60	20
(K)	60	15–30
(Li)	24	20–30
Dioxane	50	20
Methylal	20–25	0–5
Dimethylacetal	30–40	25
Di-n-butyl ether	48	40–50

The sodium dispersion-acetylene reaction in mineral oil is a good method for preparing sodium acetylide.[11] Less than one-third of the acetylene was reduced by the hydrogen liberated. When acetylene was added to a rapidly stirred dispersion of sodium in mineral oil at 110–150°, the limiting factor was control of temperature and removal of the heat of reaction. The yield based on sodium was quantitative, and the conversion of acetylene was 20% per pass. Sodium acetylide made in mineral oil was relatively stable, but easily ignited in air when dry. It was thermally stable up to about 180°. At 200° it disproportionated slowly at first, then more rapidly at a steady rate, and at the end slowed down. Disproportionation was essentially complete after 1 hour and was autocatalytic. The product is disodium acetylide (sodium carbide). Other bases, such as sodamide, sodium hydride or sodium also catalyze the disproportionation:

$$NaC_2H + NaNH_2 \longrightarrow Na_2C_2 + NH_3$$
$$NaC_2H + NH_3 \longrightarrow C_2H_2 + NaNH_2$$
$$\text{(overall)} \quad 2NaC_2H(+ NaNH_2) \longrightarrow Na_2C_2 + C_2H_2(+ NaNH_2)$$

Sodium acetylide on pumice at 100° and 0.5 mm also disproportionates to sodium carbide.[4] Lithium, calcium, barium and strontium acetylides disproportionate similarly.

Sodium hydride and dimethyl sulfoxide react to form hydrogen and "dimsylsodium" $[CH_3C(O)CH_2]^-Na^+$.[12] Acetylene or 1-alkynes added to dimsylsodium in dimethyl sulfoxide give sodium acetylide or sodioalkyne.[13] Some of the sodioalkynes are only partly soluble, but excess alkyne forms a blue-black soluble complex which reacts like free acetylide. The utility of this method is illustrated by these results:

Reactant	Acetylide	Product	% Yield
Dimethyl sulfate	NaC_2H	Propyne	90
Methyl iodide	Sodiopropyne	2-butyne	82
Acetaldehyde	NaC_2H	1-Butyn-3-ol	78
Acetophenone	LiC_2H	3-Phenyl-1-butyn-3-ol	83

Dimsylsodium can be dangerous. French[14] reported a violent explosion during one preparation of dimsylsodium by adding sodium hydride to dimethyl sulfoxide.

1.3. Reactions of Sodium Acetylide

1.3.1. ALKYLATION IN ORGANIC DILUENTS

Sodium acetylide made in organic diluents[10] has been used for reactions with dialkyl sulfates and with alkyl halides.[15] Dimethyl sulfate reacted at 90° in xylene to form propyne in 85% conversion and 2-butyne in 8% conversion. At 120°, the reaction gave 17.5% conversion to 2-butyne. Both of the methyl groups of dimethyl sulfate reacted; only one reacts in ammonia. Diethyl sulfate gave 1-butyne; 1.4 of the ethyl groups reacted. Sodium acetylide made in ammonia reacted with dimethyl sulfate in xylene to give only 50% yield of propyne. This sodium acetylide did not disperse well in the xylene.

Alkyl halides, such as n-butyl bromide, did not react with sodium acetylide in xylene.[15] A simple screening test of possible solvents showed that the best ones were dimethylformamide, hexamethylphosphoramide and dimethylacetamide. Dimethylformamide was studied further. The best diluent combination for the sodium acetylide–butyl bromide alkylation was 35–40% (by volume) of dimethylformamide in xylene. The conversion and yield of 1-hexyne was 81% after 8 hours at 25–30°. n-Butyl chloride gave 32% yield of 1-hexyne. This parallels the yields in ammonia reactions. n-Octadecyl bromide gave 1-eicosyne in 90% yield, which is much better than the liquid ammonia reaction.

n-Octadecyl bromide is not very soluble in ammonia.[16,17] No dialkylacetylenes formed in any of these alkylations.

The problem of the low solubility of higher alkyl halides in ammonia was avoided by another simple method.[16] Sodium acetylide was made in ammonia, and the ammonia was replaced by dimethylformamide. Finally, the alkyl halide was added. After 2–3 hours at 70°, 75–85% yields of the 1-alkynes (RC≡CH) were obtained (R can have 8, 10, 12, 13, 14, 16 and 18 carbon atoms). The alkynes in which R has 14, 15, 16 and 17 carbon atoms were made by reacting n-alkyl bromides with sodium acetylide in a mixture of ammonia and dimethylformamide. The yields were around 80%.[17]

Normant[18] prepared sodium acetylide in tetrahydrofuran at 45° added hexamethylphosphoramide, and then at 10–15° added RX in tetrahydrofuran (Table 4-3).

TABLE 4-3
Alkylation of Sodium Acetylide in
Tetrahydrofuran-Dimethylformamide[18]

RX	Product	Reaction Temperature (°C)	% Yield
Br(CH$_2$)$_6$Br	1,9-Decadiyne	40	71
(tetrahydropyranyl)–(CH$_2$)$_4$Br	(tetrahydropyranyl)–(CH$_2$)$_4$C≡CH	50	47
BuOCH$_2$Cl	BuOCH$_2$C≡CH	40	32
		−5	12.5
		75	18
RBr, RCl	RC≡CH(R = heptyl, amyl)	5–40	50–70
BuOtosylate	1-Hexyne	50	77

Dear[19] synthesized the toxic ingredient in *Dechapetalum toxicarium*, a glabrous shrub from Sierra Leone. The compound is very toxic to warm-blooded animals, and the powdered fruit has been used as a rat poison (hence the common name "ratsbane"). The natives use it as an arrow poison and to poison enemy water supplies, and witch doctors use it "for terrorizing the native population."[19] The toxic ingredient has been identified as ω-fluorooleic acid. In the synthesis of ω-fluorooleic acid, xylene-dimethylformamide was used as solvent for alkylating sodium acetylide with 8-fluorooctyl bromide. The yield of 10-fluoro-1-decyne was 60%. The recently available lithium acetylide-ethylenediamine complex is preferred[19] for laboratory work, because it is not necessary to use acetylene. Sodium acetylide or lithium acetylide in ammonia gives poor results because these compounds dehydrofluorinate the bromofluoroalkanes.[20] The sequence of reactions leading to ω-fluorooleic acid is an interesting example of indirect introduction of a double bond into a molecule by first forming an acetylenic bond and then semihydrogenating it:

$$F(CH_2)_8Br + NaC_2H \longrightarrow F(CH_2)_8C\equiv CH \xrightarrow[\text{(2) I(CH}_2)_7\text{Cl}]{\text{(1) NaNH}_2}$$

$$F(CH_2)_8C\equiv C(CH_2)_7Cl \xrightarrow[\text{DMSO}]{\text{NaCN}}$$
$$(89\%)$$

$$F(CH_2)_8C\equiv C(CH_2)_7CN \xrightarrow[\text{H}_2\text{O}_2]{\text{KOH}} F(CH_2)_8C\equiv C(CH_2)_7\overset{\overset{\displaystyle O}{\displaystyle \|}}{C}NH_2 \xrightarrow{\text{alcoholic KOH}}$$
$$(93.5\%) \qquad\qquad\qquad\qquad (77\%)$$

$$\text{acid} \xrightarrow[\text{catalyst}]{\text{H}_2, \text{ Lindlar's}} F(CH_2)_8CH\!=\!CH(CH_2)_7CO_2H$$
$$(94\%) \qquad\qquad\qquad (76\%)$$

Trifluoroacetic acid is the only other organic fluorine compound which is known to occur in nature. Toxicity data show that the acetylenic bond has little or no effect on the metabolic breakdown of long-chain ω-fluoroacetylenes. Trifluoroacetic acid is not formed from larger molecules by oxidation.

1.3.2. CARBONATION TO FORM PROPIOLIC ACID

Carbonation to propiolic acid may be one of sodium acetylide's most important potential uses.[11] Coupling of propiolic acid esters to butadiynedioic acid diesters gives starting materials for a series of halogenated adipic acids. Ordinarily carbonation is too slow to be commercially interesting. Sodium acetylide from liquid ammonia does not react well, because of particle size or some other surface characteristic. Dioxane is usually regarded as the best diluent. Lindsay[11] synthesized sodium propiolate in 70% yield in a 1-hour reaction of sodium acetylide prepared in mineral oil with CO_2 at 450 psig and 5°. He isolated free propiolic acid by extracting the acidified aqueous hydrolysis layer with ether.

Reaction of sodium acetylide in methylal with CO_2 at 800 psig and 25° gives 68% yield of propiolic acid, 96% pure, after $4\frac{1}{2}$ hours.[21] Xylene-dimethylformamide is claimed to be a good liquid medium for the carbonation.[22] Normant[23] used sodium naphthalene in tetrahydrofuran to convert acetylene to sodium acetylide. Carbonation of the sodium acetylide at atmospheric pressure gave 20% yield of propiolic acid.

1.3.2.1. *Fluorination of Acetylenic Acids.* Propiolic acid reacts with SF_4 at 30° to form trifluoropropyne in 60% yield.[24] At 120°, propiolyl fluoride is the product (28%, b.p. 22–23°). Acetylenedicarboxylic acid at 70° gives the acyl difluoride (51% yield, b.p. 40–45°), but at 170° hexafluoro-2-butyne is formed (80% yield).

1.3.2.2. *Conversion to Nitriles.* Saggiomo[25] prepared dicyanoacetylene by a slight modification of the Moreau and Bongrand procedure:[26] Dimethyl acetylenedicarboxylate with ammonium hydroxide gave the diamide, which was dehydrated by P_2O_5 to dicyanoacetylene. Dicyanoacetylene is relatively stable, can be stored indefinitely at dry ice temperature and is easily handled at room temperature. It polymerizes or condenses in the presence of oxygen. Dicyanoacetylene and dicyanodiacetylene are highly endothermic compounds which should produce very high temperatures (over 5000°K) when burned in oxygen or ozone.

1.3.2.3. *Esterification of Acetylenic Acids.* Acetylenedicarboxylic acid is auto-catalytic in esterification reactions, just as other strong organic acids are:[27]

Acid	pK_a	Autocatalytic
n-$C_3F_7CO_2H$	2.00	Yes
Acetylenedicarboxylic	2.65	Yes
Propiolic	3.40	No
Fumaric	4.47	No

Some esters from perfluoroacids and acetylenic alcohols, and from acetylenic acids and alcohols, are listed in Table 4-4.

2. SODIUM DERIVATIVES OF SUBSTITUTED ACETYLENES

2.1. Sodium Derivatives of Acetylenic Hydrocarbons —Preparation and Reactions

According to Lebeau,[28] propyne reacts easily with sodium in ammonia to form sodiopropyne. Herbertz[29] could not confirm this, but could make sodiopropyne by adding propyne to sodamide in ether. He also observed that diacetylene reacts with sodium in ammonia to give disodiodiacetylene; sodium in ammonia forms only sodium acetylide from acetylene, and sodium acetylide reacts with sodamide in ammonia to form disodium acetylide (sodium carbide). Sodiopropyne reacts with methyl iodide to form 2-butyne.[32] Herbertz[29] made 2-butyne in one step by the reaction of sodium acetylide, sodamide and dimethyl sulfate in ammonia (50% yield).

Benzyl chloride reacts with sodium acetylide in ammonia to form three products: $PhCH_2\overset{\displaystyle Ph}{\underset{\displaystyle |}{C}}HC{\equiv}CH$, $PhCH_2\overset{\displaystyle Ph}{\underset{\displaystyle |}{C}}{=}C{=}CH_2$ and $(PhCH_2)_2\overset{\displaystyle Ph}{\underset{\displaystyle |}{C}}C{\equiv}CH$. The α-hydrogen in the initially formed benzylacetylene is both benzylic and propargylic, and thus is more acidic than ethynyl hydrogen. It exchanges with sodium acetylide for the sodium, and the sodiobenzylacetylene reacts with additional benzyl chloride.[30]

Yen[33,34] prepared sodiophenylacetylenes by reacting substituted phenyl-acetylenes with sodium in tetrahydrofuran. These reacted with dimethyl sulfate to form $RPhC\equiv CMe$ in 48% yield.

TABLE 4-4
Esters Containing Acetylenic Groups[27]

Ester	% Yield	b.p. (°C, @ mm Hg)	m.p. (°C, solvent)[b]	Reflux Time (hr)	Catalyst
$n\text{-}C_7H_{15}CO_2CH_2C\equiv CH$	52	50–59, @ 2.2–3.0	—	11	None
$(n\text{-}C_7H_{15}CO_2CH_2)_2(C\equiv C)$	51	140–144, @ 1.0–1.5	—	13	None
$(CF_2CO_2CH_2C\equiv CH)_2$	6	74–76, @ 0.3	—	10	None
$(CF_2)(CF_2CO_2CH_2C\equiv CH)_2$	25	87–90, @ 0.5	—	7	None
$HC\equiv CCO_2(CH_2)_2C(CH_3)_3$	78	35, @ 0.6	—	10	H_2SO_4
$CH_3C(NO_2)[(CH_2)_2CC\equiv CH]_2^a$	70	—	92–93, benzene	13	H_2SO_4
$C(CH_2O_2CC\equiv CH)_4^a$	81	—	110, CH_3NO_2	15	H_2SO_4
$H(CF_2)_{10}CH_2O_2CC\equiv CH$	86	—	59–60, CH_3NO_2	19	H_2SO_4
$(CF_2)_3(CH_2O_2CC\equiv CH)_2$	6	102, @ 0.8	—		H_2SO_4
$(C\equiv C)[CO_2(CH_2)_2C(CH_3)_3]_2$	57	132–138, @ 0.9	—	10	None
$(C\equiv C)[CO_2(CH_2)_4C(CH_3)_3]_2$	82	148–148, @ 0.6	—	13	None
$(C\equiv C)[CO_2CH_2(CF_2)_{10}H]_2$	5	150–168, @ 2.5	—	18	H_2SO_4
$(C\equiv C)(CO_2CH_2C\equiv CH)_2$	4	86–92, @ 0.3	—	20	None

[a] Attempts to distill resulted in a violent explosion.
[b] Solvent used to recrystallize ester.

Sodium naphthalene in tetrahydrofuran at room temperature can transfer its metal to acetylenes. The sodium acetylides formed react with aldehydes and ketones normally, and can be carbonated to form α-acetylenic acids:[23]

Acetylenic Hydrocarbon	Acid from CO_2 Reaction	% Yield
Phenylacetylene[a]	$PhC\equiv CCO_2H$	45
Phenylacetylene	$PhC\equiv CCO_2H$	50
1-Hexyne	$BuC\equiv CCO_2H$	50
Acetylene	$HC\equiv CCO_2H$	20

Sodium phenylacetylide in ether reacts with ethyloxalyl chloride in ether to form an α-keto-β-acetylenic acid ester:[35]

$$PhC\equiv CNa + Cl\overset{O}{\overset{\|}{C}}-\overset{O}{\overset{\|}{C}}OEt \rightarrow PhC\equiv C\overset{O}{\overset{\|}{C}}-\overset{O}{\overset{\|}{C}}OEt$$
$$(20\%)$$

Nonconjugated diynes react with sodium amide in ethylene glycol dimethyl ether at 150° to form disodium derivatives which react with CO_2 in the same medium to give acids.[36]

2.1.1. REACTION OF SODIUM ALKYNYLIDES WITH EPOXIDES

Epoxides react with metal derivatives of acetylenes to form 4-hydroxyalkynes, usually in liquid ammonia. The alkynyl group attaches mainly to the least branched carbon atom of the epoxide. Sometimes the reverse occurs. Long reaction times are required to give good yields, especially in reaction of non-terminal epoxides.[37,40,41] This reaction was reviewed in 1959.[38,39]

2.1.2. REACTION OF SODIUM ALKYNYLIDES WITH EPICHLOROHYDRIN

This reaction was first reported by Haynes[42] in 1947. The chlorine atom is replaced by the acetylenic group, and the epoxide ring opens. Sodium acetylide gives 40% yield of trans-pent-2-en-4-yn-1-ol, and sodium phenylacetylide gives 15% yield of the phenyl-substituted analog. Jacobs[43] identified the by-product from sodium phenylacetylide and epichlorohydrin as α-benzylfuran. The normal product enynol oxidized by CrO_3-H_2SO_4 gave enyne aldehyde, which was oxidized by silver oxide to form the enynoic acid. Hydration of the enynoic acid gave phenylcoumalin (see structure on page 56).

Landor and Pepper[44] investigated the reaction further. 1-Octyne reacted with epichlorohydrin in ammonia in the presence of 2 moles of sodium amide to form trans-undec-2-en-4-yn-1-ol in 33% yield, but no furan. Sodium

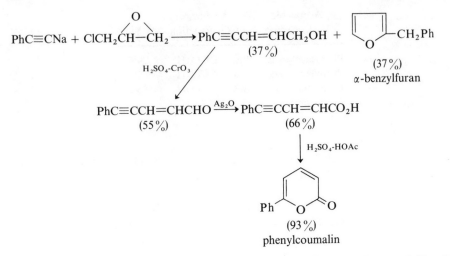

diacetylide gave the products shown. Lithium diacetylide gave better yields of the enediynol, and some 2-allenylfuran:

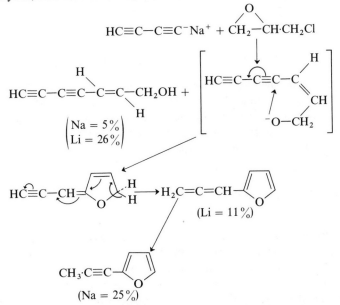

Sodium 1,3-hexadiynylide gave 20% yield of a dihydrofuran and 10% yield of the expected enediynol:

2.1.3. SODIUM ALKYNYLIDES AND CHLOROBROMOALKANES

Sodium acetylide reacts with ω-chloroalkyl bromides to form ω-chloro-1-alkynes.[45] Carbinols, ketones and Mannich bases can be made from the products by the use of standard reactions. Marszak[46] prepared products such as 1,9-dichloro-4-nonyne as intermediates to α,ω-disubstituted aliphatic compounds. He made some ω-chloro-1-alkynes by dehydrohalogenation:

$$Cl(CH_2)_8CHBrCH_2Br + NaNH_2\text{--}NH_3\text{--ether} \xrightarrow[\text{6 hr}]{\text{reflux}} \text{1-chloro-9-decyne}$$
$$(88\%)$$

The chloroalkynes react with sodamide in ammonia to form sodium chloroalkynylides, which are alkylated by α,ω-chlorobromides.

Some products from the reactions of sodium ω-chloroalkynylides are listed in Table 4-5.

TABLE 4-5
Products from ω-Chloroalkylbromides[46]

Product	b.p. (°C, @ mm Hg)
1,10-Dichloro-4-decyne	100, @ 0.3
1,5-Dichloro-5-pentadecyne	120, @ 10^{-4}
1,16-Dichloro-6-hexadecyne	140, @ 10^{-4}
7-Chloro-2-heptyn-1-ol	93, @ 0.3
(Gaseous HCHO + Grignard)	
12-Chloro-2-dodecyn-1-ol	123, @ 0.2
1-Bromo-7-chloro-2-heptyne	62, @ 0.1
1-Bromo-12-chloro-2-decyne	120, @ 0.07
1,12-Dichloro-2-dodecyne	111, @ 0.2
1,16-Dichloro-5,11-hexadecadiyne	—
1,26-Dichloro-10,16-hexacosadiyne	m.p. 27–28
1,24-Dichloro-10,14-tetracosadiyne	m.p. 30–30.5
1,18-Dimethoxy-2,8,10,16-octadecatetrayne	140, @ 10^{-4}
1,18-Dichloro-2,8,10,16-octadecatetrayne	150–160, @ 10^{-4}
1,9-Bis(dimethylamino)-4-nonyne	78, @ 10.1
5-Undecynedioic acid	m.p. 77–78
6-Heptadecynedioic acid	m.p. 94
Diethyl 7-octadecynedioate	150, @ 10^{-4}
6,12-Octadecynedioic acid	m.p. 107
11,17-Octacosadiynedioic acid	m.p. 105
11-Tridecyn-13-oloic acid	m.p. 68

2.1.4. REACTION WITH S, Se AND Te

Brandsma[47] reported a new synthesis for 1-alkynyl thio-, seleno- and telluro-ethers in 1964. A sodium alkynylide in ammonia reacts with sulfur, selenium or tellurium. The resulting salt reacts with an alkyl halide to form the ethers:

$$RC\equiv CNa + X_8 \longrightarrow RC\equiv CXNa \xrightarrow{R'\,halide} RC\equiv CXR'$$

where X = S, Se or Te. This synthesis also applies to 1,3-enynes and terminal diacetylenes. The products are listed in Table 4-6. 1,7-Octadiyne gave 40% yield of $MeSC\equiv C(CH_2)_4C\equiv CSMe$ and some $HC\equiv C(CH_2)_4C\equiv CSMe$.

TABLE 4-6
Acetylenic Thioethers, Selenoethers
and Telluroethers (RC≡C—X—R')[47]

R	X	R'	% Yield
H	S	Me	20
H	S	Et	35–39
H	S	Bu	20
Me	S	Et	40
Me	S	Me	39
Et	S	Me	50
Et	S	Et	45–52
Pr	S	Et	44–51
Bu	S	Et	59–63
t-Bu	S	Et	48–57
Ph	S	Et	58–60
Me	S	i-Pr	10
Me	Se	Et	75–80
Me	Se	i-Pr	60–70
Me	Te	Et	55–70
Vinyl	S	Me	60
1-Butenyl	S	Me	68
1-Propynyl	S	Me	65
1-Butynyl	S	Me	67

This reaction system was used to make ethers from isopropenylacetylene:[48]

b.p. (°C) @ 20 mm

$$\begin{array}{c} Me \\ | \\ CH_2{=}C{-}C\equiv C{-}SMe \end{array}$$

	b.p. (°C) @ 20 mm
—SMe	55.5
—SEt	69
—SeMe	69
—SeEt	82
—TeMe	93

3. SODIUM DERIVATIVES OF DIACETYLENE

In 1952, Herbertz[49] reported work done during 1941–1944 at Chemischen Werke Hüls on diacetylene as an acetylenic reagent. Diacetylene was a by-product component in the arc acetylene process. At the time of the work, the copper and silver derivatives were known, but no alkali metal acetylides had been reported.

3.1. Sodium Diacetylides

When 0.5 mole of diacetylene[50] was passed into 1 mole of sodium in 0.5 liter of ammonia, the blue color disappeared when half of the diacetylene was added. This indicated formation of disodium diacetylide. The last half of the diacetylene reacted with the disodium diacetylide to form monosodium diacetylide.

3.2. Reactions of Monosodium Diacetylide

Sodium diacetylide reacted with halides and sulfates to give normal products:

Reagent	Solvent	Product	% Yield	b.p. (°C, @ mm Hg)
Me_2SO_4	Ammonia	$MeC{\equiv}CC{\equiv}CH$	81	55
Et_2SO_4	Ammonia	$EtC{\equiv}CC{\equiv}CH$	100	27, @ 18
n-PrBr	Ether	$PrC{\equiv}CC{\equiv}CH$	9	53, @ 10
Vinyl bromide	NH_3	Resin		
Vinyl bromide	Decalin	$CH_2{=}CHC{\equiv}CC{\equiv}CH$ (polymerized rapidly)		

3.3. Reactions of Disodium Diacetylide

Dimethyl sulfate alkylated disodium diacetylide to form dimethyldiacetylene, m.p. 64.5°, in quantitative yield. Diethyl sulfate also reacted well.

3.4. Reactions of Sodium Methoxyvinylacetylene

Diacetylene adds 1 mole of methanol to form methoxyvinylacetylene. Methoxyvinylacetylene with sodamide in ammonia gives sodium methoxyvinyl-acetylide, which alkylates normally: Dimethyl sulfate gives a 60% yield; diethyl sulfate, 76% yield; n-propyl bromide, 15% yield. The products have the general formula $RC{\equiv}CCH{=}CHOMe$.

4. LITHIUM ACETYLIDE

4.1. Preparation of Lithium Acetylide-Ethylenediamine Complex

Since 1898 when Moissan[51] prepared lithium acetylide in liquid ammonia, no significantly different or better procedures have been reported. A patent[9] in 1957 claimed preparation of lithium acetylide from acetylene and lithium dispersion in tetrahydrofuran. Beumel and Harris[52] could not duplicate this preparation. They also failed to isolate lithium acetylide from liquid ammonia preparations because the ammonia-lithium acetylide complex[4] decomposed to lithium carbide and acetylene. In 1963, they reported a new form of lithium acetylide, the lithium acetylide-ethylenediamine complex.[52]

Formation of the complex requires two steps. The lithium dispersion first reacts with ethylenediamine, neat or in solvent, to form N-lithioethylenediamine. Vigorous stirring is necessary because ethylenediamine is not very soluble in aliphatic hydrocarbons and is dense, while lithium is insoluble and less dense. Above 85°, a fast reaction gives 90% yield of N-lithioethylenediamine after 5 hours. Aromatic hydrocarbons are better solvents. In refluxing benzene, the yields are quantitative after 1 hour. Benzene is reduced to cyclohexene in 95% yield. Apparently, reduction of the benzene speeds up the reaction with lithium. Lithium nitride, lithium hydride, lithium amide and n-butyllithium can also be used, but lithium metal is best.

N-Lithioethylenediamine in dioxane reacts exothermically with acetylene. When one-half mole of acetylene is consumed, the reaction stops. The product is dilithium acetylide. Additional acetylene eventually reacts to form colorless crystals of lithium acetylide-ethylenediamine. The second stage may be very slow if seed crystals are not available. Other good solvents for the acetylene reaction are tetrahydrofuran, ether, diethyl "Carbitol," butylamine, pyridine, ethylenediamine and hydrocarbons.

The crystals of lithium acetylide-ethylenediamine are octahedral and are usually about 1 mm across. The crystals slowly darken when exposed to light. Darkening is accelerated by free ethylenediamine. The solid hydrolyzes slowly and can be handled in air. Addition of water or to water causes vigorous evolution of acetylene, but no explosions or flashing. The solid does not detonate by impact or friction. It burns with a low red flame when ignited by a match. The only solvents which dissolve more than 0.6% of the complex are amines and dimethyl sulfoxide. Dimethylformamide and dimethylacetamide react slowly with the complex. The complex is excellent for ethynylation of carbonyl compounds (see Chapter 5; also reference 53).

4.2. Reaction of Lithium Acetylide-Ethylenediamine with ω-Fluoroalkyl Halides

In 1963, Pattison[20] reviewed earlier work on the synthesis of ω-fluoroalkynes. Attempted syntheses had caused loss of much of the fluorine, particularly when sodium acetylide in ammonia was used. The new and best method is reaction of ω-fluoroalkyl chloride or bromide with lithium acetylide-ethylenediamine. For chlorides, a temperature of 25° is best, and for bromides, 5–10°. Unreacted chloride is removed by slowly warming the reaction mixture to 60° after the initial exothermic reaction stops. Yields are as high as 92%.

Reaction of the fluoroalkyne products with ethylmagnesium bromide removes all the fluorine, but ethylmagnesium chloride under controlled conditions gives normal Grignards. The Grignards react with CO_2 to give acids, and with isocyanates to give ω-fluoro-2-alkynoamides:

$$F(CH_2)_nC\equiv MgCl \xrightarrow{C_{10}H_7NCO} F(CH_2)_nC\equiv CCONHC_{10}H_7$$
$$(72–88\%)$$

$$[F(CH_2)_nC\equiv C]_2Mg \xrightarrow{CO_2} F(CH_2)_nC\equiv CCOOH$$
$$(51–95\%)$$

The terminal $\equiv CH$ group can be replaced by halogen and by ω-fluoroalkyl groups. ω-Fluoroalkynes couple to form diynes. Some products from ω-fluoroalkynes are listed in Table 4-7.

5. LITHIUM DERIVATIVES OF SUBSTITUTED ACETYLENES

5.1. Reaction of Lithium with 1-Alkenes to form Lithium Alkynylides

Skinner and co-workers[54] in 1967 reported a promising new method for making acetylenic hydrocarbons and their derivatives. When they heated 1-hexene with lithium metal dispersion at reflux (64°), 65% of the 1-hexene was converted to lithium 1-hexynylide within 1 hour. No hydrogen evolved, and no by-products were found. The reaction is:

$$RCH=CH_2 + 4Li \longrightarrow RC\equiv CLi + 3LiH$$

Of the olefins which they tried, only the 1-alkenes below 1-heptene reacted well. Carefully purified 1-octene did not react, but addition of certain "promoters" induced reaction. The best promoter was dimethylamine, 8 mole % based on 1-octene. This caused 52.5% yield of lithium 1-octynylide to form within 4 hours at 100°.

Some other olefins did not react: 1,3-pentadiene, 1,5-hexadiene, 2-heptene and cyclooctene. The fact that such a wide variety of promoters as water, alcohol, HCl, amines and 1-hexyne were effective to some degree with 1-octene indicates that promoters for the completely unreactive olefins might be found. If this is possible, cheaper sodium metal might be used, and a wide variety of acetylenes might be made directly from relatively cheap and available olefins.

TABLE 4-7
Products from ω-Fluoroacetylenes[20]

Compound	% Yield	b.p. (°C)	(mm)
5-Fluoro-1-pentyne	21.4[b]	75.5–76	742
6-Fluoro-1-hexyne	75[b]	106–106.5	742
7-Fluoro-1-heptyne	92[b]	131.5–132	742
8-Fluoro-1-octyne	50[a], 76[b]	82–82.5	60
9-Fluoro-1-nonyne	76[b]	114	108
10-Fluoro-1-decyne	60[a]	81–82	10
N-α-Naphthyl-2-heptynoamide	77	—	—
N-α-Naphthyl-9-fluoro-2-nonynoamide	72	—	—
N-α-Naphthyl-10-fluoro-2-decynoamide	88	—	—
N-α-Naphthyl-11-fluoro-2-undecynoamide	75	—	—
9-Fluoro-2-nonynoic acid	50	121	0.2
10-Fluoro-2-decynoic acid	95	115	0.01
11-Fluoro-2-undecynoic acid	75	120–120.5	0.03
7-Fluoro-1-heptene	80	117–117.5	742
8-Fluoro-1-octene	86	140	742
9-Fluoro-1-nonene	80	104	108
10-Fluoro-1-decene	75	119	90
1-Bromo-6-fluoro-1-hexyne	86	62.5	12
1-Bromo-7-fluoro-1-heptyne	87	74	10
1-Bromo-8-fluoro-1-octyne	74	89	10
1-Bromo-9-fluoro-1-nonyne	65	102	10
1-Bromo-10-fluoro-1-decyne	86	117	10
1-Chloro-8-fluoro-1-octyne	42	112	55
1,12-Difluoro-6-dodecyne	65	130.5–131	11
1,14-Difluoro-7-tetradecyne	77	95–96	0.1
1,11-Difluoro-4,6-undecadiyne	55	89	0.05
1,12-Difluoro-5,7-dodecadiyne	41	122	0.8
1,13-Difluoro-5,7-tridecadiyne	71	99–100	0.03
1,14-Difluoro-6,8-tetradecadiyne	48	103–104	0.04
1,6-Difluorohexane		126.5–127	742
1,11-Difluoroundecane	64	108–108.5	11
1,13-Difluorotridecane		135	12

[a] Sodium acetylide in xylene-dimethylformamide
[b] Lithium acetylide-ethylenediamine.

5.2. Lithium Alkynylides in Dioxane

In 1958, Schlubach[55] reviewed methods for preparing disubstituted acetylenes. Higher alkyl halides are not very soluble in ammonia, so they react poorly with sodium alkynylides in ammonia. In addition, ammonia reacts with activated halogen atoms, such as α-haloketones, to form amines. The Grignard method is not generally applicable because acetylenic Grignards react slowly and poorly with primary alkyl halides. The reaction of dialkynylmercury with lithium to form lithium alkynylide is inconvenient because it is hard to separate the metallic mercury which is liberated. Lithium alkynylides have been made by reacting acetylenes with lithium alkyls in dioxane, but this method requires very pure dioxane.[56]

Schlubach[55] described a general synthesis of disubstituted acetylenes. He found that ordinary commercial lithium amide in dioxane would react with acetylenic compounds fast enough to form several moles of $LiC \equiv CR$ per hour. Lithium acetylide itself is insoluble, but solubility increases as the size of R increases. Lithium phenylacetylide reacts with n-butyl bromide in boiling dioxane to form phenylbutylacetylene in 46% yield. At 130°, the yield is 55%, at 150°, 71%. The reaction can be conducted satisfactorily in an autoclave, because stirring is good. Lithium phenylacetylide reacts with isopropyl bromide at 150° to give 65% yield of phenylisopropylacetylene. This is much better than the older methods for preparing acetylenes with secondary alkyl groups. t-Alkyl halides do not react even at 150°.

Active halogen compounds are also useful. Lithium 1-hexynylide reacts with chloromethyl methyl ether to form $MeOCH_2C \equiv CH$ in 67% yield. The Grignard reagent of 1-hexyne gives only 42% yield, and sodium 1-hexynylide in ammonia gives 46% yield. Lithium 1-hexynylide and ethyl chloroformate give two products:

$$BuC \equiv CLi + ClCO_2Et \longrightarrow BuC \equiv CCO_2Et + (BuC \equiv C)_3COH \xrightarrow[\text{rearrangement}]{\text{Meyer–Schuster}}$$
$$ (25\%) \qquad\quad (46\%)$$

$$\overset{\displaystyle OH}{\underset{}{(BuC \equiv C)_2C = C = CR}} \text{ (these are dyestuffs)}$$

α-Bromoacetic ester gives polymer, but ethyl bromopropionate results in a 90% yield of $MeCHBrC(OLi)(C \equiv CBu)_3$, which with KOH gives 50% yield

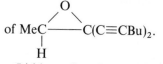

of $MeC \overset{\displaystyle O}{\overset{\diagup\;\diagdown}{\underset{\displaystyle H}{\longrightarrow}}} C(C \equiv CBu)_2$.

Lithium phenylacetylide reacts with other reagents:

$$LiC \equiv CPh + ClSO_2PhMe \longrightarrow PhC \equiv CCl$$
$$ (60\%)$$

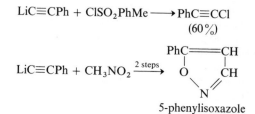

$$LiC \equiv CPh + CH_3NO_2 \xrightarrow{\text{2 steps}}$$

5-phenylisoxazole

$$\text{LiC}{\equiv}\text{CPh} + \text{ClCH}_2\overset{\displaystyle O}{\overset{\|}{\text{C}}}\text{CH}_3 \longrightarrow \text{PhC}{\equiv}\text{C}\overset{\displaystyle OH}{\underset{\displaystyle \underset{CH_3}{|}}{\overset{|}{-}\text{C}-}}\text{CH}_2\text{Cl} \text{ (alkynylation is}$$

much faster than

alkylation)

(72%)

5.3. Reaction of Lithium Alkynylides with ω-Chloroalkyl Bromides

Gautier[57] prepared some new carbinols, $\text{RR}'\overset{\displaystyle OH}{\overset{|}{\text{CC}}}{\equiv}\text{C(CH}_2)_n\text{Cl}$, by two methods: (1) selective alkylation and (2) alkynylation:

$$(1) \quad \text{MeEtC}\overset{\displaystyle OM}{\overset{|}{\text{C}}}\text{C}{\equiv}\text{CM} + \text{Br(CH}_2)_n\text{Cl}$$

$$(2) \quad \text{MeEtC}{=}\text{O} + \text{MC}{\equiv}\text{C(CH}_2)_n\text{Cl}$$

$$\longrightarrow \text{MeEt}\overset{\displaystyle OH}{\overset{|}{\text{CC}}}{\equiv}\text{C(CH}_2)_n\text{Cl}$$

He studied the effect of the alkali metal M on the alkylation reaction. Dehydrohalogenation was the most important side reaction and was at a minimum when lithium (from lithium amide) was used.

Grimmer[58] reacted 1-alkynes with lithium amide, and then added 1-chloro-ω-bromo(or iodo)alkanes to make 1-chloro- (nonterminal) alkynes. The products are given in Table 4-8. The haloacetylenes react with either NaCN or sodiomalonic esters to form acetylenic acids.

TABLE 4-8
1-Haloalkynes[58]

1-Halo-	b.p. (°C) @ 1 mm Hg	
	Cl	I
7-Undecyne	82–83	108–110
7-Tridecyne	106–107	133–135
5-Tetradecyne	—	128–130 (0.4 mm)
6-Tetradecyne	115–118	135–137
8-Tetradecyne	116–119	135–138
7-Pentadecyne	126–128	150–153
6-Hexadecyne	138–139	—
7-Hexadecyne	140–143	161–164
8-Hexadecyne	140–142	159–161
7-Heptadecyne	150–152	172–174
8-Octadecyne	135–136	155–157 (0.1 mm)

5.4. Reaction of Lithium Alkynylides with ω-Bromo Alkanols and ω-Bromo Acids

Lithium and sodium alkynylides can be alkylated with ω-bromo acids.[59] Extension of this reaction to unprotected ω-bromo alcohols is a new route to acetylenic alcohols (in addition to dehydrohalogenation, ethynylation and acetylide-epoxide reactions). In liquid ammonia, 3-bromo-1-propanol and a large excess of lithium 1-heptynylide gave 70% yield of 7-tridecyn-1-ol. This product was converted to the bromide, which was malonated by sodiomalonic ester. The malonate was decarboxylated to make 4-hexadecynoic acid. An example of acid synthesis via dilithium derivatives of acetylenic alcohols is:

$$C_{13}H_{27}Br + LiC\equiv CCH_2 \longrightarrow C_{13}H_{27}C\equiv CCH_2\overset{\overset{\displaystyle OLi}{|}}{} \quad \xrightarrow[\text{(2) sodiomalonic ester}]{\text{(1) PBr}_3}$$

$$\text{(93\%)}$$

$$C_{13}H_{27}C\equiv C(CH_2)_2CO_2H$$
$$\text{(52\%)}$$

Reaction of α,ω-dihalides with ω-acetylenic alcohols is a convenient synthesis of long-chain α,ω-diols. 1,6-Dibromohexane with propargyl alcohol in the presence of lithium amide in ammonia gives dodeca-2,10-diyne-1,12-diol in 88% yield. The acid synthesis via malonic ester gives dibasic acids.

ω-Bromo acids can also react with dilithioprop-2-yn-1-ol.[59] Products are ω-hydroxy acetylenic acids:

$$HO_2C(CH_2)_nBr + LiC\equiv CCH_2\overset{\overset{\displaystyle OLi}{|}}{} \xrightarrow[\text{(2) H}_2\text{O, H}^+]{\text{(1) NH}_3} HO_2C(CH_2)_nC\equiv CCH_2OH$$

Table 4-9 lists some hydroxy acids made by this reaction.

TABLE 4-9
Hydroxy Acetylenic Acids[59]

Acid	% Yield	m.p. (°C)
10-Hydroxydec-8-ynoic	59	60–61.5
11-Hydroxyundec-9-ynoic	76	56.5–57
14-Hydroxytetradec-12-ynoic	66	82–83
10-Hydroxydec-7-ynoic	52	45–45
12-Hydroxydodec-9-ynoic	53	60–61
15-Hydroxypentadec-12-ynoic	62	74–75
13-Hydroxytridec-9-ynoic	51	54–55
16-Hydroxyhexadec-12-ynoic	54	63–64

5.5. Reaction of Monolithium Dialkynylides with ω-Bromo Acids

Lithium alkynylides in liquid ammonia condense with ω-bromoacids to form long-chain acetylenic acids, but the yields decrease as the chain length of the alkyne increases. Ames and co-workers[60] condensed α,ω-diacetylenes with ω-bromo acids in the hope of increasing solubilities, and hence improving the possibility of preparing longer-chain acids. They made products of the type $HC \equiv C(CH_2)_m C \equiv C(CH_2)_n CO_2H$. 8-Bromooctanoic acid reacted with 5 moles of deca-1,9-diyne in the presence of 10 moles of lithium amide in ammonia to give octadeca-9,17-diynoic acid ($m = 6$, $n = 7$, 66% yield). 11-Bromo-undecanoic acid and tetradeca-1,13-diyne gave only 48% yield of the acid ($m = 10$, $n = 10$). This synthesis is no better than the method which uses monoalkylacetylenes.

Hexa-1,5-diyne was alkylated with 1 mole of n-octyl bromide (via lithium amide in ammonia) to form tetradeca-1,5-diyne; further condensation with 8-bromooctanoic acid gave docosa-9,13-diynoic acid in 62% yield.[60] This method was used to prepare the acids having three, four, five or six methylene groups between the two acetylenic bonds. Catalytic semihydrogenation of the diynoic acids over Lindlar's catalyst (quinoline present) gave the corresponding *cis,cis*-dienoic acids.

5.6. Relative Acidity of Fluorenyl and Acetylenic Hydrogen; Competitive Reactions of Lithium Derivatives

Gautier and co-workers[61] replaced both one and two hydrogen atoms on the 9-position of fluorene with metals and then reacted the metallofluorene with ω-halo-1-acetylenes:

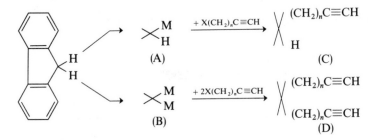

The metal exchange reaction did not occur at all:

$$RM + X(CH_2)_n C \equiv CH \not\longrightarrow RH + X(CH_2)_n C \equiv CM$$

Thus, fluorenyl hydrogen is more acidic in this reaction. Type (C) compounds undergo the Mannich reaction with formaldehyde and dialkylamine to form the usual yield of product of reaction at the acetylenic hydrogen:

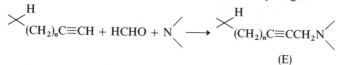

$$(E)$$

Surprisingly, the reaction at fluorenyl hydrogen to give products such as

$$(F)$$

does not occur. Alkylation of type (C) products after metallation by sodium amide in ammonia gives only reaction at the fluorenyl hydrogen. The same reaction after metallation by phenyllithium in ether gives no product at all. However, carbonation after metallation by phenyllithium in ether gives acid from the reaction at the fluorenyl hydrogen.

These reactions show that the fluorenyl hydrogen is more acidic than the acetylenic hydrogen in ammonia. The characteristic red fluorenyl anion is formed and can be alkylated. In the ether solution, the red color of the fluorenyl anion from phenyllithium disappears after about $\frac{1}{2}$ hour, the mixture becoming white. The addition of alkylating agent before the color disappears gives a low yield of product alkylated at the fluorenyl carbon. If the alkylating agent or CO_2 is added to the white mixture, alkylation does not occur at the fluorenyl carbon, but does occur at the acetylenic hydrogen. The lithium fluorenyl salt is in equilibrium with the lithium acetylide derivative, which is insoluble in ether. Thus equilibrium is shifted to acetylenic derivative:

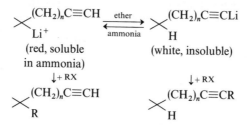

5.7. Reaction of Lithium Alkynylides with Disulfides to Form Alkynyl Thioethers

Lithium alkynylides react well with disulfides to form alkynyl thioethers.[62] This is the easiest synthesis of 1-alkylthio-1-alkynes. Yields are 70–80% when R and R' are lower alkyls:

$$R'C\equiv CLi + RSSR \xrightarrow{NH_3} R'C\equiv CSR$$

A new procedure for preparing S-alkyl, aryl, alkenyl and alkynyl phosphorothioates uses lithium alkynylides in ether or hydrocarbon diluent as the means of introducing the acetylenic group:[63]

$$(RO)_2\overset{\overset{S}{\|}}{P}S\overset{\overset{S}{\|}}{S}P(OR)_2 + R'C\equiv CLi \xrightarrow{\text{2-3 min}} (RO)_2\overset{\overset{S}{\|}}{P}SC\equiv CR' + (RO)_2\overset{\overset{S}{\|}}{P}SLi$$

These esters are related to the thioalkynyl ethers. They have exceptional insecticidal properties, but are practically nontoxic to mammals.

5.8. Reaction of Lithium Alkynylides with Sulfur and Acyl Bromides to Form 1-Acylthio-1-alkynes

1-Acylthio-1-alkynes, a new class of acetylenic compounds, are made by reacting lithium alkynylides with sulfur and then with acyl bromides:[64]

$$RC\equiv CH + BuLi \xrightarrow[\text{-10 to 20°}]{\text{ether}} RC\equiv CLi \xrightarrow[\text{-15 to 0°}]{S_8} RC\equiv CSLi$$

$$RC\equiv CSLi + R'-\overset{\overset{O}{\|}}{C}-Br \rightarrow RC\equiv C-S-\overset{\overset{O}{\|}}{C}-R'$$

where R and R' are alkyl groups.

TABLE 4-10
1-Acylthio-1-alkynes[64]

1-Acylthio-1-alkyne	b.p. (°C, @ mm Hg)	% Yield[a]
$CH_3-\overset{\overset{O}{\|}}{C}-S-C\equiv C-CH_3$	60–61, @ 10 m.p. 0–1	37
$CH_3-\overset{\overset{O}{\|}}{C}-S-C\equiv C-n\text{-}C_4H_9$	100–101, @ 10	55
$CH_3-\overset{\overset{O}{\|}}{C}-S-C\equiv C-\overset{\overset{CH_3}{/}}{\underset{\underset{CH_3}{\backslash}}{C}}-H$	75–76, @ 10	54
$\overset{\overset{CH_3}{\backslash}}{\underset{\underset{CH_3}{/}}{CH_3-C}}-\overset{\overset{O}{\|}}{C}-S-C\equiv C-\overset{\overset{CH_3}{/}}{\underset{\underset{CH_3}{\backslash}}{C}}-H$	100–102, @ 10	52

[a] Yield based on sulfur.

5.9. Lithium 1-Alkoxyalkynylides and their Reactions

Vollema and Arens[65] used salt-free solutions of metal derivatives of acetylenic ethers in reactions with epoxides. They reacted ethoxyethyne with alkali amide in ammonia and added epoxide to form $R\overset{\displaystyle OH}{\underset{\displaystyle |}{C}}HCH_2C{\equiv}COEt$. With lithium ethoxyethynylide in ammonia, ethylene oxide reacted best at 0°, and propylene oxide at 20°. Sodium and potassium ethoxyethynylides gave poor results.

Lithium alkoxyethynylide reacted with ethyl chloroacetate in ether to form an impure unstable ester, $EtOC{\equiv}CCH_2CO_2Et$ (b.p. 62–63° at 2 mm of Hg). Lithium ethoxyethynylide reacts with diethyl disulfide, but the intermediate adds $-SEt$ to form a vinyl ether, $EtSCH{=}\overset{\displaystyle OEt}{\underset{\displaystyle |}{\underset{\displaystyle SEt}{C}}}$. The intermediate could not be isolated because the secondary reaction is very fast. The mixed ether-thioether formed in a modified reaction:

$$LiC{\equiv}COEt + EtSSO_2Et \longrightarrow EtSC{\equiv}COEt \xrightarrow{H_2O,\,H^+} EtSCH_2CO_2Et$$

$$\xrightarrow[+\ EtSLi]{} EtSCH{=}\overset{\displaystyle OEt}{\underset{\displaystyle SEt}{C}}$$

5.10. Lithium Ethylthioethynylide and Its Reactions

Lithium amide reacts with ethylthioethyne in ammonia to form lithium ethylthioethynylide, which reacts with epichlorohydrin in ammonia to give two products:[67]

$$ClCH_2\overset{\displaystyle O}{\overset{\displaystyle \diagup\,\diagdown}{CH-CH_2}} + LiC{\equiv}CSEt \xrightarrow{NH_3} HOCH_2CH{=}CHC{\equiv}CSEt + \;\diagdown\!\!\diagup\text{—}CH_2SEt$$

Reaction time (hr)	(1) % Yield	(2) % Yield
5	62	8
16	54	17
24	52	30

The cyclization in the presence of base is another example of nucleophilic addition of an alcohol to an acetylenic thioether, the addend attaching to the β-carbon of the acetylenic bond. Note that lithium ethoxyethynylide reacts normally with epichlorohydrin to form $\overset{\displaystyle O}{\overset{\diagup\diagdown}{CH_2-CHCH_2C}}\equiv COEt$, 60% yield. Interestingly, bis-(ethylthioethyne)magnesium or bis(ethoxyethyne)magnesium gives yet another kind of product, $CH_2ClCH\overset{\displaystyle OH}{\overset{|}{CH}}CH_2C\equiv CXEt$, where X is O or S.[65]

Lithium ethylthioethynylide in ether poured onto solid CO_2 gives the acid $EtSC\equiv CCO_2H$ in good yield.[68] The reaction with ethyl chloroacetate gives the ethyl ester of the acid.

5.11. Lithium Vinylthioethynylide

Vinylthioethyne reacts with lithium amide in ammonia to form the lithium derivative, which reacts normally with alkyl halides and with acetone:[69]

$$LiC\equiv CSCH=CH_2 \xrightarrow{+\ RBr} RC\equiv CSCH=CH_2$$
$$(R = Bu, 80\%; Me, 65\%)$$

$$\xrightarrow{+\ acetone} Me_2\overset{\displaystyle OH}{\overset{|}{C}}C\equiv CSCH=CH_2$$
$$(75\%)$$

Vinylthioethyne develops a brown color fairly rapidly at room temperature, but remains colorless for several days at $-70°$. The alkyl and hydroxyalkyl derivatives are more stable.

5.12. Lithium Ethylselenoethyne

Ethylselenoethyne is hard to prepare by the sodium acetylide–selenium reaction because it reacts further to form $EtSeC\equiv CSeEt$.[47,70] This secondary reaction probably involves a nucleophilic attack at Se by bases, analogous to the formation of bis(dialkylphosphino)ethynes from dialkylethynylphosphines.[71] A good method for preparing ethylselenoethyne is the reaction of bis-(ethylseleno)ethyne with phenyllithium in ether:

$$PhLi + EtSeC\equiv CSeEt \longrightarrow LiC\equiv CSeEt + PhSeEt + by\text{-}products$$
$$\xrightarrow{H_2O} HC\equiv CSeEt$$

This is a useful synthesis for alkyl phenyl selenides. The sulfur analogs react similarly.

6. CALCIUM CARBIDE

Calcium carbide, CaC_2, is much less reactive than sodium acetylide or lithium acetylide. Calcium carbide in dry benzene does not react with chlorine at 0 or $50°$.[72] Addition of a trace of water starts the vigorous evolution of a flammable gas, probably chloroacetylenes. Chlorine saturated with water gives benzene hexachloride, by the addition of chlorine to benzene.

Kazarian[73] first used calcium carbide–KOH mixtures as a reagent for making acetylenic glycols. KOH and CaC_2 in inert diluents react with ketones to form the acetylenic glycols in good yield. Kazarian thought the reagent was $KC\equiv C-CaOH$, which reacted first like $KC\equiv CH$, and then at the $-CaOH$ bond. This formulation is unlikely, because a simple mixture of KOH and calcium carbide will not react with alkyl sulfates or alkyl halides. If the $KOH-CaC_2$ mix in a diluent is heated first to 150°, and then cooled, it will react with alkyl sulfates and alkyl bromides to give 1-alkynes in modest yield.[74]

The literature contains very few references to the organic chemistry of calcium carbide. This very economical source of the acetylenic group is relatively inert, presumably because of its crystal structure.

7. GRIGNARD REAGENTS OF ACETYLENES

7.1. Acetylene

Acetylene reacts with ethylmagnesium bromide in ether to form a dark, dense, viscous lower layer of $BrMgC\equiv CMgBr$ (acetylene diGrignard). Excess acetylene might be expected to react further to form the monoGrignard, $HC\equiv CMgBr$, but reaction is incomplete even if acetylene is used under pressure.[37] Acetylene diGrignard prepared in dibutyl ether-benzene is powdery and easy to stir.[75] Acetylene Grignard reagents can be alkylated or carbonated to give products which can be assumed to involve acetylene monoGrignard. Acetylene diGrignard can be made to give mostly monosubstituted acetylenic products.[76]

One of the best procedures for making ethynylmagnesium bromide (acetylene monoGrignard) uses tetrahydrofuran as a solvent. Acetylene reacts with ethylmagnesium bromide in THF to give a clear solution of a Grignard reagent which reacts easily with aldehydes and ketones to form ethynylcarbinols.[77] In ether, the same reaction gives mostly glycols. In tetrahydrofuran, the solution of monoGrignard disproportionates at 40° to acetylene and acetylene diGrignard.

Acetylene Grignard reagents are not widely used (for a review of Grignard reagents, see reference 78). Gouin[79] recently described the reaction of acetylene Grignard reagents with tetrahydropyran and tetrahydrofuran derivatives to prepare acetylenic products (see table on page 72.)

7.2. Grignard Reagents of Substituted Acetylenes

The Grignard reagents of substituted acetylenes are usually easier to make than the acetylene Grignards and give cleaner reactions because disubstitution is not

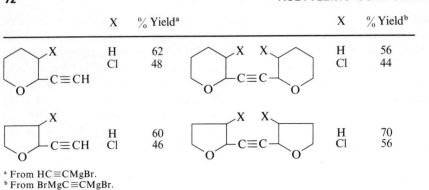

	X	% Yield[a]		X	% Yield[b]
	H	62		H	56
	Cl	48		Cl	44
	H	60		H	70
	Cl	46		Cl	56

[a] From $HC{\equiv}CMgBr$.
[b] From $BrMgC{\equiv}CMgBr$.

a competing side reaction. Consequently, Grignards of substituted acetylenes are much more generally used.

7.2.1. RATE OF REACTION OF ACETYLENIC COMPOUNDS WITH GRIGNARD REAGENTS

Wotiz[80] reported the first study of the rate of reaction of Grignard reagents with acetylenes. He determined the rate of evolution of hydrocarbon from the reaction of the Grignards with 1-hexyne. The relative rates for the reaction

$$BuC{\equiv}CH + RMgX \longrightarrow BuC{\equiv}CMgX + RH \text{ (gas)}$$

are given in Table 4-11. When R is methyl, halide reactivity is $Cl > Br \cong I$, but when R is ethyl, $Cl > Br > I$. The rate for methyl Grignards is the lowest. The rate increases as the number of β-hydrogens in R increases, so hyperconjugation in R is important. The same order of reactivity holds for dialkylmagnesiums and 1-hexane.[81] The reaction has at least two steps, and the first

TABLE 4-11
Relative Rates of Reaction of Grignard Reagents with 1-Hexyne[80]

RMgX			RMgX		
R	X	Relative Rate	R	X	Relative Rate
Me	I	6	Et	Br	100
Me	Br	6	Et	Cl	155
Me	Cl	16	i-Pr	Br	210
Pr	Br	59	Allyl	Br	435
Et	I	71			

half of the alkyl groups in the Grignard reagent is more reactive than the second half.

Wotiz subsequently determined the rate of reaction of various acetylenes with a single Grignard reagent, ethylmagnesium bromide.[82] Reactions in ether showed:

(1) Steric factors aside, the 1-alkynes reacted at about the same rate.

(2) Triethylamine increased the rate of reaction of 1-hexyne by a factor of 5, but dioxane added to the ether had no effect.

(3) Butoxyacetylene reacted 5 times as fast as 1-hexyne, but methyl propargyl ether (a β-acetylenic ether) reacted only 1.6 times as fast. Electron attraction by oxygen is more effective in the α-acetylenic ether, and this makes the acetylenic hydrogen more available for reaction.

(4) Propargyl bromide reacted rapidly but gave less than 15 % of the expected ethane; at least three reactions occurred:

$$\text{EtMgBr} + \text{HC} \equiv \text{CCH}_2\text{Br}$$

$\rightarrow$ ethane + BrMgC≡CCH$_2$Br (expected from reaction at the —C≡CH group)

$\rightarrow$ EtCH=C=CH$_2$ (from coupling at Br and rearrangement)

$\rightarrow$ PrC≡CH (from coupling at Br, no rearrangement)

The main reaction was coupling, which is surprising because Grignard reagents have always been assumed to react faster with acidic hydrogen than in coupling reactions.

(5) The lower rate of reaction of phenylacetylene than 1-hexyne must be caused by steric hindrance.

The acidities of some substituted acetylenes determined by the rate of exchange with D_2O in dimethylformamide[83] do not parallel the acidities determined by the rate of reaction with ethylmagnesium bromide:[82]

	Relative Rate	
	Exchange Reaction	Grignard Reaction
$C_4H_9C \equiv CH$	0.058	1.3
$C_4H_9OC \equiv CH$	—	>6.5
$CH_3OC \equiv CH$	2.0	—
$C_6H_5C \equiv CH$	1	1
p-$BrC_6H_4C \equiv CH$	2.1	1.2
p-$ClC_6H_4C \equiv CH$	4.8	2.2

This suggests that the Grignard reaction is not merely a protolysis, but involves a hindered transition state. A four-center transition state may be involved, similar to the one pictured for reactions of terminal acetylenes with mercuric salts in the presence of tertiary amines:[83a]

$$\left[\begin{array}{c} -C\equiv C-H \\ \vdots \\ Mg-R \end{array}\right]^{\ddagger}_{\pm} \qquad \left[\begin{array}{c} -C\equiv C-H-NR_1 \\ \vdots \\ Hg-Cl \end{array}\right]$$

$$\text{Grignard} \qquad\qquad \text{HgCl}_2\text{-NR}_3$$

Dielectric constant changes were used to determine the rates of reaction of 1-hexyne with substituted phenylmagnesium bromides.[84] The method is good as long as the dielectric constant changes, and nothing precipitates from solution. The reaction is accelerated by increased electron density at the α-carbon of the Grignard, and the attack is electrophilic. Relative rates determined this way are listed in Table 4-12.

TABLE 4-12[84]

$$\text{Y}-\text{PhMgBr} + \text{BuC}\equiv\text{CH} \xrightarrow{31.5°}$$
$$\text{YC}_6\text{H}_5 + \text{BuC}\equiv\text{C}-\text{MgBr}$$

Y	k (liters/mole-sec) $\times 10^{-4}$)	Relative Reactivity
m-CF$_3$	0.22	2
m-Cl	0.33	3
p-Cl	0.6	6
H	2.80	25
p-Me	6.22	60
p-Me[a]		100

[a] Reaction with ethylmagnesium bromide.

7.2.2. COMPOSITION OF GRIGNARD REAGENTS

Wotiz[85] showed that the Schlenk equilibrium[86] does occur:

$$2\text{RMgBr} \longleftrightarrow \text{R}_2\text{Mg} + \text{MgBr}_2$$

He added different amounts of MgBr$_2$ to Et$_2$Mg, then added 1-hexyne and measured the ethane evolved. The rate decreased with increasing amounts of MgBr$_2$, and in a mixture with 1:1 Mg-to-Br ratio, the rate was the same as with ordinary ethylmagnesium bromide. Equilibration was very rapid, being about 95% complete in 10 minutes.

Halogen-free diethylmagnesium reacts with 1-hexyne in ether three times as fast as ethylmagnesium bromide does.[87] When dioxane is added to the Grignard, the rate increases. Dry ice does not carbonate the Grignard reagent of 1-hexyne, but it does carbonate bis(1-hexynyl)magnesium (73% yield). It is difficult and hazardous to prepare halogen-free diethylmagnesium, but the same order of reactivity can be obtained with ethylmagnesium bromide if dioxane is added. Apparently dioxane shifts the Schlenk equilibrium to the right to form more diethylmagnesium.

7.2.3. MECHANISM OF REACTIONS OF ACETYLENES WITH ORGANOMAGNESIUM COMPOUNDS

Dessy[88] reacted 1-deutero-1-acetylenes with various Grignard reagents. Deuterium reduces the reactivity with ethylmagnesium bromide by a factor of at least 4.3, so cleavage of the C—D bond must be involved in the transition state. The terminal bond is nearly broken in the transition state, and the new bond to the alkyl group of the Grignard has started to form. Thus, the reaction has to be at least a three-center process. The isotope effect is greater in the latter half of the reaction. Data indicated second-order kinetics both with 1-hexyne and 1-hexyne-d_1. These facts are explained by the following equations:

$$R_2Mg + MgX_2 \longleftrightarrow R_2Mg \cdot MgX_2 \longleftrightarrow 2RMgX \text{ (unknown equilibrium, so actual reagent is called ZMgR)}$$

$$\begin{array}{ccc} R'C{\equiv}CH & R'C{\equiv}C\cdots H \\ + & \longrightarrow & \mid \quad \mid \longrightarrow R'C{\equiv}CMgZ + RH \\ ZMgR & Z{-}Mg\cdots R \\ & \text{(transition state)} \end{array}$$

Bond breaking is more important in forming the transition state than bond making. The rate is proportional to the number of β-hydrogens on R, and this may be due to stabilization of the incipient carbanion by hyperconjugation. The rate depends on the electron-withdrawing power of R'; the more electronegative R' is, the faster is the reaction.

7.3. Reactions of Grignard Reagents of Substituted Acetylenes

7.3.1. CARBONATION OF PROPARGYLIC GRIGNARDS

The propargylic Grignard reagent from 1-bromo-2-heptyne carbonates to a mixture of acetylenic and allenic acids:[89]

$$\begin{array}{ccc} & & \overset{\displaystyle CO_2H}{\overset{\displaystyle |}{}} \\ BuC{\equiv}CCH_2MgBr + CO_2 \xrightarrow{\text{ether}} BuC{\equiv}CCH_2CO_2H & + & BuC{=}C{=}CH_2 \\ & (36\% \text{ yield}) & (68\% \text{ of mix}) \\ & \xrightarrow{\text{dioxane}} (5\% \text{ yield}) & (84\% \text{ of mix}) \end{array}$$

7.3.2. CARBONATION OF 1-ACETYLENIC GRIGNARDS

The order of mixing the reagents can be important: When the Grignard reagent of 1-hexyne in dioxane is poured onto dry ice, the acid yield is 38%, but the reverse addition gives 60% yield.[87]

Dihalocarbenes do not react with phenylacetylene or 1-hexyne, but they do add to the olefinic bond of enynes to form dihalocyclopropylacetylenes. The Grignard reagents of these acetylenes carbonate well:[90]

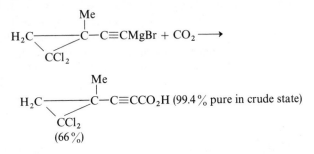

Kucherov[91] carbonated Grignard reagents to prepare substituted α-acetylenic acids. Some of his products are $EtMeCC\equiv CCO_2H$,

$$H_2C \overset{\displaystyle Me}{\underset{\displaystyle \underset{CCl_2}{\diagdown}}{\overset{\displaystyle |}{\rule[0.5ex]{4em}{0.4pt}}}} C-C\equiv CMgBr + CO_2 \longrightarrow$$

and $Me_2C=CH(CH_2)_2\underset{\displaystyle Me}{\overset{\displaystyle \overset{OH}{|}}{C}}-C\equiv CCO_2Me.$

Carbonation of Grignards of substituted acetylenes is a key step in the synthesis of tropinone and of pseudo-pelleterine:[92]

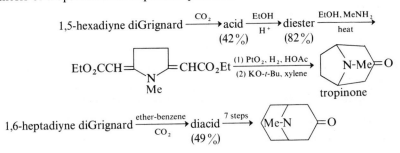

7.3.3. REACTION OF EPOXIDES WITH 1-ACETYLENIC GRIGNARDS

Acetylenic Grignards react well with epoxides in tetrahydrofuran[93,94] and in benzene.[95] If magnesium halides are present in the Grignard, they can act as

Lewis acids and catalyze the rearrangement of the epoxides to carbonyl compounds. These carbonyl compounds can react with the Grignard to give acetylenic carbinols, isomeric with the desired products. Halogen ions, particularly bromide and iodide, open the epoxide to form α-hydroxyhalides. This can occur in Grignard reactions unless $MgBr_2$ is removed, and it can occur in liquid ammonia if an acetylide has reacted with an organic halide in the previous step, leaving MX in solution.

7.3.4. REACTION OF 1-ACETYLENIC GRIGNARDS WITH HALOGEN COMPOUNDS

Acetylenic Grignards react well with organohalogen compounds, as a few recent examples illustrate:

$$BrMgC\equiv C(CH_2)_8CO_2MgBr + BrCH_2C\equiv CCH_2C\equiv CEt \xrightarrow{\text{THF, CuCN}}$$

9,12,15-octadecatriynoic acid (m.p. 76°)[96]
(74%)

Semihydrogenation of the triynoic acid in the presence of palladium catalyst gave 88% yield of linolenic acid.

1-Propynylmagnesium bromide reacts with $ClC\text{-}C\equiv CMe$ to form (with Me substituents above and below the C)

$MeC\equiv CC\text{-}C\equiv CMe$ (with Me substituents above and below) in low yield. Phenylethynylmagnesium bromide reacts much better, to give 43% yield of the corresponding diyne.[97]

Pabon[99] used Osbond's[100] Grignard alkylation method to prepare 4,7,10,13-nonadecatetraynoic acid:

$$C_5H_{11}(C\equiv CCH_2)_3Br + XMgC\equiv C(CH_2)_2CO_2MgX \xrightarrow{Cu_2Cl_2}$$

$$C_5H_{11}(C\equiv CCH_2)_4CH_2CO_2H$$
(47%)

In this and many other successful Grignard alkylation reactions, cuprous chloride serves as a catalyst. Pabon has presented an excellent description of his experimental methods.[99]

Grignard reactions are used to make skipped diynes. Taniguchi[101] reviewed the literature on skipped diynes in 1966. These diynes are hard to prepare and isolate because they isomerize easily to form conjugated diacetylenes. In fact, much of the older literature work was probably actually on the isomerized diynes. The simplest skipped diyne, 1,4-pentadiyne, has not been reported.

Taniguchi made several substituted 1,4-pentadiynes by the Grignard alkylation method:

$$RC{\equiv}CMgBr + BrCH_2C{\equiv}CR' \xrightarrow[\text{THF}]{\text{Cu}_2\text{Cl}_2} RC{\equiv}CCH_2C{\equiv}CR'$$

Sodium acetylide, which is more basic, reacted with propargyl bromide to give poor yields of skipped diynes. The Grignard reaction was used to prepare the compounds in Table 4-13. The ultraviolet spectra indicated very little, if any, conjugation through the methylene group.

TABLE 4-13
1,3- and 1,4-Diynes[101]

1,4- and 1,3-Diynes	Method[a]	Time (hr)	% Yield
$n\text{-}C_4H_9C{\equiv}CCH_2C{\equiv}CH$	1	1	50.5
$n\text{-}C_4H_9(C{\equiv}C)_2CH_3$	2	3	82
$C_6H_5C{\equiv}CCH_2C{\equiv}CH$	1	0.66	52
$C_6H_5(C{\equiv}C)_2CH_3$	2	3	54
$n\text{-}C_4H_9C{\equiv}CCH_2C{\equiv}CC_6H_5$	1	0.66	52
$n\text{-}C_4H_9(C{\equiv}C)_2CH_2C_6H_5$	2	72	64
$C_6H_5C{\equiv}CCH_2CC_6H_5$	1	1	56
$C_6H_5(C{\equiv}C)_2CH_2C_6H_5$	3	7	57
$p\text{-}CH_3C_6H_4C{\equiv}CCH_2C{\equiv}CH$	1	1	42
$p\text{-}CH_3C_6H_4(C{\equiv}C)_2CH_3$	2	24	66
$p\text{-}CH_3C_6H_4C{\equiv}CCH_2C{\equiv}CC_6H_5$	1	24	60
$p\text{-}CH_3C_6H_4(C{\equiv}C)_2CH_2C_6H_5$	3	—	—

[a] Method 1: Grignard alkylation reaction.
     2: Base-catalyzed isomerization of 1,4-diyne.
     3: 1,4-Diyne isomerized during chromatography on alumina.

Vinylic bromides are also reactive in Grignard alkylations:[102]

$$RCH{=}CHBr + BrMgC{\equiv}CR' \longrightarrow RCH{=}CHC{\equiv}CR'$$

Acetylenic Grignard reagents react with 2,3-dichlorotetrahydropyran to form a series of 2-alkynyl-3-chlorotetrahydropyrans.[98] The 2-halotetrahydropyrans show the characteristic reactivity of α-halogen ethers, just as glycosyl halides do. Zelinski used the Grignard alkylation reaction to make 2-phenylethynyltetrahydropyran[103] as a model for reactions contemplated with tetraacetyl-α-D-glucopyranosyl bromide.[104] The product hydrogenated normally, and hydrated and formed acetals as expected. For the glucosylation reaction, Zelinski reacted 1 mole of tetraacetyl-α-D-glucopyranosyl bromide with 12 moles of phenylethynylmagnesium bromide. The product consisted of levorotatory crystals, m.p. 135°. Recrystallization of the crude product gave

33% of a monohydrate, m.p. 125°, which had the same specific rotation. The Grignard and subsequent reactions can be represented as:

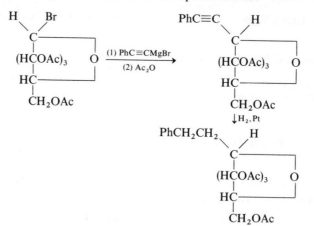

In similar reactions, acetylene diGrignard gave only tars.

One chlorine in cyanuric chloride can react with alkynyl Grignard reagents to form alkynyldichlorotriazines:[104a]

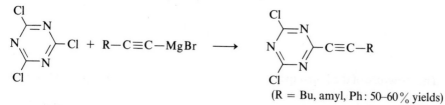

(R = Bu, amyl, Ph: 50–60% yields)

α-Acetylenic ketones are usually made by reacting an acid chloride with a metal acetylide or an acetylenic Grignard reagent:

$$RC{\equiv}CM + ClCR' \longrightarrow RC{\equiv}CCR'$$
$$\quad\quad\quad\quad\quad\overset{\|}{O}\quad\quad\quad\quad\overset{\|}{O}$$

Other acetylenic ketones have been made by careful oxidation of secondary acetylenic alcohols:

$$\underset{OH}{RCH}(CH_2)_nC{\equiv}CR' \longrightarrow \underset{O}{RC}(CH_2)_nC{\equiv}CR'$$

where $n = 0$ or an integer. For ketones in which n is greater than 2, a new synthesis has been developed.[105a] An acetylenic nitrile is reacted with a Grignard reagent, and the intermediate metalloimide is hydrolyzed by acid:

$$RMgBr + NC(CH_2)_nC{\equiv}CR' \longrightarrow \underset{O}{RC}(CH_2)_nC{\equiv}CR'$$

(R = Ph, R' = H or CH_3: 80% yield)

Allylvinylacetylenes are made by reacting vinylacetylene Grignard reagent with allyl bromides in ether:[105]

$$CH_2{=}CHC{\equiv}CMgBr + BrCH_2CH{=}CRR' \longrightarrow CH_2{=}CHC{\equiv}CCH_2CH{=}CRR'$$

7.4. Grignard Reagents of Diacetylenes

Gusev[106] prepared acetals from t-diacetylenic carbinols and then cleaved them with KOH to form diacetylenic aldehyde acetals:

$$\underset{\substack{|\\ OH}}{Me_2C}C{\equiv}CC{\equiv}CCH(OEt)_2 + KOH \text{ (trace)} \xrightarrow[\text{vacuum}]{140°} \underset{(52\%)}{HC{\equiv}CC{\equiv}CCH(OEt)_2} + \text{acetone}$$

He also prepared acetals of diacetylenic hydrocarbons by reacting Grignard reagents with ethyl orthoformate:

$$RC{\equiv}CC{\equiv}CMgX + HC(OEt)_3 \longrightarrow RC{\equiv}CC{\equiv}CCH(OEt)_2$$

R	% Yield
H	52.5
Me	54.6
Pr	54.5
Bu	55.7

The structure of the R group had no effect on the yield. Aqueous HCl hydrolyzed the acetals to free diacetylenic α-aldehydes.

Vinyl ethers react with the hydroxyl group of diacetylenic carbinols to "block" the hydroxyl during Grignard reactions at the terminal ethynyl hydrogen.[107] The hydroxyl group is regenerated by hydrolysis in dioxane-HCl.

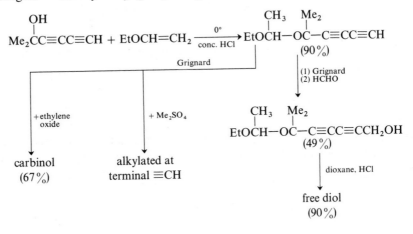

7.5. Acetylenic Zinc Grignard Reagents

Golse[108] reacted zinc with allyl bromide in tetrahydrofuran, and then added $RC\equiv CH$, followed by ethyl chloroethoxyacetate, to make α-ethoxy-β-acetylenic acid esters:

$$Zn + CH_2=CHCH_2Br \longrightarrow BrZnCH_2CH=CH_2 \xrightarrow{+\ RC\equiv CH} RC\equiv CZnBr \xrightarrow[\overset{|}{OEt}]{+\ ClCH-CO_2Et}$$

$$RC\equiv C\overset{\overset{\displaystyle OEt}{|}}{C}HCO_2Et \text{ (R is propyl, butyl, amyl, hexyl or phenyl)}$$

Phenylacetylene reacts with ethylzinc chloride to form $PhC\equiv CZnCl$. $PhC\equiv CMgX + ZnCl_2$ give the same product in ether. The zinc Grignard reagent reacts with acyl chlorides to give 40–70% yields of α-ketoacetylenes,

$$PhC\equiv C\overset{\overset{\displaystyle O}{||}}{C}R.^{[109]}$$

References

1. Vaughn, T. H., et al., J. Org. Chem., **2**, 1 (1937).
2. Coffman, D. D., Org. Syn., **20**, 40 (1940).
3. Pomerantz, P., et al., J. Res. Natl. Bur. Stds., **52**, 51 (1954).
4. Corbellini, M., and Turner, L., Chem. Ind. (Milan), **42**, 251 (1950); Chem. Abstr., **54**, 19250 (1960).
5. Masdupuy, E., Ann. Chim. (Paris), **2**, 527 (1957); Chem. Abstr., **52**, 2627 (1958).
6. Ernst, O., and Nicodemus, O., German Patent 494,575 (Nov. 21, 1926).
7. Schulenberg, W., German Patent 535,071 (Feb. 8, 1929).
8. Matignon, C., Compt. Rend., **124**, 775 (1897); **125**, 1033 (1897).
9. BASF, A-G, British Patent 771,708 (Apr. 3, 1957); Chem. Abstr., **51**, 18510 (1957).
10. Rutledge, T. F., J. Org. Chem., **22**, 649 (1957).
11. Lindsay, K. L., Perilstein, W. L., and Zachry, J. B., in "Metal-Organic Compounds," Advances in Chemistry Series, Vol. 23, p. 69, Washington, D.C., American Chemical Society, 1959.
12. Corey, E. J., and Chaykovsky, M., J. Am. Chem. Soc., **84**, 867 (1962).
13. Kriz, J., Benes, M. J., and Peska, J., Tetrahedron Letters, 2881 (1965).
14. French, F. A., Chem. Eng. News, 48 (Apr. 11, 1966).
15. Rutledge, T. F., J. Org. Chem., **24**, 840 (1959).
16. Jenny, E. F., and Meier, Kd., Angew. Chem., **71**, 245 (1959).
17. Grimmer, G., and Hildebrandt, A., Ann. Chem., **685**, 154 (1965).
18. Normant, J. F., Bull. Soc. Chim. France, 859 (1965).
19. Dear, R. E. A., and Pattison, F. L. M., J. Am. Chem. Soc., **85**, 622 (1963).
20. Pattison, F. L. M., and Dear, R. E. A., Can. J. Chem., **41**, 2600 (1963).
21. Pachter, I. J. (to Ethyl Corp.), U.S. Patent 2,799,703 (July 16, 1957); Chem. Abstr., **52**, 1206 (1958).
22. Kurtz, A. (to Union Carbide Corp.), British Patent 986,083 (Mar. 17, 1965); Chem. Abstr., **62**, 14504 (1965).

23. Normant, J. F., and Angelo, B., *Bull. Soc. Chim. France*, 354 (1960).

24. Hasek, W. R., Smith, W. C., and Engelhardt, V. A., *J. Am. Chem. Soc.*, **82**, 543 (1960).

25. Saggiomo, A. J., *J. Org. Chem.*, **22**, 1171 (1957).

26. Moreau, C., and Bongrand, J. C., *Bull. Soc. Chim.*, 846 (1909); *Ann. Chim.*, **14**, 5 (1920).

27. Radell, J., *et al.*, *J. Phys. Chem.*, **69**, 928 (1965).

28. Lebeau, P., and Picon, M., *Compt. Rend.*, **157**, 138 (1913).

29. Herbertz, T., *Chem. Ber.*, **92**, 541 (1959).

30. Ando, T., and Tokura, N., *Bull. Chem. Soc. Japan*, **31**, 351 (1958); *Chem. Abstr.*, **53**, 289 (1959).

31. Ando, T., and Tokura, N., *Bull. Chem. Soc. Japan*, **30**, 259 (1957); *Chem. Abstr.*, **52**, 331 (1958).

32. Heisig, G. B., and Davis, H. M., *J. Am. Chem. Soc.*, **57**, 339 (1935).

33. Yen, V.-Q., *Ann. Chim* (*Paris*), **7**, 785 (1962); *Chem. Abstr.*, **59**, 5043 (1963).

34. Yen, V.-Q., *Ann. Chim.* (*Paris*), **7**, 799 (1962); *Chem. Abstr.*, **59**, 5044 (1963).

35. Lapkin, I. I., and Andreichikov, Yu. S., *Zh. Organ. Khim.*, **1**, 480 (1965); *Chem. Abstr.*, **63**, 1692 (1965).

36. Adams, B. F., and Wotiz, J. H. (to Diamond Alkali Co.), U.S. Patent 3,235,577 (Feb. 15, 1966); *Chem. Abstr.*, **64**, 12556 (1966).

37. Raphael, R. A., "Acetylenic Compounds in Organic Synthesis," London, Butterworth, 1955.

38. Parker, R. E., and Isaacs, N. S., *Chem. Rev.*, **59**, 737 (1959).

39. Gaylord, N. G., and Becker, E. J., *Chem. Rev.*, **49**, 413 (1951).

40. Sondheimer, F., *J. Chem. Soc.*, 877 (1950).

41. Inhoffen, H. H., *et al.*, *Chem. Ber.*, **89**, 853 (1956).

42. Haynes, L. J., *et al.*, *J. Chem. Soc.*, 1583 (1947).

43. Jacobs, T. L., Dankner, D., and Dankner, A. R., *J. Am. Chem. Soc.*, **80**, 864 (1958).

44. Landor, S. R., and Pepper, E. S., *J. Chem. Soc.* (*C*), 2283 (1966).

45. Gautier, J. A., and Miocque, M., *Ann. Pharm.* (*France*), **23**, 317 (1965).

46. Marszak, I., Guermont, J. P., and Epsztein, R., *Bull. Soc. Chim. France*, 1807 (1960); *Chem. Abstr.*, **55**, 18585 (1961).

47. Brandsma, L., Wijers, H. E., and Jonker, C., *Rec. Trav. Chim.*, **83**, 208 (1964).

48. Radchenko, S. I., and Petrov, A. A., *Zh. Organ. Khim.*, **1**, 2115 (1965); *Chem. Abstr.*, **64**, 11076 (1966).

49. Herbertz, T., *Chem. Ber.*, **85**, 475 (1952).

50. Armitage, J. B., Jones, E. R. H., and Whiting, M. C., *J. Chem. Soc.*, 44 (1951).

51. Moissan, H., *Compt. Rend.*, **127**, 911 (1898).

52. Beumel, O. F., Jr., and Harris, R. F., *J. Org. Chem.*, **28**, 2775 (1963).

53. *Ibid.*, **29**, 1872 (1964).

54. Skinner, D. L., Peterson, D. J., and Logan, T. J., *J. Org. Chem.*, **32**, 105 (1967).

55. Schlubach, H. H., and Repenning, K., *Ann. Chem.*, **614**, 37 (1958).

56. Raphael, R. A., "Acetylenic Compounds in Organic Synthesis," London, Butterworth, 1955.

57. Gautier, J. A., Miocque, M., and d'Engenieres, M. D., *Bull. Soc. Chim. France*, 1368 (1963).

58. Grimmer, G., and Kracht, J., *Chem. Ber.*, **96**, 3370 (1963).

59. Ames, D. E., Covell, A. N., and Goodburn, T. G., *J. Chem. Soc.*, 5889 (1963).

60. *Ibid.*, 4373 (1965).

61. Gautier, J. A., Miocque, M., and Moskowitz, H., *Compt. Rend.*, **260**, 1988 (1965); *J. Organometall. Chem.*, **1**, 212 (1964).

62. Nooi, J. R., and Arens, J. F., *Rec. Trav. Chim.*, **80**, 244 (1961).

63. Miller, B., *J. Am. Chem. Soc.*, **82**, 6205 (1960).

64. Wijers, H. E., *Rec. Trav. Chim.*, **84**, 1284 (1965).

65. Vollema, G., and Arens, J. F., *Rec. Trav. Chim.*, **82**, 305 (1963).

66. Nooi, J. R., and Arens, J. F., *Rec. Trav. Chim.*, **81**, 533 (1962).

67. Vollema, G., and Arens, J. F., *Rec. Trav. Chim.*, **78**, 140 (1959).

68. Arens, J. F., *Advan. Org. Chem.*, **2**, 117 (1960).

69. Brandsma, L., and Arens, J. F., *Rec. Trav. Chim.*, **80**, 237 (1961).

70. Brandsma, L., Wijers, H. A., and Arens, J. F., *Rec. Trav. Chim.*, **81**, 583 (1962).

71. Voskuil, W., and Arens, J. F., *Rec. Trav. Chim.*, **81**, 993 (1962).

72. Dermer, O. C., and Hertzler, D. V., *Proc. Oklahoma Acad. Sci.*, **44**, 104 (1964).

73. Kazarian, L., *J. Gen. Chem. USSR, Engl. Transl.*, **4**, 1347 (1934); *Chem. Abstr.*, **29**, 3978 (1935).

74. Lyon, A. M., and Rutledge, T. F. (to Air Reduction Co.), U.S. Patent 2,724,008 (Nov. 15, 1955).

75. Bachmann, W. E., and Controulis, J., *J. Am. Chem. Soc.*, **73**, 2639 (1951).

76. Jacobs, T. L., *Org. Reactions*, **5**, 1 (1949).

77. Skatteböl, L., Jones, E. R. H., and Whiting, M. C., *Org. Syn.*, **39**, 56 (1959).

78. Kharasch, M. S., and Reinmuth, O., "Grignard Reactions of Non-Metallic Substances," p. 66, Englewood Cliffs, N.J., Prentice-Hall, 1954.

79. Gouin, L., *Ann. Chim. (Paris)*, **5**, 529 (1960); *Chem. Abstr.*, **55**, 8399 (1961).

80. Wotiz, J. H., Hollingsworth, C. A., and Dessy, R. E., *J. Am. Chem. Soc.*, **77**, 103 (1955).

81. Petrov, A. A., and Kormer, V. A., *Zh. Obshch. Khim.*, **30**, 216 (1960).

82. Wotiz, J. H., Hollingsworth, C. A., and Dessy, R. E., *J. Org. Chem.*, **20**, 1545 (1955).

83. Dessy, R. E., Okuzimi, Y., and Chen, A., *J. Am. Chem. Soc.*, **84**, 2899 (1962).

83a. Dessy, R. E., Budde, W. L., and Woodruff, C., *J. Am. Chem. Soc.*, **84**, 1172 (1962).

84. Dessy, R. E., and Salinger, R. M., *J. Org. Chem.*, **26**, 3519 (1961).

85. Wotiz, J. H., Hollingsworth, C. A., and Dessy, R. E., *J. Org. Chem.*, **21**, 1063 (1956).

86. Schlenk, W., and Schlenk, W., Jr., *Chem. Ber.*, **62**, 920 (1929).

87. Wotiz, J. H., Hollingsworth, C. A., and Dessy, R. E., *J. Am. Chem. Soc.*, **78**, 1221 (1956).

88. Dessy, R. E., Wotiz, J. H., and Hollingsworth, C. A., *J. Am. Chem. Soc.*, **79**, 358 (1957).

89. Wotiz, J. H., *J. Am. Chem. Soc.*, **72**, 1637 (1950).

90. Vo-Quang, L., and Cadiot, P., *Bull. Soc. Chim. France*, 1418 (1965).

91. Kucherov, V. F., *et al.*, *Izv. Akad. Nauk SSSR, Otd. Khim. Nauk*, 484 (1962); *Chem. Abstr.*, **57**, 16382 (1962).

92. Parker, W., Raphael, R. A., and Wilkinson, D. I., *J. Chem. Soc.*, 2433 (1959).

93. Zderic, J. A., and Limon, D. C., *J. Am. Chem. Soc.*, **82**, 2304 (1960).

94. Slezak, F. B., *et al.*, *J. Org. Chem.*, **26**, 3137 (1961).

95. Jones, E. R. H., Mansfield, G. H., and Whiting, M. C., *J. Chem. Soc.*, 3208 (1954).

96. Kraevskii, A. A., and Preobrazhenski, N. A., *Zh. Obshch. Khim.*, **34**, 618 (1965); *Chem. Abstr.*, **63**, 2893 (1965).

97. Gracheva, G. D., and Zakharova, A. I., *Zh. Organ. Khim.*, **2**, 965 (1966); *Chem. Abstr.*, **64**, 11247 (1966).

98. Riobe, O., *Compt. Rend.*, **231**, 1312 (1950); **236**, 2073 (1953).

99. Pabon, H. J. J., van der Steen, D., and van Dorp, D. A., *Rec. Trav. Chim.*, **84**, 1319 (1965).

100. Osbond, J. M., and Wickens, J. C., *Chem. Ind. (London)*, 1288 (1959).

101. Taniguchi, H., Mathai, I. M., and Miller, S. I., *Tetrahedron*, **22**, 867 (1966).

102. Garwood, R. F., Oskay, E., and Weedon, B. C. L., *Chem. Ind. (London)*, 1684 (1962).

103. Zelinski, R., and Louvar, J., *J. Org. Chem.*, **23**, 807 (1958).

104. Zelinski, R., and Meyer, R. E., *J. Org. Chem.*, **23**, 810 (1958).

104a. Chretien-Bessiere, Y., *et al.*, *Compt. Rend. (C)*, **264**, 1298 (1967).

105. Petrov, A. A., *et al.*, *Zh. Obshch. Khim.*, **31**, 352 (1961); *Chem. Abstr.*, **57**, 10988 (1962).

105a. Gautier, J. A., Miocque, M., and Mascrier-Demagnez, L., *Bull. Soc. Chim. France*, 1551 (1967).

106. Gusev, B. P., and Kucherov, V. F., *Izv. Akad. Nauk SSSR, Ser. Khim.*, 851 (1965); *Chem. Abstr.*, **63**, 11342 (1965).

107. Gusev, B. P., and Kucherov, V. F., *Izv. Akad. Nauk SSSR, Ser. Khim.*, 1067 (1962); *Chem. Abstr.*, **57**, 16384 (1962).

108. Golse, R., Liermann, A., and Bussiere, H., *Bull. Soc. Pharm. Bordeaux*, **101**, 233 (1962); *Chem. Abstr.*, **58**, 13789 (1963).

109. Vereshchagin, L. I., Yashina, O. G., and Zarva, T. V., *Zh. Organ. Khim.*, **2**, 1895 (1966); *Chem. Abstr.*, **66**, 46074 (1967).

PART TWO

Copper, Silver, Zinc, Cadmium and Mercuric Derivatives of Acetylenes

1. COPPER ACETYLIDES

In 1947, Brameld[1] published an extensive study of copper acetylide formation and properties. He also reviewed earlier literature and noted that the conditions of preparation of copper acetylides can affect their compositions and explosive nature significantly.

1.1. Cuprous Acetylide

Acetylides from cuprous salt solutions can be made in very explosive form or in relatively stable form. As the acidity of the cuprous solution increases, explosiveness usually increases. Cuprous acetylides prepared in the presence of reducing agents such as hydrazine, hydroxylamine or formaldehyde are more stable than those prepared without a reducing agent. This indicates "complex" formation, or a change in crystal structure. Cuprous acetylide which has a metallic luster was more explosive than any other cuprous acetylide made.

Cuprous iodide reacts with 1 mole of potassium acetylide in ammonia at $-78°$ to form orange-colored CuC_2H, which disproportionates at $45°$ to acetylene and dark red Cu_2C_2.[2] Excess potassium acetylide gives K_2C_2 and $K_2[Cu(C_2H)]$. Acetylene and cuprous iodide in ammonia give Cu_2C_2. According to x-ray analysis, Cu_2C_2 is similar to calcium carbide. The monohydrate is less explosive than Cu_2C_2. Cu_2C_2 is obviously more stable than CuC_2H. Schlubach[3] found that aqueous cupric sulfate, ammonium hydroxide and hydroxylamine hydrochloride reacted with acetylene to give only Cu_2C_2 under all conditions explored. Schlubach also made the explosive cuprous derivative of methyldiacetylene. Silver methyldiacetylide was even more highly explosive.

Supported cuprous acetylide catalysts are fairly stable. The usual preparation involves impregnating a solid with a cupric salt, reducing with formaldehyde or other reducing agent, and then exposing the wet solid to acetylene. Copenhaver and Bigelow[4] have described in detail the preparation of Reppe's cuprous catalyst for the acetylene-formaldehyde reaction.

1.2. Cupric Acetylide

Cupric solutions and acetylene give explosive acetylides. Cupriammonium salts do not form acetylides. All of Brameld's[1] cupric acetylides fall into two classes: (1) amorphous black precipitates which explode with a report, sparks and flashes, to form black cupric oxide; these are more explosive than ordinary cuprous acetylide; (2) lustrous metallic plates which explode on gentle tapping, sometimes when touched under solution, with a bright flash and report, to form metallic copper flakes. Cupric acetylides have not been used as catalysts.

One problem in handling acetylene is the formation of copper acetylides on brass fittings, valves, etc. It is likely that basic copper carbonate plays a part in the formation of acetylide on copper alloys, and so does air. The amount and explosiveness of the acetylides decrease with decreasing copper content of the alloys.[1] There are two sets of conditions which favor formation of acetylides on copper or copper alloys: (1) contact with ammonia, water vapor and acetylene (or lime sludge from slaking calcium carbide), or (2) water vapor and acetylene. Nitrogen inhibits copper acetylide formation. Explosive copper acetylides may form on copper and on brasses which contain 50% copper or more, when surfaces are exposed to acetylene under certain conditions. Clean metals require moisture for acetylide formation. None is formed in dry acetylene. Metal surfaces contaminated with acids or sodium hydroxide readily form explosive acetylides (see reference 5). Thus, acetylene must be handled in carefully cleaned and maintained equipment, and contamination with acids or bases must be avoided. The copper content of brass fittings should be below 50%.

1.3. Uses of Heavy Metal Acetylides

The most important use for cuprous acetylide is as catalyst for acetylene reactions. These are usually supported on a solid such as silica, carbon or alumina.

Acetylides of copper, silver and mercury give uniform, low molecular weight polymers when they are used as catalysts for polymerizing ethylene, propylene and ethylene-1-butene mixtures.[6] Low concentrations of cuprous acetylide give higher molecular weight polymers. These polymers are high-density polyolefins.

1.4. Complexes of Cuprous Derivatives of Substituted Acetylenes

Coates[7] made some tertiary phosphine and arsine complexes of cuprous and silver derivatives of substituted acetylenes. In the infrared, the metal-acetylenic orbital interactions appeared weaker than in the polymeric uncomplexed derivatives, $(RC\equiv CCu)_x$. The relatively high melting points indicate reasonable stability:

Complex	m.p. (°C)
t-BuC$\equiv$CCu(PMe$_3$)	105
t-BuC$\equiv$CCu(PMe$_2$)	95
PhC$\equiv$CAg(PEt$_2$)	78
PhC$\equiv$CAg(AsEt$_3$)	89

1.5. Reactions of Cuprous Derivatives of Substituted Acetylenes with Aromatic Halides

Diarylacetylenes are usually made by elimination reactions (see Chapter 3). Aryl bromides react with sodium phenylacetylide to form diarylacetylenes. Excess potassium amide must be present in the ammonia solution. Bromobenzene and sodium phenylacetylide give only 26% yield of diphenylacetylene.[8] Benzyne is the intermediate. In 1963, Stephens and Castro[9] reported an important new synthetic method, similar to the reaction of aliphatic halides with alkali metal acetylides. They found that aryl iodides react with cuprous arylacetylides in refluxing pyridine to give good yields of diarylacetylenes:

$$ArI + CuC\equiv CAr' \longrightarrow ArC\equiv CAr' + CuI$$

Some of the products were incorrectly identified at first, but were later identified correctly.[10] The products obtained are listed in Table 4-14. Cuprous alkynylides react to form arylalkylacetylenes.

1.5.1. REACTION WITH o-AMINOARYL IODIDES

When aryl iodides which have an *ortho* nucleophilic group are used, the corresponding heterocyclic compounds form. In a detailed study published in 1966, Castro and co-workers[10] showed that the reaction of o-aminoaryl iodides

TABLE 4-14[9]

$$PhC\equiv CCu + ArI \longrightarrow PhC\equiv CAr + CuI$$

Ar	% Yield PhC≡CAr[a]
Phenyl	87
p-Methoxyphenyl	99
o-Methoxyphenyl	91
p-Aminophenyl	76
p-Carboxyphenyl	85
p-Hydroxyphenyl	82
p-Nitrophenyl	75
o-Nitrophenyl	84

[a] Yield of purified product.

with CuC≡CR in dimethylformamide gives indoles directly and that the yields are high despite the insolubility of the acetylides. The acetylides are soluble in pyridine, but the products from reactions in pyridine are either all uncyclized acetylenic or a mixture of uncyclized acetylenic and cyclized product from the acetylenic compound. These products are listed in Table 4-15. The effect of solvent is emphasized by the reaction of o-iodoaniline and cuprous phenylacetylide:

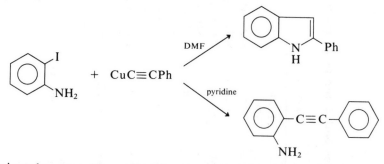

o-Aminotolan cannot be cyclized by cuprous catalyst in pyridine, but it can be cyclized easily in DMF. The cuprous catalyst is essential for cyclization.

For the preparation of 2-substituted indoles, a two-step reaction is best. Pyridine is the solvent in the first step, and DMF in the cyclization step:

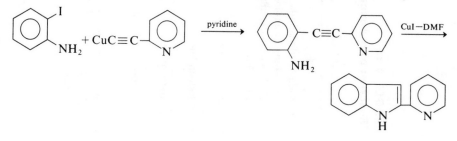

TABLE 4-15

Reaction of *o*-Aminoaryl Iodides with Cuprous Acetylides (CuC≡CR)[10]

Aryl Iodide	R	Solvent	Product	% Yield	Yield[b] after Cyclization (%)
o-Iodoaniline	Phenyl	DMF[c]	2-Phenylindole	89	
o-Iodo-N-ethylaniline	Phenyl	DMF	1-Ethyl-2-phenylindole	50	
2-Iodo-4-methylaniline	Phenyl	DMF	5-Methyl-2-phenylindole	90	
4-Hydroxy-2-iodoaniline	Phenyl	DMF	5-Hydroxy-2-phenylindole	57	
o-Iodoaniline	*n*-Propyl	Pyridine	2-*n*-Propylindole / *o*-Aminophenyl-*n*-propylacetylene	{70 / 17	87
o-Iodoaniline	*n*-Butyl	Pyridine	2-*n*-Butylindole[d] / *o*-Aminophenyl-*n*-butylacetylene	{35.4 / 19.5	55
o-Iodoaniline	Ethyl	Pyridine	2-Ethylindole / (*o*-Aminophenylethyl)acetylene[d]	{12 / 28	24
o-Iodoaniline	2-Pyridyl	Pyridine	2-(*o*-Aminophenylethyl)pyridine / 2-(2'-Pyridyl)indole	50 / 0	40
o-Iodo-N-ethylaniline	*n*-Propyl	Pyridine	1-Ethyl-2-propylindole[d] / *o*-Ethylaminophenyl-*n*-propylacetylene	50 / 5	

[a] Yield of purified product, based on halide.
[b] Overall yield based on halide of indole, after treating with CuI in DMF.
[c] Dimethylformamide.
[d] Mixtures.

1.5.2. REACTION WITH o-HALOPHENOLS

o-Halophenols react faster than o-haloanilines, so the bromophenol can be used instead of the iodophenol. In pyridine, alkylation and cyclization give good yields of benzofurans in one step:

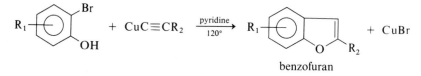

benzofuran

Good yields can also be obtained in one step in dimethylformamide. No un-cyclized acetylenic product is isolated from any of these reactions. Table 4-16 lists the products obtained with halophenols.

TABLE 4-16
Reaction of Cuprous Acetylides (CuC≡CR) with o-Halophenols to form Benzofurans[10]

Halophenol	R	Solvent	Product	% Yield[a]
o-Iodophenol	Phenyl	DMF	2-Phenylbenzofuran	88
o-Iodophenol	n-Propyl	Pyridine	2-n-Propylbenzofuran	60
o-Bromophenol	Phenyl	Pyridine	2-Phenylbenzofuran	53
2,4-Dibromophenol	Phenyl	Pyridine	5-Bromo-2-phenylbenzofuran	55
2,4-Dibromophenol	n-Propyl	Pyridine	5-Bromo-2-n-propyl-benzofuran	40
2,4-Dibromophenol	2-Pyridyl	Pyridine	5-Bromo-2-(2-pyridyl)-benzofuran	38
o-Bromophenol	2-Pyridyl	Pyridine	2-(2-Pyridyl)benzofuran	50
3,5-Diiodo-4-hydroxy-pyridine	Phenyl	DMF	7-Iodo-2-phenylfuro-[3,2-c]pyridine	86

[a] Purified product, based on halide.

1.5.3. REACTION WITH o-HALOBENZOIC ACIDS

o-Halobenzoic acids are so reactive that the chloro compounds can be used and cuprous iodide can be employed as a catalyst. The reaction proceeds at room temperature in either pyridine or dimethylformamide to give phthalides directly. The products are given in Table 4-17.[10]

1.5.4. REACTION WITH OTHER SUBSTITUTED HALOBENZENES

Castro[10] prepared a variety of substituted tolans to illustrate the scope of his reaction (Table 4-18).

TABLE 4-17[10]

$$\text{(o-halobenzoic acid, } R_1,\ Cl,\ CO_2H) + CuC{\equiv}CR_2 \longrightarrow \text{(phthalide,\ }R_1,\ {=}CHR_2) + CuCl$$

o-Halobenzoic Acid	Acetylide or Acetylene	Solvent	In situ[a]	Product	% Yield[b]
o-Iodobenzoic acid	Phenylacetylene	DMF	Yes	3-Benzylidenephthalide	90
o-Bromobenzoic acid	Phenylacetylene	DMF	Yes	3-Benzylidenephthalide	53
o-Chlorobenzoic acid	Phenylacetylene	DMF	Yes	3-Benzylidenephthalide	39
o-Chlorobenzoic acid	Cuprous phenylacetylide	Pyridine	No	3-Benzylidenephthalide	65
2,4-Dichlorobenzoic acid	Cuprous phenylacetylide	Pyridine	No	3-Benzylidene-5-chlorophthalide	69
o-Iodobenzoic acid	Ethyl propiolate	DMF	Yes[c]	Ethyl 3-phthalylideneacetate	39
o-Bromobenzoic acid	Ethyl propiolate	DMF	Yes[c]	Ethyl 3-phthalylideneacetate	15
o-Iodobenzoic acid	Propargyl alcohol	DMF	Yes[c]	3-Phthalylideneethanol	6
o-Iodobenzoic acid	Cuprous n-propylacetylide	Pyridine	No	3-n-Propylisocoumarin	40
o-Iodobenzoic acid				3-Butylidenephthalide	22

[a] With cuprous iodide and N-ethylpiperidene as catalysts.
[b] Yield of purifed material, based on halide charged.
[c] Reactions run at room temperature.

TABLE 4-18
Preparation of Substituted Tolans[10]

Halide[a]	CuC≡CR, R	Product	% Yield[c]
o-Diiodobenzene	Phenyl	o-Bis(phenylethynyl)benzene	61
m-Diiodobenzene	Phenyl	m-Bis(phenylethynyl)benzene	42
p-Diiodobenzene	Phenyl	p-Bis(phenylethynyl)benzene	45
o-Iodoaniline	Phenyl	o-Aminotolan	59
o-Iodo-N-ethylaniline	Phenyl	o-Ethylaminotolan	5[d]
o-Iodobenzamide	Phenyl	o-Carboxamidotolan	47
o-Iodobenzamide	n-Propyl	o-Carboxamidophenyl-n-propylacetylene	50
o-Iodobenzyl alcohol	Phenyl	o-Hydroxymethyltolan	50
3-Iodopyridine	Phenyl	2-Phenylethynylpyridine	47
2-Iodopyridine	Phenyl	2-Phenylethynylpyridine	25
Picryl chloride[b]	Phenyl	2,4,6-Trinitrophenylphenylacetylene	34
o-Iodoaniline	2-pyridyl	2-(o-Aminophenylethynyl)pyridine	50
2-Iodo-4-methylaniline	Phenyl	2-Amino-5-methylphenylphenyl-acetylene	92

[a] Pyridine is solvent unless noted.
[b] Dimethylformamide solvent.
[c] Purified product, based on halide.
[d] 1-Ethyl-2-phenylindole is major product.

1.5.5. CATALYTIC REACTIONS

In an effort to avoid the use of molar amounts of cuprous salts, Castro carried out the reaction in solution in the presence of a small amount of cuprous iodide. He obtained the same products as in the stoichiometric reaction, but the yields were considerably lower (10–15%).

1.5.6. SIDE REACTIONS

A major side reaction in the case of unreactive phenols is Straus coupling of the acetylenic compound (see Chapter 6).

o-Bromothiophenol gave a ligand exchange reaction:

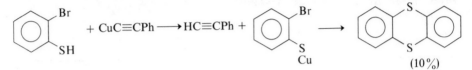

1.5.7. MECHANISM

The rate of reaction of *para*-substituted iodobenzenes with cuprous phenyl-acetylide is: $p\text{-NO}_2 > p\text{-H} > p\text{-MeO}$.[9] This is the same as the order of halogen exchange between cuprous halides and *para*-substituted aryl halides. This suggests that the new arylation is a homolytic reaction, and it probably follows a concerted path:

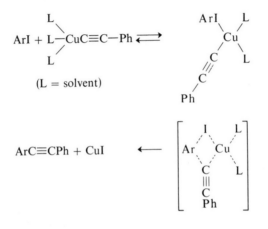

1.5.8. THIOPHENE AND FURAN IODIDES

Atkinson[11] applied the aryl halide–cuprous acetylide reaction to thiophene iodides and furan iodides. This is much better than similar reactions between acetylenic Grignard reagents and thiophene iodides.[12] The results of this study are summarized in Tables 4-19 and 4-20.

1.5.9. OTHER VARIATIONS

Campbell has used the alkylation method to make cyclic acetylenes (see Chapter 6). Iodoferrocenes were reacted with cuprous arylacetylides to form 85% yields of ferrocenylarylacetylenes.[14] Diiodoferrocenes gave 60% yield of symmetrical bis(arylacetylene)ferrocene products.

TABLE 4-19

Reaction of Thiophene Iodides with Cuprous Acetylides[11]

$$R\text{—}\underset{S}{\text{thiophene}}\text{—I} + CuC\equiv CR' \xrightarrow[\text{pyridine, 2–6 hr}]{\text{reflux}} R\text{—}\underset{S}{\text{thiophene}}\text{—}C\equiv CR'$$

Product	Constants	% Yield
R = —CHO; R' = —Me;	m.p. 78–79°	61
R = —Ph; R = —Me;	m.p. 43–44°	51
R = —Me; R' = —CH(OEt)$_2$	b.p. 98–99°, @ 0.4 mm	85
R = —H; R' = —CH$_2$OH	b.p. 88–89°, @ 5 mm	67
R = —H; R' = —CH=CH—[furan]	m.p. 60–62°	60
R = —CO$_2$Et; R' = —CH=CH—[furan]	b.p. 150–152°, @ 1 mm	55
R = [thiophene]; R' = —CH$_2$—CH$_2$OH	m.p. 66–67°	51
R = [thiophene]; R' = —CH=CH$_2$	b.p. 80–85°, @ 0.005 mm	48
R = [Me-thiophene]; R' = —CH=CH$_2$	m.p. 61°	53
R = [EtO$_2$C-thiophene]; R' = —CH=CH$_2$	m.p. 110°	43
R = [AcOCH$_2$-thiophene]; R' = —CH=CH$_2$	m.p. 52–53°	—

2. CUPROUS-CATALYZED ALKYLATION OF ACETYLENES

Kurtz[15] in 1962 reported a new alkylation system—the catalytic reaction of allyl halides with acetylenes (see also references 16 and 17). All earlier syntheses of allylacetylenes required anhydrous systems, as in the Grignard or alkali metal acetylide reactions. Kurtz used aqueous systems and controlled the pH

TABLE 4-20
Reaction of Furan Iodides with Cuprous Acetylides[11]

$$R-\text{furan}-I \ + \ R'-C{\equiv}CCu \ \longrightarrow \ R-\text{furan}-C{\equiv}C-R'$$

Product	Constants	% Yield
$R = -H; R' = -CH_2OH$	b.p. 70–73°, @ 10 mm	67
$R = -Me; R' = -CH_2OH$	b.p. 88–91°, @ 7 mm	65
$R = -CO_2Et; R' = -Me$	b.p. 68–70°, @ 7 mm	60
$R = -H; R' = -CH_2Ph$	b.p. 112–115°, @ 1 mm	58

around 7–9 to minimize hydrolysis of the allyl halide. In the first reaction tried under these conditions, allyl chloride and phenylacetylene gave allylphenyl-acetylene in 29% yield. Since allylacetylene cannot be separated from allyl chloride by distillation, acetylene reacted best in a continuous apparatus in which the product could be obtained as 90–96% allylacetylene. Two moles of allyl chloride and one of acetylene gave diallylacetylene. Other reactions are summarized in Table 4-21.

TABLE 4-21
Catalytic Reaction of Allylic Chlorides with Acetylenes[15]

Acetylenic Compound	Allylic Chloride	Product	% Yield
Propargyl alcohol	Allyl chloride	1-Hexen-4-yn-6-ol	75
Propargyl alcohol	Methallyl chloride	2-Methyl-1-hexen-4-yn-6-ol	74
Propargyl alcohol	Crotyl chloride	3-Methyl-1-hexen-4-yn-6-ol + 2-hepten-5-yn-7-ol	65[a]
Propargyl alcohol	1,4-Dichloro-2-butene	5-Undecen-2,9-diyne-1,11-diol	
1-Butyn-3-ol	Allyl chloride	1-Hepten-4-yn-6-ol	85
3-Methyl-1-butyn-3-ol	Allyl chloride	6-Methyl-1-hepten-4-yn-6-ol	59
Acetylene	Methallyl chloride	2-Methyl-1-penten-4-yne	84[b]

[a] These two products are explained by assuming crotyl chloride rearranges:

$$CH_2{=}CH-\underset{CH_3}{CHCl} \ \rightleftharpoons \ CH_3CH{=}CHCH_2Cl \quad \xrightarrow{\substack{+ \text{ propargyl} \\ \text{alcohol}}} \quad \substack{1 \text{ part } CH_2{=}CH-\underset{CH_3}{CHC}{\equiv}CCH_2OH \\ + \\ 3 \text{ parts } CH_3CH{=}CHCH_2C{\equiv}CCH_2OH}$$

[b] Amount of product in the crude reaction mixture.

Sevin[18] extended the reaction to propargyl and allyl halides and tosylates. The reaction with propargylic halides gave diynes and allenynes:

$$RC{\equiv}CH + R'R''\overset{\overset{\displaystyle X}{|}}{C}C{\equiv}CH \xrightarrow{Cu^+} RC{\equiv}C\overset{\overset{\displaystyle H}{|}}{C}=C=CR'R'' + RC{\equiv}C\overset{\overset{\displaystyle R'}{|}}{\underset{\underset{\displaystyle R''}{|}}{C}}-C{\equiv}CH$$

$$\text{allenyne} \qquad\qquad \text{diyne}$$

Only 1–2% of the cuprous salt was enough to catalyze the reaction. Water, alcohol and dimethyl sulfoxide were good solvents. Since the reaction liberates an acid, a base is necessary; primary amines lead to faster rates than secondary or tertiary amines. Some bases directed the propargylic alcohol-propargyl bromide reaction to the allenyne (Table 4-22). The directive effect of bases depended on the propargylic halide. Ammonium hydroxide was the most effective. The reaction of methylbutynol with propargyl chloride gave 80% yield of allenyne in the presence of ammonium hydroxide. Propargyl chloride gave the highest yield, followed by the tosylate, bromide and iodide.

TABLE 4-22[18]

$$(CH_3)_2CH(OH){-}C{\equiv}CH + BrCH_2{-}C{\equiv}CH \longrightarrow$$
$$(CH_3)_2CH(OH){-}C{\equiv}C{-}CH=C=CH_2$$

Base	Minutes	% Yield	Base	Minutes	% Yield
NaOH	180	Traces	$(CH_3)_3CNH_2$	30	60
NH_4OH	30	75	NH_2OH^a	60	60
$C_2H_5NH_2$	60	30	$CH_3N\diagup\bigcirc\diagdown O$	30	50
$(C_2H_5)_2NH$	60	10			
$(C_2H_5)_3N$	60	Traces	$N\diagdown\bigcirc$	60	Traces

a 20% of stoichiometric amount; slowly added sodium carbonate.

Some of the diynes required as GLC standards were made by the Grignard method:[19,20]

$$Me_2\overset{\overset{\displaystyle OMgBr}{|}}{C}{-}C{\equiv}CMgBr + ICH_2C{\equiv}CH \longrightarrow$$

$$Me_2C{\equiv}CCH=C=CMe_2 + HC{\equiv}C\overset{\overset{\displaystyle Me_2}{|}}{C}C{\equiv}CCH_3$$
$$(20\%) \qquad\qquad (70\%)$$

3. SILVER ACETYLIDES

Contrary to general belief, the formation of precipitates with ammoniacal silver nitrate is not a reliable diagnostic test for terminal acetylene groups. Acetylenes vary widely in the rate of reaction of the ethynyl group with ammoniacal silver nitrate.[21] Thus, 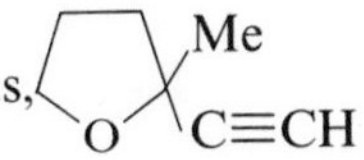 and $HC{\equiv}CCMe_2$ form precipitates instantly in the cold. $HO(CH_2)_3C(Me)C{\equiv}CH$ forms a precipitate only after prolonged heating. $PhCH_2OC(Me)_2C{\equiv}CH$ does not react even on prolonged heating. Infrared spectra give no clues to explain these differences.

Agawa[22] tried to use his finding that silver phenylacetylide is soluble in pyridine as a method for coupling acid halides with acetylenes:

$$R'COCl + AgC{\equiv}CR \xrightarrow[\text{pyridine}]{/\!\!/} R'\overset{\displaystyle O}{\overset{\|}{C}}C{\equiv}CR + AgCl \qquad (1)$$

Instead, he obtained acetylenic pyridine compounds from the nucleophilic attack by silver phenylacetylide on the pyridinium-acyl halide salt:

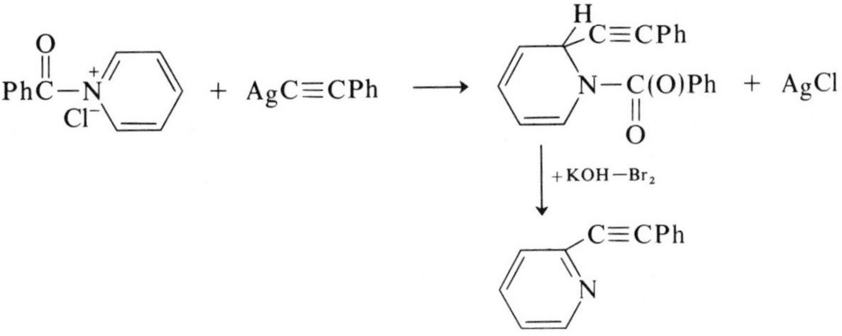

Some silver acetylides, such as silver 1-hexynylide, are soluble in carbon tetrachloride, chloroform and benzene. Others such as silver propynylide and silver phenylacetylide are insoluble. Solutions of the soluble silver acetylides do react with acyl halides according to Agawa's reaction [reaction (1)].

4. ZINC-COPPER COUPLES

Terminal acetylenes react with methylene iodide and zinc-copper couple. This is a method of introducing a methyl group into the acetylene.[24] The reaction gives several products:

$$\underset{(1)}{RC{\equiv}CH} + CH_2I_2 + Cu{-}Zn \longrightarrow \underset{(2)}{RC{\equiv}CMe} + \underset{(3)}{RCH{=}C{=}CH_2} + \underset{(4)}{RCH_2C{\equiv}CH}$$

The reaction usually requires refluxing for 8–15 days in ether and gives the products shown in Table 4-23. Tetrahydrofuran is a better solvent than ether. With phenylacetylene, the reaction in THF goes as well in a few hours as it does in 8–15 days in ether, and the yield of the allene (3) increases to 7.5%. Diacetylenes, $RC\equiv C-C\equiv CH$, give up to 30% yield of $RC\equiv C-C\equiv CMe$ after 1–2 days in refluxing ether.

TABLE 4-23
Reaction of Terminal Acetylenes with CH_2I_2 + Zn—Cu Couple[24]

R in $RC\equiv CH$	% Unreacted (1)	% Yield (2)	(3)
Ph	35	37.5	Trace
p-Tolyl	35	35	
Propyl	47.5	25.5	3
Butyl	51	20	5
Amyl	64.5	15	3

5. ZINC ACETYLIDES

Nast[25] reacted acetylenes with zinc dialkyls and diaryls to form zinc acetylides:

$$ZnPh_2 + 2PhC\equiv CH \xrightarrow[1 \text{ hr}]{20°} Zn(C\equiv CPh)_2$$
$$(80\%)$$

Zinc phenylacetylide is not explosive or pyrophoric. It decomposes at 200°. It is soluble in ammonia, and if the solution is cooled to $-78°$, colorless crystals of the diammoniate form. With a $1:1$ ratio of reactants, the product is $PhZnC\equiv CPh$ (80% yield). This acetylide is soluble in tetrahydrofuran and slowly disproportionates in THF to insoluble $Zn(C\equiv CPh)_2$. Zinc amide reacts with acetylene in ammonia to form zinc acetylide diammoniate, another nonexplosive acetylide. All of the zinc acetylides hydrolyze very easily.

Phenylacetylene reacts with diethylzinc in hexamethylphosphoramide to give 50% yield of zinc phenylacetylide in less than 8 seconds.[26] Zinc phenylacetylide couples in the presence of cupric bromide to form diphenyldiacetylene.

6. CADMIUM ACETYLIDES

A similar reaction is used to prepare cadmium acetylides:[27] $Ph_2Cd + PhC\equiv CH \longrightarrow Cd(C\equiv CPh)_2$. This acetylide is a crystalline nonpyrophoric, easily hydrolyzed solid. Cadmium diamide reacts with potassium acetylide in ammonia to give $K_2Cd(C\equiv CH)_4$.

7. MERCURIC ACETYLIDES

Dessy[28] concluded that the halogen acid cleavage of carbon-mercury bonds is a four-center reaction. Electrophilic proton and nucleophilic halide ion attach themselves to the C—Hg bond simultaneously:

This is an S_F2 reaction. Dessy studied the mechanism of formation of carbon-mercury bonds in order to establish the S_F2 character of the (reverse) acid cleavage of these bonds.[23] He reacted acetylenes with mercuric halide in amine solvents. When he used phenylacetylene, which oxidizes slightly at high concentrations in solution, he carefully excluded oxygen. The extensive kinetic study suggested a mechanism. In a pre-rate-determining step, the acetylene, amine and mercuric halide form a complex. In the rate-determining step, the complex "slips" from the π configuration to a σ C—Hg bond and concertedly loses HX, to form $R'C\equiv CHgX$. $R'C\equiv CHgX$ reacts further with $R'C\equiv CH$ to give the final product $(R'C\equiv C)_2Hg$:

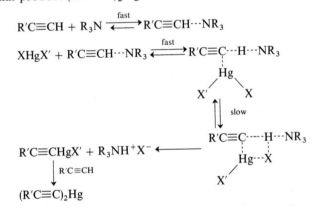

where $X' = X$ or R.

If there is a single mechanism for acid cleavage of C—Hg bonds, by the principle of microscopic reversibility the same mechanism must apply to the reverse reaction. Although Dessy studied only the —C≡C—Hg cleavage reaction, the mechanism will also apply to the formation of other C—Hg bonds via sp^2 or sp^3 carbon. Some π complex is involved, and "slip" from the π- to the σ-bonded structure is reasonable. The effects of this complexing are not apparent as a mechanistic deviation in the acid cleavage reaction, so it represents at most a shoulder on the potential energy surface. Thus, it will not greatly affect the back reaction, i.e., formation of the C—Hg bond. This kinetic study confirms the four-center (S_F2) nature of both the formation and cleavage of C—Hg bonds.

7.1. Application of Mercuric Acetylides

Mercury derivatives of arylacetylenes are claimed to be agricultural herbicides.[29] Reaction of aralkyne with mercuric oxide and sodium hydroxide gave compounds such as bis(2-naphthylethynyl)mercury, and bis(1-thienylethynyl)-mercury.

7.2. Preparation of 1-Nitrosoacetylenes

Robson[30] added NOCl to di-1-hexynylmercury in chloroform or tetrahydrofuran at $-78°$. The product was 1-nitroso-1-hexyne. At room temperature, the blue-green color faded, and the acetylenic band in the infrared disappeared at the same time.

References

1. Brameld, V. F., Clark, M. T., and Seyfang, A. P., *J. Soc. Chem. Ind.*, **66**, 346 (1947).
2. Nast, R., and Pfab, W., *Z. Anorg. Allgem. Chem.*, **292**, 287 (1957); *Chem. Abstr.*, **52**, 6996 (1958).
3. Schlubach, H. H., *et al.*, *Ann. Chem.* **568**, 141 (1950).
4. Copenhaver, J. W., and Bigelow, M. H., "Acetylene and Carbon Monoxide Chemistry," New York, Reinhold Publishing Corp.; 1949.
5. Feitknecht, W., and Hugi-Carmes, L., *Schuliz. Arch. Angew. Wiss. Tech.*, **23**, 328 (1957); *Chem. Abstr.*, **52**, 3578 (1958).
6. Sun Oil Co., British Patent 811,139 (Apr. 2, 1959); *Chem. Abstr.*, **53**, 18549 (1959).
7. Coates, G. E., and Parkin, C., *J. Inorg. Nucl. Chem.*, **22**, 59 (1961); *Chem. Abstr.*, **56**, 13777 (1962).
8. Scardiglia, F., and Roberts, J. D., *Tetrahedron*, **3**, 197 (1958).
9. Stephens, R. D., and Castro, C. E., *J. Org. Chem.*, **28**, 3313 (1963).
10. Castro, C. E., Gaughan, E. J., and Owsley, D. C., *J. Org. Chem.*, **31**, 4071 (1966).
11. Atkinson, R. E., Curtis, R. F., and Phillips, G. T., *Chem. Ind.* (*London*), 2101 (1964); *Chem. Abstr.*, 62, 6450 (1965); *J. Chem. Soc.* (*C*), 578 (1967).
12. Brown, D., *et al.*, *J. Chem. Soc.* (*C*), 89 (1966).
13. Campbell, I. D., *et. al.*, *Chem. Commun.*, 87 (1966).
14. Rausch, M. D., Siegel, A., and Klemann, L. P., *J. Org. Chem.*, **31**, 2703 (1966).
15. Kurtz, P., *Ann. Chem.* **658**, 6 (1962).
16. Kurtz, P., (to Farbenfabriken Bayer), U.S. Patent 2,884,464 (Apr. 28, 1959); British Patent 775,723 (May 29, 1957).

17. Kleinschmidt, R. F. (to General Aniline and Film Corp.), U.S. Patent 2,542,517 (Feb. 20, 1951); *Chem. Abstr.*, **45**, 7594 (1951).

18. Sevin, A., Chodkiewicz, W., and Cadiot, P., *Tetrahedron Letters*, 1953 (1965).

19. Petrov, A. A., *et al.*, *Zh. Obshch. Khim.*, **31**, 3525 (1961); *Chem. Abstr.*, **57**, 10988 (1962).

20. van der Steen, D., Pabon, H. J. J., and van Dorp, D. A., *Rec. Trav. Chim.*, **82**, 1015 (1963).

21. Favorskaya, T. A., and Sergievskaya, O. V., *Zh. Obshch. Khim.*, **30**, 132 (1960); *Chem. Abstr.*, **54**, 21032 (1960).

22. Agawa, T., and Miller, S. I., *J. Am. Chem. Soc.*, **83**, 449 (1961).

23. Dessy, R. E., Budde, W. L., and Woodruff, C., *Am. Chem. Soc.*, **84**, 1172 (1962).

24. Vo-Quang, L., and Cadiot, P., *Bull. Soc. Chim. France*, 1525 (1965).

25. Nast, R., Künzel, O., and Müller, R., *Chem. Ber.*, **95**, 2155 (1962).

26. Oppenheim, W., and Shorr, L. M., *Israel J. Chem.*, **2**, 121 (1964); *Chem. Abstr.*, **61**, 14791 (1964).

27. Nast, R., and Richers, C., *Z. Anorg. Allgem. Chem.*, **319**, 320 (1963); *Chem. Abstr.*, **59**, 3942 (1963).

28. Dessy, R. E., and Kim, J., *J. Am. Chem. Soc.*, **83**, 1167 (1961).

29. Iwai, I., and Yura, Y. (to Sankyo Co., Ltd), Japanese Patent 11,124(1961); *Chem. Abstr.*, **56**, 4794 (1962).

30. Robson, E., and Tedder, J. M., *Proc. Chem. Soc.*, 13 (1963).

PART THREE

Boron, Aluminum, Gallium, Thallium, Silicon and Germanium Compounds of Acetylenes

Introduction

In 1967, Davidsohn and Henry[1] published a review covering acetylenic compounds of B, Al, Ga, Si, Ge, Sn, Pb, P, As, Sb and Bi. It includes an excellent discussion of hazards and safety precautions. This is recommended reading for anyone starting work with these acetylenic compounds.

1. BORON COMPOUNDS OF ACETYLENES

1.1. Alkynylboronates

In 1960, Matteson[2] reported a new class of compounds, the α,β-acetylenic boronic esters, represented by dibutyl acetyleneboronate, $HC\equiv CB(OBu)_2$. Dibutyl acetyleneboronate is a useful reagent for making new kinds of unsaturated boronic esters which are not accessible by other methods. Acetylene Grignard reagent in tetrahydrofuran added to tributyl borate in ether at $-70°$ gives 57 % yield of dibutyl acetyleneboronate (b.p. 31° at 0.3 mm of Hg). It is important to use pure acetylene. Good stirring and low temperature are necessary during addition of the Grignard reagent to the borate ester. During the product work-up, dilute acids or pure hydroxylic solvents can be tolerated, but aqueous bases, even sodium bicarbonate, easily hydrolyze the $B{-}C\equiv$ bond. In a similar reaction, the Grignard reagent of 1-hexyne gives 40% yield of dibutyl 1-hexynyl-1-boronate. Grignard reagents react better than sodium alkynylides,[3] and the products are purer.

Dibutyl acetyleneboronate is a fairly good dienophile, giving 25% yield of adduct with cyclopentadiene after 15 hours in refluxing chlorobenzene. The corresponding ethylenic boronate is more active; the yield is 54% after only 3 hours at 90°. The hexanethiol radical adds easily to give a 72% yield of olefinic sulfide.

Giraud[4] prepared other acetylenic boronates: $Ar_2BC\equiv CR\cdot$ pyridine,

$$Ph_2BC\equiv C\overset{\overset{\displaystyle R}{|}}{C}{=}CH_2\cdot \text{pyridine and } PhB(C\equiv CR)_2\cdot\text{pyridine.}$$

Sodium alkynylboronates have been made (see Table 4-24):[5]

$$Na(R_3BH) + R'C\equiv CH \xrightarrow[\text{cyclohexane}]{\text{benzene or}} Na(R_3BC\equiv CR')$$
$$(1)$$

Acetylene itself gives disubstituted products: $Na_2(R_3BC\equiv CBR_3)$.

TABLE 4-24
Sodium Alkynylboronates,
$Na(R_3BC\equiv CR')$[5]

R	R'	m.p. (°C)	% Yield
Me	Me	163	68
Me	Et	168	65
Me	Ph	146 (dec.)	78
Et	Me	89	89
Et	Et	65	87
Et	Ph	129	98
Pr	Me	120	95
Pr	Et	134	97
Pr	Ph	177	77

Alkyldiboranes react with product (1), displacing BR_3 with R_2BH, which is a stronger Lewis acid. The product is $Na(R_2BH{-}C\equiv CR')$. Dialkylboron halides react to form different products under different conditions:

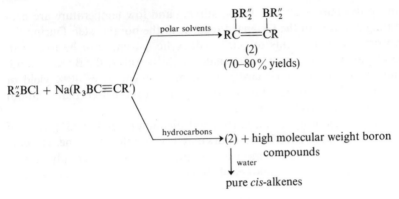

1.2. Other Boron-Acetylenic Compounds

Table 4-25 lists some other boron-acetylenic compounds.

2. ALUMINUM COMPOUNDS OF ACETYLENES

2.1. Reaction of Dialkylaluminum Chlorides with Sodium Vinylacetylide

Sodium vinylacetylide reacts with dialkylaluminum chlorides to form compounds such as $Et_2AlC{\equiv}CCH{=}CH_2$ and $i\text{-}Bu_2AlC{\equiv}CCH{=}CH_2$.[9] These acetylides are spontaneously flammable in air. The compounds on standing or when heated give 1,4-polymerization products which contain allenic bonds.

2.2. Reaction of Alkylaluminum Compounds with Terminal Acetylenes

Mole[10] observed that the substitution reaction:

$$RC{\equiv}CH + R'_3Al \longrightarrow RC{\equiv}CAlR'_2 + R'H$$

gave high yields when R = phenyl, 1-naphthyl or *n*-octyl, and when R′ = methyl, ethyl, propyl or isobutyl. Wilke[11] and Ziegler[12] had studied such reactions earlier and reported that addition across the acetylenic bond was the only reaction. In Mole's reactions, trimethylaluminum and phenylacetylene at 110° for $1\frac{1}{2}$ hours gave 73% yield of (phenylethynyl)dimethylaluminum (m.p. 100–106°). Hydrolysis of the product in acidified D_2O gave $PhC{\equiv}CD$. Thus, the ethynyl carbon was attached directly to aluminum.

The reaction of aluminum alkyls with acetylenes is probably not too different from the reaction of gallium alkyls with acetylenes (see section 3).[13] Mole's

TABLE 4-25
Compounds with Boron Attached to Acetylenic Carbon

Acetylenic Compound	Boron Compound	Conditions	Products	% Yield	Reference
$NaC{\equiv}CR''$	$RR'NBCl_2$	Ether, $-60°$, N_2	$RR'NB(C{\equiv}CR'')_2$	45–60	6
$NaC{\equiv}CCH_3$	$Me_2NB(Ph)Cl$	Ether, $-60°$, N_2	$\overset{\text{Ph}}{\underset{\vert}{Me_2N}}BC{\equiv}CCH_3$	74	6
$BrMgC{\equiv}CMgBr$	R_2BI	Chloroform, N_2	$R_2BC{\equiv}CBR_2$	—	7

R	b.p. (°C) @ 1 mm
i-Pr	55
Pr	80
i-Bu	78
Bu	99
(spontaneously flammable)	

Acetylenic Compound	Boron Compound	Conditions	Products	% Yield	Reference
$RC{\equiv}CMgBr$	$Ph_2BOCH_2CH_2I$	Pyridine	$Ph_2BC{\equiv}CR \cdot$ pyridine	—	8

R	m.p. (°C)
H	150
Me	170
Ph	158
p-BrPh	165
Me_3Si	130
Me_3SiCH_2	178
EtS	156
Ph_2B	170

Acetylenic Compound	Boron Compound	Conditions	Products	% Yield	Reference
Mg_2C_2	$Ph_2BOCH_2CH_2I$			41, 48, 69, 77, 41, 55, 44, 27	
$PhC{\equiv}CMgBr$	$BF_3 \cdot$ pyridine	THF	$[(PhC{\equiv}C)_4B]_2Mg$	60	8
$\overset{CH_3}{\underset{\vert}{CH_2{=}CC{\equiv}CMgBr}}$	Bu_2BCl		$\overset{CH_3}{\underset{\vert}{CH_2{=}CC{\equiv}CBBu_2}}$		9
$RC{\equiv}CNa$	$ClB(NR_2)_2$	Saturated hydrocarbon, $-60°$	$RC{\equiv}CB(NR'_2)_2$	32–55	9a
$RC{\equiv}CNa$	$Cl_2BNR'_2$	Saturated hydrocarbon, $-60°$	$(RC{\equiv}C)_2BNR'_2$	45–75	9a

results also confirm the reaction of vinylacetylene with triisobutylaluminum to form diisobutylaluminum vinylacetylide.[9]

2.3. Reaction of Aluminum Hydrides with Terminal Acetylenes

Some authors have reported that aluminum hydrides add to acetylenes, and some have found metallation to form aluminum-acetylene compounds. Surtees[14] studied the problem of addition versus substitution. Four reactions occurred when he mixed phenylacetylene and dialkyl-aluminum hydrides:

$$PhC{\equiv}CH + R_2AlH \longrightarrow PhC{\equiv}CAlR_2, \text{metallation} \qquad (1)$$

$$PhC{\equiv}CAlHR, \text{metallation} \qquad (2)$$

$$PhCH{=}CHAlR_2, \text{monoaddition} \qquad (3)$$

$$PhCH_2CH(AlR_2)_2, \text{diaddition} \qquad (4)$$

He reacted phenylacetylene with 3 moles of dialkylaluminum hydride in cyclohexane or toluene. The course of the reaction depended on the conditions; it could be either mainly substitution or mainly addition (Table 4-26). Thus,

TABLE 4-26
Reaction of Phenylacetylene with Dialkylaluminum Hydrides[14]

R (in R_2AlH)	Conditions Temperature (°C)	Time (min.)	(1)	(2)	(3)	(4)	% Unreacted PhC≡CH
				% Yield of			
Me	65–75	40	16	—	18	15	30
	105–110	10	17	—	15	10	8
	65–75 (3 moles PhC≡CH)	40	32	—	32	5	0
Et	55–60	30	34	—	44	21	0
Ph	60–70	30	0	28	41	23	4
	60–70 (no solvent)		19	9	34	27	2
	40 (+5 moles Et₃N)	3	74	17	0	0	7

addition of triethylamine greatly increased the substitution (metallation) reactions (1) and (2).

2.4. Reaction of Sodium Aluminum Hydride with Terminal Acetylenes

Zakharkin[17] reacted sodium or lithium aluminum hydride with 1-alkynes in tetrahydrofuran to obtain good yields of $MAl(C\equiv CR)_4$. These reacted like typical alkali metal acetylides: $NaAl(C\equiv CBu)_4$ alkynylated propionaldehyde and crotonaldehyde, to give 70 and 80% yields, respectively, of carbinols. $NaAl(C\equiv CPh)_4$ reacted with CO_2 at 120–150° to give 60% yield of phenyl-propiolic acid. In other carbonation reactions, the yields were 60–75%.[18]

3. GALLIUM COMPOUNDS OF ACETYLENES— REACTION OF GALLIUM ALKYLS AND ALKYL HYDRIDES WITH ACETYLENES

Eisch[13] compared the reaction of aluminum alkyls and of gallium alkyls with olefins and acetylenes. He showed that diethylgallium hydride adds across olefins to form Et_2GaR (an excellent synthesis for these unsymmetrical gallium alkyls).

Aluminum triethyl adds to acetylene at 40–60° to form $AlEt_2(CH=CHEt)$, while triethylgallium gives mostly substitution:

$$GaEt_3 + HC\equiv CR \longrightarrow GaEt_2C\equiv CR + C_2H_2$$

$$\downarrow \uparrow \text{heat}$$

$$2GaEt_3 + Ga(C\equiv CR)_3$$

On Pauling's electronegativity scale, aluminum is 1.5 and gallium is 1.6. In spite of this, gallium alkyls are less effective Lewis acids than aluminum alkyls. The most striking difference between these alkyls is in their reaction with terminal acetylenes:

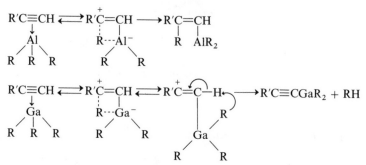

The net effect of gallium is to make the terminal acetylenic hydrogen more acidic. Contrary to these results, Mole[10] was able to make substitution the major reaction (see section 2.2).

4. THALLIUM COMPOUNDS OF ACETYLENES

Nast and Kaeb[19] in 1966 reported the first thallium acetylenic compounds: $Me_2TlC\equiv CR$ (R = Ph, Me) and $Me_2TlC\equiv CTlMe_2$ were made by reacting Me_2TlNH_2 with an acetylenic hydrocarbon in ammonia. They also reacted thallium trichloride with a metal acetylide in ammonia:

$$TlCl_3 \cdot 4NH_3 + MC\equiv CR \longrightarrow M[Tl(C\equiv CR)_4]$$

where R = Ph or Me, and M = Na, K or Ph_4P.

5. SILICON COMPOUNDS OF ACETYLENES

5.1. Ethynylsilanes

Ethylene adds silane at 500° to form ethylsilane and diethylsilane. Acetylene, however, gives some ethynylsilane by substitution, but mostly ethynyldivinylsilane, by addition and substitution.[20a] Gilman[20] reacted dilithium acetylide with triphenylchlorosilane to form bis(triphenylsilyl)acetylene (m.p. 156°). A by-product of this reaction was triphenylsilylacetylene. He obtained 85% yield of 1-chloro-2-triphenylsilylacetylene by adding triphenylchlorosilane to 1,2-dichloroethylene and 2 moles of phenyllithium in tetrahydrofuran. Trichloroethylene and triphenylsilyllithium, however, gave 1-chloro-2-triphenylsilylacetylene in low yield because of complicating side reactions. Some cleavage reactions of bis(triphenylsilyl)acetylene are:

$$Ph_3SiC\equiv CSiPh_3 \quad \begin{array}{l} \xrightarrow[\text{(2) water}]{\text{(1) } Ph_3SiLi} (Ph_3Si)_2 + HC\equiv CSiPh_3 \\ (93\%) (87\%) \\ \xrightarrow[\text{(2) water}]{\text{(1) } LiPh} Ph_4Si + HC\equiv CSiPh_3 \\ (94\%) (75\%) \\ \xrightarrow[\text{19 hr}]{\text{Grignard reagent}} \text{no reaction} \end{array}$$

Other acetylene- and chloroacetylene-silicon compounds are given in Table 4-27.

5.2. Silicon-Enyne Compounds

Vinylacetylene Grignard reagent reacts with R_3SiCl to give $R_3SiC\equiv CCH=CH_2$, where R is methyl, ethyl or phenyl.[25] Similar derivatives of isopropenylacetylene can be made by dehydrating the corresponding silicon enynol with $KHSO_4$.

TABLE 4-27
Acetylenic Silicon Compounds

Acetylenic Reagent	Silicon Reagent	Solvent	Product	% Yield	Reference
$NaC\equiv CH$	$(Me_2Si)_2SO_4$	Ether	$Me_3SiC\equiv CH$	68	21
	SiX_4		$X_3SiC\equiv CH, X_2Si(C\equiv CH)_2,$ $Si(C\equiv CH)_4$		22
$HC\equiv CMgBr$	R_3SiBr	THF	$R_3SiC\equiv CH$		23
	R_2SiBr_2		$R_2Si(C\equiv CH)_2$		
$LiC\equiv CCl$	Me_3SiCl	Ether	$Me_3SiC\equiv CCl +$ $Me_3SiC\equiv CH$	54	24
	$SiCl_4$	Ether	$Si(C\equiv CCl)_4$ (explodes if dried)		24
$Me_3SiC\equiv CCl$	PhLi	Ether	$Me_3SiC\equiv CCl +$ $Me_3SiC\equiv CH$		24

5.3. Silicon-Acetylenic Carbinol Compounds

Most of the compounds in this series have been made by Russian workers. Shikhiev[26] reacted propargyl alcohol Grignard reagent with triethylchlorosilane in the presence of cuprous chloride–mercuric chloride catalyst to obtain $Et_3SiC\equiv CCH_2OH$. Shostakovskii[27] prepared the Grignard reagents from the carbinols he made by reacting ethylene oxide or propylene oxide with sodium acetylide in ether. These Grignards reacted with trimethylchlorosilane to form 40% yield of the trimethylsilylacetylenic alcohols. The method also works well with tertiary acetylenic alcohol Grignard reagents. Perveev[28] reported some reactions which demonstrated that the silylacetylenes form normally reactive Grignard reagents:

$$HC\equiv CMgBr + MeEt_2SiCl \xrightarrow[10\,hr]{THF} Et_2MeSiC\equiv CH \xrightarrow[(2)\ ClCH_2C(O)CH_3]{(1)\ EtMgBr\text{-}ether}$$
$$(60\%)$$

$$\underset{(72\%)}{Et_2MeSiC\equiv C\underset{\underset{}{|}}{\overset{\overset{OH}{|}}{C}}(CH_3)CH_2Cl} \xrightarrow{KOH\text{-}ether} \underset{(78\%)}{Et_2MeSiC\equiv C\overset{O}{\underset{\underset{CH_3}{|}}{C}}\!\!-\!\!CH_2} \xrightarrow{EtNH_2}$$

$$\underset{(79\%)}{Et_2MeSiC\equiv C\underset{\underset{CH_3}{|}}{\overset{\overset{NHEt}{|}}{C}}\!\!-\!\!CH_2OH}$$

Shostakovskii[29] also reacted dialkyldichlorosilanes with the Grignard reagents of acetylenic alcohols. The Grignard of 3-methyl-1-butyn-3-ol reacted

$$\underset{|}{\overset{OH}{}}$$

with dimethyldichlorosilane to form $Me_2Si(C{\equiv}CCMe_2)_2$ (64% yield). Diethyl- and dipropyldichlorosilane gave the corresponding silicon compounds in 50% yield. Kuznetsova[30] prepared compounds by the same reaction:

$$\underset{|}{\overset{OH}{}}$$
$$p\text{-}C_6H_4[Si(Me)_2C{\equiv}CCMe_2]_2$$

is an example. He dehydrated the carbinol by heating with $KHSO_4$ at 70–80°

$$\overset{Me}{\underset{|}{}}$$

and made $p\text{-}C_6H_4[Si(Me)_2C{\equiv}CC{=}CH_2]_2$ in 60% yield. The hydroxyl group in secondary silicon acetylenic alcohols can be converted to Cl by reaction with thionyl chloride in pyridine.[31]

5.4. Silylacetylenes as Bactericides and Fungicides

The compounds $PhC{\equiv}CSiMe_3$ and $BuC{\equiv}CSiMe_3$ are claimed to be bactericides and fungicides.[32] They inhibit the growth of *Staphylococcus aureus* and of *Hormodendron*, a fungus which produces slime in jet fuels.

5. GERMANIUM COMPOUNDS OF ACETYLENES

6.1. Ethynylgermanes

Sodium acetylide reacts with GeX_4 to form $GeX_3C{\equiv}CH$, $GeX_2(C{\equiv}CH)_2$ and $Ge(C{\equiv}CH)_4$.[22] These are the only known compounds of acetylene with the germanium-acetylenic carbon bond.

6.2. Germanium Compounds of Substituted Acetylenes

All of the germanium-substituted acetylene compounds known have been made by the Grignard procedure used for reactions of acetylenic carbinols with chlorosilanes. Some new acetylenic germanium products have been made by reacting R_3GeX with acetylenic Grignards (Table 4-28).[33]

The Grignard reagent of methylbutynol reacts with tributylgermanium chloride in ether to give 37% yield of the carbinol $Bu_3GeC{\equiv}CC(Me)_2OH$.[34] The hydroxyl group reacted normally with PCl_5, with acrylonitrile and with vinyl ethers (to form acetals).

Table 4-28
Acetylenic Germanium Compounds[33]

	b.p. (°C, @ mm Hg)
$Et_3GeC{\equiv}CC(Me)_2OH$	80, @ 1
$Bu_3GeC{\equiv}CCH_2CH{=}CH_2$	95, @ 0.2
$Et_3GeCH_2C{\equiv}CCH_2CH{=}CH_2$	111, @ 11
$Et_3GeC{\equiv}CC(Me){=}CH_2$	97, @ 23
$Et_3GeC{\equiv}CCH_2OH$	94, @ 3
$Et_3GeC{\equiv}CCH(OH)Pr$	106, @ 1
$Et_3GeC{\equiv}CC{\equiv}CEt$	118, @ 5

Shikhiev[35] prepared a series of organogermanium diacetylenic compounds by a coupling reaction:

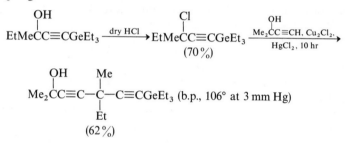

$$
\underset{\text{(70\%)}}{EtMe\overset{\displaystyle OH}{\overset{|}{C}}C{\equiv}CGeEt_3} \xrightarrow{\text{dry HCl}} EtMe\overset{\displaystyle Cl}{\overset{|}{C}}C{\equiv}CGeEt_3 \xrightarrow[\text{HgCl}_2,\ 10\ \text{hr}]{Me_2CC{\equiv}CH,\ Cu_2Cl_2,}
$$

$$
\underset{\text{(62\%)}}{Me_2\overset{\displaystyle OH}{\overset{|}{C}}C{\equiv}C{-}\overset{\displaystyle Me}{\underset{\displaystyle Et}{\overset{|}{\underset{|}{C}}}}{-}C{\equiv}CGeEt_3}\ \text{(b.p., 106° at 3 mm Hg)}
$$

References

1. Davidsohn, W. E., and Henry, M. C., *Chem. Rev.*, **67**, 73 (1967).
2. Matteson, D. S., and Peacock, K., *J. Am. Chem. Soc.*, **82**, 5759 (1960); *J. Org. Chem.*, **28**, 369 (1963).
3. Sharanina, L. G., Zavgorodnii, V. S., and Petrov, A. A., *Zh. Obshch. Khim.*, 36, 1275 (1966); *Chem. Abstr.*, **65**, 15412 (1966).
4. Giraud, D., Soulie, J., and Cadiot, P., *Compt. Rend.*, **254**, 319 (1962).
5. Binger, P., and Koester, R., *Tetrahedron Letters*, 1901 (1965).
6. Soulie, J., *Compt. Rend., Ser. C.*, 262, 376 (1966).
7. Hartmann, H., and Birr, K. H., *Z. Anorg. Allgem. Chem.*, **299**, 174 (1959); *Chem. Abstr.*, **53**, 17888 (1959).
8. Soulie, J., and Willemart, A., *Compt. Rend.*, **251**, 727 (1960).
9. Petrov, A. A., Zavgorodnii, S. V., and Kormer, V. A., *Zh. Obshch. Khim.* **32**, 1349 (1962); *Chem. Abstr.*, **58**, 1481 (1963).
9a. Soulie, J., and Cadiot, P., *Bull. Soc. Chim. France*, 3846, 3950 (1966).
10. Mole, T., and Surtees, J. R., *Chem. Ind. (London)* 1727 (1963).
11. Wilke, G., and Müller, H., *Ann. Chem.*, **629**, 222 (1960).
12. Ziegler, K., in (Zeiss, H., editor) "Organometallic Chemistry," p. 232, New York, Reinhold Publishing Corp., 1960.

13. Eisch, J. J., *J. Am. Chem. Soc.*, **84**, 3830 (1962).
14. Surtees, J. R., *Australian J. Chem.*, **18**, 14 (1965); *Chem. Abstr.*, **62**, 7787 (1965).
15. Lab. Riuniti Studi e Richerche S.p.a., Belgian Patent 610,213 (May 14, 1962); *Chem. Abstr.*, **57**, 1665 (1962).
16. Chini, P., *et al.*, *Chim. Ind.* (*Milan*), **44**, 1220 (1962); *Chem. Abstr.*, **58**, 13973 (1963).
17. Zakharkin, L. I., and Gavrilenko, V. V., *Izv. Akad. Nauk SSSR, Otd. Khim. Nauk*, 1146 (1963); *Chem. Abstr.*, **59**, 8772 (1963).
18. Zakharkin, L. I., Gavrilenko, V. V., and Ivanov, L. L., *Izv. Akad. Nauk SSSR, Ser. Khim.*, 2066 (1964); *Chem. Abstr.*, **62**, 7629 (1965).
19. Nast, R., and Kaeb, K., *J. Organometallic Chem.*, **6**, 456 (1966).
20. Gilman, H., and Aoki, D., *Chem. Ind.* (*London*), 1619 (1961).
20a. Wright, D. G., and Rochow, E. G., *J. Am. Chem. Soc.*, **76**, 3897 (1954).
21. Shostakovskii, M. F., Komarov, N. V., and Yarosh, O. G., *Izv. Akad. Nauk SSSR, Ser. Khim.*,101 (1966); *Chem. Abstr.*, **64**, 12712 (1966).
22. Davidsohn, W., and Henry, M. C., *J. Organometallic Chem.*, **5**, 29 (1966).
23. Shchukovskaya, L. L., Pal'chik, R. I., and Petrov, A. A., *Dokl. Akad. Nauk SSSR*, **136**, 1354 (1961); *Chem. Abstr.*, **55**, 18564 (1961).
24. Viehe, H. G., *Chem. Ber.*, **92**, 3064 (1959).
25. Stadnichuk, M. D., and Petrov, A. A., *Zh. Obshch. Khim.*, **30**, 3890 (1960); *Chem. Abstr.*, **55**, 23328 (1961).
26. Shikhiev, I. A., Abdullaev, N. D., and Akhundova, G.Yu., *Azerb. Khim. Zh.*, 50 (1965); *Chem. Abstr.*, **63**, 9977 (1965).
27. Shostakovskii, M. F., Atavin, A. S., and Egorov, N. V., *Zh. Obshch. Khim.*, **35**, 809 (1965); *Chem. Abstr.*, **63**, 7033 (1965).
28. Perveev, F.Ya., and Bogatkin, R. A., *Zh. Obshch. Khim.*, **35**, 801 (1965); *Chem. Abstr.*, **63**, 7035 (1965).
29. Shostakovskii, M. F., Shikhiev, I. A., and Komarov, N. V., *Dokl. Akad. Nauk SSSR*, **109**, 344 (1956); *Chem. Abstr.*, **51**, 1826 (1957).
30. Kuznetsova, V. P., and Smetankina, N. P., *Zh. Obshch. Khim.*, **35**, 913 (1965); *Chem. Abstr.*, **63**, 7033 (1965).
31. Shostakovskii, M. F., Komarov, N. V., and Pukhnarevich, V. B., *Dokl. Akad. Nauk SSSR*, **136**, 846 (1961); *Chem. Abstr.*, **55**, 18563 (1961).
32. Merker, R. L. (to Dow Corning Corp.), French Patent 1,403,705 (June 25, 1965); *Chem. Abstr.*, **63**, 13973 (1965).
33. Mazerolles, P., *Compt. Rend.*, **251**, 2041 (1960).
34. Shikhiev, I. A., and Abdullaev, N. D., *Zh. Obshch. Khim.*, **35**, 1348 (1965); *Chem. Abstr.*, **63**, 16377 (1965).
35. Shikhiev, I. A., Aslanov, I. A., and Mikhmandarova, N. T., *Zh. Obshch. Khim.*, **35**, 459 (1965); *Chem. Abstr.*, **63**, 624 (1965).

PART FOUR

Tin, Arsenic, Bismuth, Antimony and Lead Derivatives of Acetylenic Compounds

1. BACKGROUND

The compounds of tin, arsenic, lead, antimony and bismuth which have $M-C \equiv C-$ bonds are grouped together because they are made by similar reactions and have similar properties. More organotinacetylenes have been reported than any of the others.

Before 1958, only organotin derivatives of acetylenic hydrocarbons had been made. Beerman[1] reported bis(triphenyltin)acetylene and bis(triethyltin)acetylene in 1954. These organotinacetylenes hydrolyze very easily, and react with silver ion or with cuprous salt-ammonia to give silver or cuprous acetylides. Iodine cleaves the $Sn-C$ bond, and so do Grignard reagents. In 1958, Johnson[2] reported organotin compounds from propargyl aldehyde acetal:

$$\text{acrolein} + Br_2 + \text{ethyl orthoformate} + EtOH \xrightarrow[\text{(2) } Ag^+]{\text{(1) KOH}}$$

$$AgC \equiv CCH(OEt)_2 \xrightarrow[\text{warm acetone}]{Ph_3SnBr} Ph_3SnC \equiv CCH(OEt)_2 \text{ (m.p. } 59°)$$

The Grignard reagent did not react as well as the silver salt with triphenyltin bromide. The tin-carbon bond is easily hydrolyzed by dilute acid or weak alkali.

Most acetylenic tin, arsenic, lead, antimony and bismuth compounds have been made by the reaction of an organometal halide with a metal-acetylene compound, usually a Grignard reagent or alkali metal acetylide:

$$R_nMX_m + XMgC \equiv C- \text{ (or } NaC \equiv C-, \text{ or } LiC \equiv C-) \longrightarrow R_nM(C \equiv C-)_m$$

2. ORGANOTINACETYLENES

2.1. Reaction of Organotin Halides with Metal Acetylides or Grignard Reagents

In 1955, LeQuan and Cadiot[3] reviewed the earlier literature on organotin-acetylenic compounds and described their own extensive work. They reacted organotin halides with acetylenic Grignard reagents, using 20–50% excess magnesium for liquid acetylenics (less for solids), usually in ether or tetrahydrofuran. A period of 1–2 hours at 30–40° was sufficient for monoacetylenes, but diynes required 2–4 hours. Products from triphenyltin halides are stable to water, so the reaction mixtures were hydrolyzed by saturated ammonium chloride solution. Trimethyltin products are less stable and more difficult to isolate. Either bromo- or iodo-tin compounds react well. Some products made by the reaction $R_3SnX + BrMgC\equiv CR' \longrightarrow R_3SnC\equiv CR'$ are listed in Table 4-29. Products from the reaction of diacetylenic diGrignard reagents are listed in Table 4-30.

TABLE 4-29
Reaction of Organotin Halides with Acetylenic Grignard Reagents[3]

Product	Solvent	% Yield	b.p. (°C, @ mm Hg)	m.p. (°C)
$Me_3SnC\equiv CH$	THF	15	95–96	—
$Me_3SnC\equiv CPh$	Ether	40	107, @ 1.5	—
$Me_3SnC\equiv CC(CH_3)=CH_2$	Ether	30	40–42, @ 5	—
$Me_3SnC\equiv C\langle\bigcirc\rangle$	Ether	20	68–70, @ 3	—
$Ph_3SnC\equiv CMe$	THF	85	—	74–75
$Ph_3SnC\equiv CPh$	THF	80	—	62
$Ph_3SnC\equiv CCH=CH_2$	THF	58	—	58–59
$Ph_3SnC\equiv C\langle\bigcirc\rangle$	THF	66	—	105–106
$Ph_3SnC\equiv CCH_2OH$	THF	80	—	66–68
$(MeC\equiv C)_4Sn$	—	65	—	139[a]
$Ph_3SnC\equiv CC\equiv CMe$	—	40[a]	—	—
$Ph_3SnC\equiv CC\equiv CH$	—	30	—	99 (dec.)

[a] See reference 4.

TABLE 4-30[4]

$$R_3SnX + XMgC\equiv C-R''-C\equiv CMgX \longrightarrow R_3SnC\equiv C-R''-C\equiv CSnR_3$$

Product	Solvent	% Yield	m.p. (°C)
$Ph_3SnC\equiv CC\equiv CSnPh_3$	THF	35	245 (dec.)
$Ph_3SnC\equiv C(CH_2)_3C\equiv CSnPh_3$	Ether + THF	40	105
$Ph_3SnC\equiv C(CH_2)_4C\equiv CSnPh_3$	Ether + THF	50	148
$Ph_3SnC\equiv C-\langle\bigcirc\rangle-C\equiv CSnPh_3$	THF	15	2–5
$Ph_3SnC\equiv CC_{14}H_8C\equiv CSnPh_3$	THF	57	225

Trisubstituted tin halides also reacted well with alkali alkynylides in 1 : 5 ether : liquid ammonia at −40°. Sodium amide and the acetylenic compound formed sodium alkynylide in 4–15 minutes at −50°. Reaction with the trisubstituted tin bromide or iodide required about an hour. Triphenyltin iodide reacted with sodium acetylide to form triphenylstannylacetylene, but triphenyltin bromide tended to give disubstitution. With 2 moles of triphenyltin iodide, bis(triphenylstannyl)acetylene was the major product. Different products are given in Table 4-31.[4]

TABLE 4-31[4]

$$R_3SnX + NaC{\equiv}CR' \longrightarrow R_3SnC{\equiv}CR'$$

Product	% Yield	m.p. (°C)
$Ph_3SnC{\equiv}CH$	70	35–36
$Ph_3SnC{\equiv}CSnPh_3$	80	152
$Ph_3SnC{\equiv}CBr$	75	104–105
$Ph_3SnC{\equiv}CC{\equiv}CH$	30	99 (dec.)
$Ph_3SnC{\equiv}CC{\equiv}CMe$	40	Oil
$Ph_3SnC{\equiv}CC{\equiv}CPh$	60	88
$Ph_3Sn(C{\equiv}C)_3SnPh_3$	30	170 (dec.)
$Sn(C{\equiv}CMe)_4$	73	150
$Me_2Sn(C{\equiv}CPh)_2$	50	66–67

Other syntheses of $R_3SnC{\equiv}CSnR_3$ from acetylene diGrignard or sodium acetylide are reported.[5] In other reactions, disodium diacetylide and trialkyltin chlorides give 76–94% yields of $R_3SnC{\equiv}CC{\equiv}CSnR_3$, where R is cyclohexyl, p-chlorophenyl or p-tolyl.[6] The same reaction with diphenyl- or di-α-naphthylarsenic chloride gives the corresponding arsenic compounds.

In the trimethyltin series, sodium alkynylides gave 50% yield, while Grignard reagents gave only 30% yield. The alkynylide method was also faster and produced mixtures which were easier to work up and separate.

In moist air, trimethyltinacetylenes hydrolyze to the acetylenic hydrocarbon and trimethyltin hydroxide, but they are stable for several years in sealed tubes. They are soluble in ordinary organic solvents. The triphenyltin products are usually solids, soluble in ether, benzene and acetone, and slightly soluble in ethanol and in hydrocarbons. Organotinacetylenes hydrolyze in acid and in strong base, and cannot be analyzed for −CH≡CH by the silver nitrate method. Grignard reagents replace the alkynyl group by the alkyl group of the Grignard. Stannyl-acetylenes hydrogenate completely in the presence of Raney nickel. Hydrolysis of the Sn−C bond is an electrophilic substitution on the acetylenic carbon atom by a proton:

$$HO: \quad Sn-C\equiv CR \longrightarrow HO\cdots Sn^+\cdots C\equiv CR \longrightarrow HO-Sn^+ + HC\equiv CR$$

Infrared spectra show absorption at $2000–2150 \text{ cm}^{-1}$ for $-C\equiv C-$ vibration. The products having terminal acetylene groups absorb normally around 3300 cm^{-1}. NMR spectra and ultraviolet spectra are also normal.

A plot[4] of electronegativity of "metal" atom versus wave length of IR absorption for terminal ethynyl groups in products of the series of "metals" C, Si, Ge, Sn and Pb showed that the π electrons of the triple bond interact with the d orbitals of the "metal." This delocalizes the π electrons and thus influences the mobility of the C—H. The greater the electronegativity of the "metal," the higher is the wavelength of absorption.

Lithium cyclohexylacetylide reacts with MX_4 or with Rb_2MCl_2 to form $(C_6H_{11}C\equiv C)_4M$:[8]

M	% Yield
Si	45
Ge	32
Sn	44
Pb	22

Lithium p-bromo- and p-chlorophenylacetylides react with the same halides to form $(p\text{-}XC_6H_4C\equiv C)_4M$ in 22–57% yields.[9]

Other preparations of tin acetylenics include the reaction of sodium vinylacetylide with R_3SnCl, and the reverse reaction of 1-bromobut-3-en-1-yne with R_3SnNa.[10] An attempt to react bromoacetylene with Me_3SnNa in ammonia gave $Me_3SnC\equiv CBr$ and $Me_3SnC\equiv CSnMe_3$, and none of the expected $Me_3SnC\equiv CH$.[11] $Et_3SnC\equiv CCH=CH_2$ has been prepared by three reactions in ammonia:[12]

(1). Excess vinylacetylene plus $(Et_3Sn)_2$, with sodium as catalyst.

(2). Excess vinylacetylene plus $NaSnEt_3$.

(3). 1-Bromobutadiene plus $NaSnEt_3$ (elimination-substitution).

2.2. Reaction of Acetylenes with Trisubstituted Tin Oxides

Acetylenes react with trisubstituted tin oxides to give $R_3SnC\equiv CR'$. Acetylene and $(Me_3Sn)_2O$ at 10 atmospheres pressure give 65% yield of $Me_3SnC\equiv CH$, b.p. 98°.[13] Diacetylene and $(Et_3Sn)_2O$ give a mixture of mono- and disubstituted diacetylene. Sodium acetylide and tripropyltin oxide give very little $Pr_3SnC\equiv CH$. Ethers of propargyl alcohol react with triethyltin oxide in refluxing benzene to give $Et_3SnC\equiv CCH_2OR$.[13] 1-Butyn-3-ol and triethyltin oxide give 20%

yield of the O—Sn compound and 43% yield of $Et_3SnO\overset{\displaystyle CH_3}{\underset{\displaystyle |}{CH}}-C\equiv CSnEt_3$.
The latter is formed in 91% yield by reaction of the 1-butyn-3-ol with
Et_3SnOMe at $-10°$.[14]

Substituted acetylenes, $RC\equiv CH$, react with $(R'_3Sn)_2O$. Water is removed by
azeotroping or by calcium hydride:[15]

$$RC\equiv CH + (R'_3Sn)_2O \longrightarrow RC\equiv CSnR'_3$$

R	R'	% Yield
Phenyl	Ethyl	82
Phenyl	Butyl	90
Phenyl	Phenyl	79
p-Methoxyphenyl	Ethyl	90
MeOCH=CH—	Ethyl	82
CN	Ethyl	83

2.3. Reaction of Acetylenes with Trisubstituted Tin Hydroxides

Acetylene reacts with Pr_3SnOH at $115°$ at an initial pressure of 15 atmospheres
to give 37% yield of $Pr_3SnC\equiv CH$. The triethyl- and tributyltinacetylenes form
in 20% yields.[16] Vinylacetylene gives $Et_3SnC\equiv CCH=CH_2$ in 63% yield.

3. ORGANOARSENICACETYLENES

Organoarsenic halides react with acetylenic Grignard reagents just as organotin
halides do (Table 4-32).[17]

Sodium alkynylides also react well:

$$Ph_2AsCl + NaC\equiv CCH_3 \xrightarrow{\text{hexane}} Ph_2AsC\equiv CCH_3$$
$$(96\%)$$

$$Ph_2AsCl + NaC\equiv CC\equiv CH \xrightarrow{NH_3} Ph_2AsC\equiv CC\equiv CAsPh_2 \text{ (m.p. }115°)$$
$$(40\%)$$

Acetylene monoGrignard reacts with $AsCl_3$ in tetrahydrofuran to give 62%
yield of $As(C\equiv CH)_3$, m.p. 49–50°.[18] Acetylenic diGrignard reacts with R_2AsI
in ether to give 16–43% yields of $R_2AsC\equiv CAsR_2$.[18a]

The ethynyl group in ethynyldiphenylarsine ($Ph_2AsC\equiv CH$) reacts normally:[17]

Reagent	Condensing Agent	Product	% Yield	m.p. (°C)
$Ph_2C=O$	KOH	$\overset{\overset{\textstyle OH}{\textstyle \vert}}{Ph_2AsC\equiv CCPh_2}$	87	136
	Grignard	,,	60	
Cyclohexanone	KOH	$Ph_2AsC\equiv C\overset{OH}{\bigcirc}$	87	57
CO_2	Grignard	$Ph_2AsC\equiv CCO_2H$	58	130

The arsenic atom is oxidized by hydrogen peroxide to give 90–95% yield of the oxide or hydroxide. Hydroxides can be dehydrated to oxides.

TABLE 4-32
Reaction of Organoarsenic Halides with Acetylenic Grignard Reagents[17]

$$R_{3-n}AsX_n + R'(C\equiv C)_mMgX \xrightarrow{\text{THF}} R_{3-n}As[(C\equiv C)_mR']_n$$

R	R'	n	m	% Yield	m.p. (°C)	b.p. (°C, @ mm Hg)
Ph	Me	1	1	86		128, @ 1
Ph	Me	2	1	85		75, @ 10^{-2}
Ph	Me	3	1	92	131	
Ph	Me	1	2	76	60	
Ph	Me	1	3	60	125	
Ph	Et	1	1	92		110, @ 10^{-1}
Ph	Ph	1	2	55	63	
Ph	Ph	2	1	63	63	
Ph	Cyclohex-1-enyl	1	1	70	42	
Ph	Pr	1	2	75	40	
Ph	H	1	1	85	23	
Ph	H	1	2	48	55	
Et	Me	1	2	83		

4. ORGANOBISMUTHACETYLENES

Hartmann[19] used sodium acetylides to prepare aromatically substituted bismuth acetylenic compounds:

$$R_2BiCl + NaC\equiv CH \longrightarrow R_2BiC\equiv CBiR_2$$

$$R_2BiCl + NaC\equiv CPh \longrightarrow R_2BiC\equiv CPh$$

He prepared $(p\text{-ClC}_6\text{H}_4)_2\text{BiC}\equiv\text{CBi}(p\text{-ClC}_6\text{H}_4)_2$ (m.p. 135°) and bis(p-tolyl)-bismuthacetylene in tetrahydrofuran. Diphenylbismuth chloride did not react. The bismuth compounds are soluble in chloroform, tetrahydrofuran, benzene and acetone.

5. ORGANOANTIMONYACETYLENES

Similar reactions are used to prepare dialkylantimonyacetylenes: Sodium acetylides are reacted with dialkylantimony bromide in ammonia or in tetrahydrofuran.[20] The disubstituted derivative $\text{Me}_2\text{SbC}\equiv\text{CSbMe}_2$ (b.p. 116° at 17 mm Hg) formed in ammonia, while the monosubstituted derivative was produced in THF. However, bis(isopropyl)antimonyacetylene was made in THF (65% yield, b.p. 68° at 15 mm Hg). Disodium diacetylide and diisopropyl-antimony bromide gave 35% yield of $[(i\text{-Pr})_2\text{SbC}\equiv\text{C}]_2$ (b.p. 118°).

Antimony trichloride and acetylene monoGrignard in tetrahydrofuran gave 63% yield of $\text{Sb}(\text{C}\equiv\text{CH})_3$ (m.p. 71°).[18]

6. ORGANOLEADACETYLENES

Acetylenic Grignards or alkali metal acetylides in ammonia are not as good as alkali metal acetylides in pentane for the reaction:[21]

$$\text{R}_3\text{PbX} + \text{MC}\equiv\text{CR}' \longrightarrow \text{R}_3\text{PbC}\equiv\text{CR}'$$

R	R'	% Yield	m.p. (°C)
Ph	Me	50	
Ph	Et	53	64
Ph	Ph	52	56
Et	H	30	b.p. 110, 2.5 mm

Propargyl Grignards give mostly allenic lead compounds:

$$\text{HC}\equiv\text{CCH}_2\text{MgX} + \text{R}_3\text{PbX} \longrightarrow 70\% \text{ yield}, 90\% \text{ is allenic } (\text{Ph}_2\text{PbCH}=\text{C}=\text{CH}_2)$$

In 1965, Masson and Cadiot[22] reviewed previous work on organolead acetylenic compounds, and reported some of their recent experiments. Triaryl-lead halides reacted slowly with acetylenic Grignards, but trialkyllead halides reacted normally. Sodium acetylides were better than Grignard reagents. The addition of solid triphenyllead iodide to sodamide-ammonia-diacetylene (or acetylene) gave both mono- and disubstituted lead acetylenes, depending on the reaction time and the ratio of sodamide to acetylenic hydrocarbon. A large excess of acetylene gave 1:1 mixtures of mono- and disubstituted products. Equimolar sodamide-acetylene and 2 moles of sodamide with

3 moles of diacetylene gave 90–95 % of disubstituted product after only 10 minutes reaction. The sodium derivative of triphenyltinacetylene reacted with triphenyllead iodide to give $Ph_3SnC\equiv CPbPh_3$. The acetylenic lead compounds prepared in this work are given in Table 4-33.

TABLE 4-33
Organoleadacetylenes[22]

$$R_3PbI + NaC\equiv CR' \longrightarrow R_3PbC\equiv CR'$$

R	R'	% Yield	b.p. (°C, @ mm Hg)	m.p. (°C)
Ph	Br	28[a]		95
Ph	H	50[a]	Oil	
Ph	PbPh$_3$	80[b]		136
Ph	Me	50[c]		65
Ph	Et	53[c]		64
Ph	Ph	52[d]		56
Et	H	30[e]	110, @ 2.5	
Et	PbEt$_3$	50[e]		
Et	Me	40[e]	81, @ 1.5	
Et	Et	64[e]	105, @ 3	
Et	Ph	42[c]	66, @ 1	
Ph		30[a]		50
Ph		53[d]		84
Et		30[e]	95, @ 1.5	
Ph	—C≡CH	30[a]		93 (dec.)
Ph	—C≡CPbPh$_3$	80[a]		187 (dec.)
Ph	—C≡CMe	42[a]		55
Ph	—C≡CPh	55[a]		81

[a] Ammonia solvent.
[b] Hexane.
[c] Benzene.
[d] Toluene.
[e] Pentane.

The lead-acetylenic carbon bond is not very stable. The aryl derivatives decompose in acid or base. The phenyl compounds are stable at room temperature. The aliphatic products are more sensitive to hydrolysis and must be stored under nitrogen at $-50°$. In the infrared, the C≡C vibration band is very intense and shows a bathochromic effect compared to the corresponding hydrocarbons. Bathochromic effects are apparent in ultraviolet spectra also, particularly with the aromatic compounds.

Very little is known about the reactions of alkynyllead compounds. Triethylphenylethynyllead and triethylhexynyllead react with acetyl chloride to give 80% yield of α-acetylenic ketones:[22a]

$$Et_3PbC\equiv CR + Cl\overset{O}{\underset{\|}{C}}CH_3 \longrightarrow CH_3\overset{O}{\underset{\|}{C}}C\equiv CR$$

These are much better yields than those obtained with the corresponding Grignard reagents. The alkynyllead compounds react exothermically with phenyl isocyanate to form 1,3,6-trisubstituted uracils:

$$Et_3PbC\equiv CR + 2PhNCO \longrightarrow$$

7. USES

Hartmann[23] claimed that a number of tin, arsenic, antimony, silicon and germanium acetylenic compounds are antiknock agents and pesticides. He reacted a slurry of organometallic halide, such as Et_3SnCl, in ammonia with 1 or 2 equivalents of sodium or lithium acetylide (Table 4-34).

TABLE 4-34
Acetylenic Bis(organometallic) Compounds
(RMC≡CMR)[23]

R	M	b.p. (°C, @ mm Hg)	m.p. (°C)
Ph$_3$	Si	—	156
(PhCH$_2$)$_3$	Sn	—	94
(α-Naphthyl)	As	—	232
Ph$_2$	As	—	100.5
Me$_2$	Sb	120, @ 19	—
Ph$_2$	Sb	—	111
Ph$_2$	Ge	—	126.7
Ph$_2$	Bi	—	184 (dec.)
Ph$_3$	Pb	—	138.5
Et$_3$	Sb	122, @ 1.5	—
Bu$_2$	P	162, @ 3	—

Propynyltrimethyllead and butynyltrimethyllead are gasoline additives for improving octane rating.[24]

References

1. Beerman, C., and Hartmann, H., *Z. Anorg. Chem.*, **276**, 20 (1954).
2. Johnson, O. H., and Holum, J. R., *J. Org. Chem.*, **23**, 738 (1958).
3. LeQuan, M., and Cadiot, P., *Bull. Soc. Chim. France*, 35 (1965).
4. Masson, J. C., *et al.*, *Compt. Rend.*, **257**, 1111 (1963).
5. Hartmann, H., and Honig, H., *Angew. Chem.*, **69**, 614 (1957). Zavgorodnii, V. S., and Petrov, A. A., *J. Gen. Chem. USSR, Engl. Transl.*, **36**, 1485 (1966).
6. Hartmann, H., Karbstein, B., and Reiss, W., *Naturwissenschaften*, **52**, 59 (1965); *Chem. Abstr.*, **62**, 11852 (1965).
7. Mirskov, R. G., and Vlasov, V. M., *Zh. Obshch. Khim.*, **36**, 562 (1966); *Chem. Abstr.*, **65**, 744 (1966).
8. Hartmann, H., and Meyer, K., *Naturwissenschaften*, **52**, 303 (1965); *Chem. Abstr.*, **63**, 5670 (1965).
9. Hartmann, H., and El A'ssar, M. K., *Naturwissenschaften*, **52**, 304 (1965); *Chem. Abstr.*, **63**, 5670 (1965).
10. Zavgorodnii, V. S., and Petrov, A. A., *Zh. Obshch. Khim.*, **32**, 3527 (1962); *Chem. Abstr.*, **58**, 12592 (1963).
11. Zavgorodnii, V. S., and Petrov, A. A., *Zh. Obshch. Khim.*, **35**, 931 (1965); *Chem. Abstr.*, **63**, 7033 (1965).
12. Zavgorodnii, V. S., and Petrov, A. A., *Zh. Obshch. Khim.*, **33**, 2791 (1963); *Chem. Abstr.*, **59**, 15297 (1963).
13. Shostakovskii, M. F., *et al.*, *Dokl. Akad. Nauk SSSR*, **163**, 390 (1965); *Chem. Abstr.*, **63**, 11601 (1965).
14. Shostakovskii, M. F., *et al.*, *Zh. Obshch. Khim.*, **35**, 47 (1965); *Chem. Abstr.*, **62**, 11368 (1965).
15. Newmann, W. P., and Kleiner, F. G., *Tetrahedron Letters*, 3779 (1964).
16. Shostakovskii, M. F., *et al.*, *Dokl. Akad. Nauk SSSR*, **158**, 918 (1964); *Chem. Abstr.*, **62**, 2788 (1965).
17. Benaim, J., *Compt. Rend.*, **261** (Group 8), 1996 (1965).
18. Voskuil, W., and Arens, J. F., *Rec. Trav. Chim.*, **83**, 1301 (1964).
18a. Kuz'min, K. I., and Pavlova, L. A., *J. Gen. Chem. USSR, Engl. Transl.*, **36**, 1483 (1966).
19. Hartmann, H., Habenicht, G., and Reiss, W., *Z. Anorg. Allgem. Chem.*, **317**, 54 (1962); *Chem. Abstr.*, **58**, 2470 (1963).
20. Hartmann, H., and Kühl, G., *Angew. Chem.*, **68**, 619 (1956).
21. Masson, J. C., *et al.*, *Compt. Rend.*, **257**, 1111 (1963).
22. Masson, J. C., and Cadiot, P., *Bull. Soc. Chim. France*, 3518 (1965).
22a. Davies, A. G., and Puddephatt, R. J., *Tetrahedron Letters*, 2265 (1967).
23. Hartmann, H., German Patent 1,062,244 (July 30, 1959); *Chem. Abstr.*, **55**, 11303 (1961).
24. Ballinger, P. (to California Research Corp.), U.S. Patent 3,185,553 (May 25, 1965); *Chem. Abstr.*, **63**, 8403 (1965).

PART FIVE

Acetylenic Nitrogen, Phosphorus and Tellurium Compounds

1. COMPOUNDS WITH NITROGEN ATTACHED DIRECTLY TO ACETYLENIC CARBON

1.1. Preparation of 1-Aminoacetylenes (Yneamines)

In 1960, Wolf[1] reported the first 1-amino-1-acetylene. Lithium phenylacetylide and N-bromophthalimide or N-bromosuccinimide reacted to form phenyl-bromoacetylene in 55% yield, but lithium phenylacetylide and N-chlorodiethylamine gave 2.3% yield of phenyldiethylaminoacetylene. Phenylacetylene Grignard gave 1.7% yield.

Later, Viehe[2] described a different reaction. 1-Chloro-2-phenylacetylene reacts with lithium alkylamine derivatives to form $PhC\equiv CN\diagup_{\diagdown}$ in 85% yield.

t-BuC$\equiv$CCl does not react with LiNMe$_2$, but t-BuC$\equiv$CF gives 48% yield of t-BuC$\equiv$CNMe$_2$.[3] Montijn[4] used a different kind of reaction: Lithium amines react with α-acetylenic ethers to form 1-aminoalkynes:

$$RC\equiv COEt + \diagdown_{\diagup}NLi \longrightarrow RC\equiv CN\diagup_{\diagdown} + LiOEt$$

Ficini made a wide variety of yneamines.[5] If the molecule $-\overset{|}{X}C=\overset{|}{C}-A$ (X = O or halogen, A = halogen) reacts with a metal, A$^-$ is removed and the product is an acetylene or allene. However, if A is nitrogen, it is not eliminated; with magnesium, for example, the nitrogen-containing vinyl Grignard reagent forms. If two halogens and a nitrogen are attached to the carbon atoms, dehydrohalogenation by metal gives yneamine. Dichloroeneamines react with RLi to give yneamines:[6] $-CCl=CCl-N\diagup_{\diagdown} \longrightarrow -C\equiv CN\diagup_{\diagdown}$ Hexamethyl-phosphoramide ether is the best solvent for the reaction. Trichloroethylene-amines are similar. They react with butyllithium to form lithium alkynylides of the yneamine:

$$CCl_2=CClNR_2 + 2BuLi \longrightarrow LiC\equiv CNR_2 \xrightarrow{RX} R'C\equiv CNR_2$$

Some yneamines prepared by these reactions are listed in Table 4-35.

1.2. Preparation of 1-Acetylenic Diazonium Compounds

An acetylenic diazonium compound was made by a substitution reaction similar to the reactions which form yneamines:[7]

$$PhC\equiv CAg + ClN\equiv NPh-p-Cl \longrightarrow p-ClC_6H_4N=NC\equiv CPh \text{ (m.p. } 115°)$$
$$(35\%)$$

TABLE 4-35
1-Acetylenic Amines[6]

Product	% Yield	b.p. (°C, @ mm Hg)
$PhC{\equiv}CNEt_2$	85	75, @ 0.2
$HC{\equiv}CNPh_2$	65	97, @ 0.1
$BuC{\equiv}CN(Ph)Me$	75	88, @ 0.1
$MeC{\equiv}CN(Ph)Me$	65	96, @ 6
$HC{\equiv}CNEt_2$	32	70, @ 300
$PrC{\equiv}CB(Ph)Me$	61	70, @ 0.06
$CH_2{=}CHCH_2C{\equiv}CN(Ph)Me$	Impure, decomposed	

1.3. Reactions of 1-Aminoacetylenes

1.3.1. HYDRATION

Hydration usually gives the ketone with carbonyl alpha α to the amine group:

$$-CH_2\overset{\overset{O}{\|}}{C}NR_2.^8$$ 1-t-Butyl-2-diethylaminoacetylene hydrates this way, but 1-n-butyl-2-diethylaminoacetylene hydrates on the β-carbon to give

$$Bu\overset{\overset{O}{\|}}{C}CH_2-NEt_2.^9$$

1.3.2. ADDITION OF AMINES

The direction of addition of amines depends on the structure of the alkyne-amine. $PhC{\equiv}CNEt_2$ adds diethylamine to give $PhCH{=}C(NEt_2)_2.^9$ 1-Diethyl-amino-1-hexyne adds diethylamine to form $Bu\overset{\overset{NEt_2}{|}}{C}{=}CHNEt_2$ (20% in 3 days). Aniline adds to bis(dimethylamino)acetylene in ether in the presence of acid to form $Me_2NCH_2\overset{\overset{NMe_2}{|}}{C}{=}NPh$, 80% yield.[10]

1.3.3. ADDITION OF HYDROXYLAMINE

1-t-Butyl-2-dimethylaminoacetylene adds hydroxylamine in ether in the presence of acid to form t-$BuCH_2\overset{\overset{NMe_2}{|}}{C}{=}NOH$, 73% yield.[10]

1.3.4. ADDITION OF HYDRAZINE[10]

$$2PhC\equiv CNMe_2 + H_2NNH_2 \xrightarrow[20°]{MeCN,\ H^+} (PhCH_2\overset{\overset{\displaystyle NMe_2}{|}}{C}=N)_2$$
$$(50\%)$$

1.3.5. ADDITION OF ALCOHOLS

1-Dimethylamino-2-phenylacetylene adds alcohol in ether at 20° in the presence of acid to form $PhCH=\overset{\overset{\displaystyle NMe_2}{|}}{C}OEt.$[10]

1.3.6. ANHYDRIDIZATION REACTIONS

Perhaps the most useful property of alkyneamines is their avidity for water. They accept water formed in condensations so well that the reactions frequently take place under extremely mild conditions. Thus, 1-dimethylamino-2-phenyl-acetylene in benzene at 10° converts benzoic acid to benzoic anhydride in 98% yield in only 5 minutes.[10,11] The alkyneamine hydrates to ketone in the process. Carbodiimides and 1-alkoxyacetylenes also accept water, but not as well. Alkyneamines also consume water formed by the low-temperature reaction of alcohols with HCl to form RCl. Alkyneamines are also excellent coupling agents in peptide syntheses.[12]

1.3.7. CYCLOADDITION REACTIONS[10]

1-Diethylamino-2-phenylacetylene reacts with 2 moles of dimethyl acetylene-dicarboxylate in ether at room temperature to form the expected hexasubstituted benzene in 80% yield:

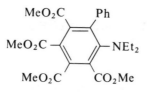

The alkyneamine reacts with *p*-phenylenediisocyanate in dioxane at room temperature by 1,3-dipolar addition to give 91% yield of

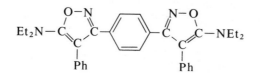

1.3.8. OTHER ADDITION REACTIONS

Acyl halides add to alkynylamines at room temperature in toluene to give high yields of adducts:[10a]

Methyl bromide adds to form two final products, a "cyclobutanecyanine," and an allenecarboxamide:[10a]

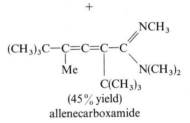

(16% yield)
"cyclobutanecyanine"

+

(45% yield)
allenecarboxamide

Protonation by an acid gives a "cyclobutanecyanine" in which the methyl group from methyl bromide is replaced by hydrogen from the acid.

2. COMPOUNDS WITH PHOSPHORUS ATTACHED TO ACETYLENIC CARBON

2.1. Introduction

In 1921, de Mahler[13] reacted acetylene diGrignard with PCl_3, but the structure of his product is doubtful. Bergmann[14] prepared some arylethynylphosphinic acids in 1933. Hartmann began his study of acetylenic phosphorus compounds in 1956. He made bis(diphenylphosphino)acetylene,[15] $R_2PC\equiv CH$ and $R_2PC\equiv CPR_2$, where R can be aliphatic or aromatic.[16,17] Hartmann converted these products to phosphorus oxides, sulfides and selenides.[18,19]

Perveev[20] made (2-methyl-3-pentyn-2-ol)yl–phosphine. Voskuil[21] prepared $R_2PC\equiv CH$ and alkylated the sodium derivatives in ammonia. He also prepared triethynylphosphine and isomerized α-acetylenic phosphines to β-acetylenic phosphines by sodium amide.[22] β-Acetylenic and allenic phosphines are formed directly from propargyl Grignard and phosphorus halides, or by KOH isomerization of α-acetylenic phosphines. Cherbuliez[23] and others have studied the isomerization reactions of propargyl phosphites and phosphonates.

Ionin[24] prepared ethyl pentadiynyl- and hexadiynylphosphonates, and ethyl propyn-1-yl-, allenyl- and (3-pent-1-yn)ylphosphonates[25] (see also reference 26). Viehe,[27] in 1962, and Hoffmann,[28] in 1964, reported studies on triphenyl-phenylethynylphosphonium bromide. Sturtz[29] prepared phosphonates from long-chain acetylenes.

2.2. 1-Acetylenic Phosphines

2.2.1. PREPARATION

In 1966, Charrier[30] reported extensive work on the reaction of disubstituted phosphorus halides with acetylenic Grignard reagents to form acetylenic phosphines. This method gave good yields, as Chodkiewicz[32] and Voskuil[21] had reported earlier:

$$\diagdown\!\!\!\diagup PCl + BrMgC\!\equiv\!CR \xrightarrow[N_2]{THF} \diagdown\!\!\!\diagup PC\!\equiv\!CR$$
$$(50\text{–}90\%)$$

Et_2PCl reacted best at $-10°$. Ph_2PCl reacted with Grignard reagents of conjugated polyacetylenes at $-20°$ and with Grignards of diethynylbenzenes at reflux in tetrahydrofuran.

Chodkiewicz[32] prepared ethynyldiphenyl phosphine by a carbinol cleavage reaction:

$$\underset{\displaystyle |}{\overset{\displaystyle OH}{Me_2CC\!\equiv\!CPPh_2}} \xrightarrow[heat]{KOH} HC\!\equiv\!CPPh_2$$
$$(35\text{–}50\%)$$

Charrier[30] obtained 90% yield by direct reaction of Ph_2PCl with $BrMgC\!\equiv\!CH$ in tetrahydrofuran in the presence of excess acetylene. Without acetylene, the yield was 70%. Diacetylene monoGrignard reacted with Ph_2PCl instantly at $-20°$ to form 35% yield of $Ph_2PC\!\equiv\!CC\!\equiv\!CH$. A second mole of Ph_2PCl reacted at $0°$ to form $Ph_2PC\!\equiv\!CC\!\equiv\!CPPh_2$, 42% yield.

Table 4-36 lists acetylenic phosphines, oxides and sulfides prepared by Charrier.[30]

2.2.2. PROPERTIES

Dialkylalkynylphosphines are distillable liquids which smell like phosphine. They easily oxidize and polymerize, so they must be kept under nitrogen in

TABLE 4-36
Acetylenic Phosphines, Phosphine Oxides and Phosphine Sulfides[30]

Acetylenic Compound	Phosphine m.p. (°C)	Phosphine Yield (%)	Phosphine Oxide m.p. (°C)	Phosphine Oxide Yield (%)	Phosphine Sulfide m.p. (°C)	Phosphine Sulfide Yield (%)
$(C_6H_5)_2P-C\equiv CH$	35	90	68	92	—	—
$(C_6H_5)_2P-C\equiv C-P(C_6H_5)_2$	86	72[b]	164[b]	—	186[b]	—
$(C_6H_5)_2P-C\equiv C-CH_3$	33	56	94	51	88	68
$(C_6H_5)_2P-C\equiv C-C_6H_5$	43	93	102	87	113	76
$(C_6H_5)_2P-C\equiv C-C(OH)(CH_3)_2$	76	65	162	78	127	73
$(C_6H_5)_2P-C\equiv C-C(OH)(C_6H_5)_2$	143	45	247	79	177	67
$(C_6H_5)_2P-C\equiv C-CH_2-(9\text{-anthranyl})$	178	74	—	—	—	—
$(C_6H_5)_2P-C\equiv C-$⬠(cyclopentenyl)	42	72	130	74	93	61
$(C_6H_5)_2P-C\equiv C-$⬡(cyclohexenyl)	60	70	120	78	120	69
$(C_6H_5)_2P-C\equiv C-$(cycloheptenyl)	Supercooled	114	40[a]	—	—	—
$(C_6H_5)_2P-C\equiv C-CH=C(C_6H_5)_2$	Supercooled	136	32[a]	—	—	—
$(C_6H_5)_2P-C\equiv C-C\equiv CH$	52	35	—	—	—	—
$(C_6H_5)_2P-C\equiv C-C\equiv C-P(C_6H_5)_2$	105	42	—	—	—	—
$(C_6H_5)_2P-C\equiv C-C\equiv C-CH_3$	61	76	84	71	71	58
$(C_6H_5)_2P-C\equiv C-C\equiv C-CH_2-CH_2-CH_3$	44	78	64	67	—	—
$(C_6H_5)_2P-C\equiv C-C\equiv C-C_6H_5$	75	77	131	74	89	63
$(C_6H_5)_2P-C\equiv C-C\equiv C-C\equiv C-CH_3$	131	65	—	—	—	—
$(C_6H_5)_2P-C\equiv C-$⬡$-C\equiv C-P(C_6H_5)_2$	204	69	256	75	—	—
$(C_6H_5)_2P-C\equiv C-$⬡$-C\equiv C-P(C_6H_5)_2$	199	45	262	63	—	—

Acetylenic Compound	Phosphine b.p. (°C, @ mm Hg)	Phosphine Yield (%)	Phosphine Oxide b.p. (°C, @ mm Hg)	Phosphine Oxide Yield (%)
$(C_2H_5)_2P-C\equiv CH$	128	48	—	—
$(C_2H_5)_2P-C\equiv C-CH_3$	165	50	—	—
$(C_2H_5)_2P-C\equiv C-C_6H_5$	105, @ 1	52	160, @ 0.6	30
$(C_2H_5)_2P-C\equiv C-C\equiv C-CH_3$	85, @ 1	40	—	—
$(C_2H_5)_2P-C\equiv C-$⬡(cyclohexenyl)	120, @ 2	50	140, @ 0.3	30

[a] Calculated on Ph$_2$PCl.
[b] From reference 33.

refrigerated sealed tubes. Diphenylalkynylphosphines are solids, stable to dilute acid and dilute alkali, but hydrolyzed by strong alkali to Ph_2POH and the acetylene.[33] They are not cleaved by cuprous or silver ion. The acetylene groups absorb normally in the infrared.[21]

2.2.3. REACTIONS[30]

(a) Hydrogenation: The phosphine group poisons palladium catalysts, but acetylenic phosphines can be reduced to saturated phosphines over Raney nickel.

(b) Oxidation: Hydrogen peroxide oxidizes the phosphines to phosphine oxides at 20° in 10–15 minutes. Acetic acid is the best solvent for the oxidation of $Ar_2PC\equiv CR$; acetone is best for $Et_2PC\equiv CR$. Sulfur in carbon disulfide oxidizes the phosphines to phosphine sulfides.

(c) Salts: Methyl iodide in ether or carbon disulfide gives phosphonium salts:

$$R_2PC\equiv CR' + MeI \longrightarrow \overset{\overset{\displaystyle I^-}{\displaystyle |}}{\underset{\underset{\displaystyle Me}{\displaystyle |}}{R_2\overset{+}{P}}}-C\equiv CR'$$

(d) Alkynylation: Chodkiewicz[32] and Charrier[30] studied alkynylation reactions. Alkynylation of excess ketone in cold tetrahydrofuran, with anhydrous KOH present, was complete in only 10–20 minutes:

$$Ph_2PC\equiv CH + R_2C=O \longrightarrow Ph_2PC\equiv C\overset{\overset{\displaystyle OH}{\displaystyle |}}{C}R_2$$

Ketone	% Yield
Acetone	63
Cyclohexanone	74
Benzophenone	85
Fluoroenone	85
Anthrafuchsone	90

(e) Carbonation:

$$Ph_2PC\equiv CMgBr + CO_2 \xrightarrow[60\ kg/cm^2]{THF,\ 48\ hr} Ph_2PC\equiv CCO_2H$$
$$(65\%)$$

(f) Reaction with boron halides: Compounds with acetylenic carbons attached both to boron and phosphorus can be made:

$$Ph_2PC\equiv CMgBr + 3ClBPh_2 \xrightarrow[-20°]{THF} Ph_2PC\equiv CBPh_2 \text{ (m.p. 280°)}$$
$$(64\%)$$
$$\updownarrow$$
$$Ph_2\overset{+}{P}=C=C=BPh_2$$

(g) Addition of amines:

$$Ph_2\overset{\uparrow O}{P}C{\equiv}CH + HNR_2 \xrightarrow[\text{15-20°}]{\text{ether}} Ph_2\overset{\uparrow O}{P}CH{=}CHNR_2$$
$$(70\text{-}80\%)$$

(h) Lithium derivatives: The reaction of ethynyldibutylphosphine (dibutyl-phosphinoethyne) with 1 equivalent of lithium amide in ammonia gives the lithium alkynylide, which reacts normally with alkyl iodides and with ketones:[21]

$$n\text{-}Bu_2PC{\equiv}CLi \xrightarrow{+RI} Bu_2PC{\equiv}CR\ (R = Me, Et)$$

$$\xrightarrow{+RR'C{=}O} Bu_2PC{\equiv}C\overset{\overset{\displaystyle OH}{|}}{C}RR'\ \text{(acetone, cyclohexanone)}$$

(i) Mannich reaction: Under conditions used for the Mannich reaction with phenylacetylene and with ethylthioethyne, dibutylphosphinoethyne yields acetylene and N,N-diethylaminomethylphosphine.

(j) Addition of thiols: Radical addition of ethanethiol in the presence of azobis(isobutyronitrile) gives the product from addition of ·SEt to the β-carbon:

$$Bu_2PC{\equiv}CH + \cdot SEt \longrightarrow Bu_2P\dot{C}{=}CHSEt + EtSH \longrightarrow Bu_2P\overset{\overset{\displaystyle H}{|}}{C}{=}\overset{\overset{\displaystyle H}{|}}{C}SEt + \cdot SEt$$

Attempted ionic addition of sodium ethanethiolate gives no product from ionic addition, but forms only bis(dibutylphosphino)ethyne:[21]

$$Bu_2PC{\equiv}CH + EtS^- \rightleftharpoons Bu_2PSEt + HC{\equiv}C^- \tag{1}$$

$$HC{\equiv}C^- + Bu_2PC{\equiv}CH \rightleftharpoons Bu_2PC{\equiv}C^- + C_2H_2 \tag{2}$$

$$Bu_2PC{\equiv}C^- + Bu_2PSEt \rightleftharpoons Bu_2PC{\equiv}CPBu_2 + EtS^- \tag{3}$$

$$Bu_2PC{\equiv}CH + Bu_2PC{\equiv}C^- \rightleftharpoons Bu_2PC{\equiv}CPBu_2 + HC{\equiv}C^- \tag{4}$$

$$Bu_2PC{\equiv}CH + EtS^- \rightleftharpoons Bu_2PC{\equiv}C^- + EtSH \tag{5}$$

$$EtSH + HC{\equiv}C^- \rightleftharpoons EtS^- + C_2H_2 \tag{6}$$

Reactions (1) and (4) are nucleophilic substitutions on P, the P—C≡ bond is broken, and the carbanion HC≡C:⁻ is the leaving group. Since bis(dibutyl-phosphino)ethyne is insoluble in ammonia, the yield is good. The loss of gaseous acetylene helps push the equilibrium in the same direction. If these equilibria constitute a true picture of the reaction, a catalytic amount of ethanethiolate or sodamide in ammonia should convert dibutylphosphino-ethyne into bis(dibutylphosphino)ethyne. This reaction does give 90% yield in practice.

Reaction (3) is also proven to be reversible: Bis(dibutylphosphino)ethyne reacts with excess sodium acetylide to form dibutylphosphinoethyne. This reaction can also be used in preparative schemes. Bis(dibutylphosphino)ethyne also reacts with phenyllithium in ether to give a good yield of dibutylphosphino-ethyne:

$$Bu_2PC\equiv CPBu_2 + BuLi \longrightarrow Bu_2PC\equiv CH + Bu_2PPh$$

Similar cleavages occur with silicon compounds:[34]

$$Ph_3SiC\equiv CSiPh_3 + PhLi \longrightarrow Ph_3SiC\equiv CH + Ph_4Si$$

Voskuil and Arens[21] utilized reaction (3) to prepare acetylenic phosphines:

$$R'C\equiv C^- + EtXPr_2 \xrightarrow{NH_3} R_2PC\equiv CR' + EtX^- (X = O, S)$$

The necessary $EtXPR_2$ is easily made from R_2PCl and $EtXH$. Another reaction can be used to make the acetylenic phosphines:

$$PCl_3 + EtOH \longrightarrow EtOPCl_2 \xrightarrow{+2RMgCl} EtOPR_2 \xrightarrow{R'C\equiv CH} R'C\equiv CPBu_2$$

This method did not work for $R_2PC\equiv CH$.

2.3. Triethynylphosphine, Arsine and Stibine

Chodkiewicz[32] reacted ethynylmagnesium bromide with PCl_3, but obtained only a black polymer. Voskuil and Arens[22] found they could use this reaction to prepare triethynylphosphine by following certain precautions. The reaction must be conducted at low temperature ($-30°$). The Grignard solution (prepared by Skattebøl's procedure[35]) must be added to the PCl_3. Care is necessary during work-up to avoid explosions. They had one very violent explosion, perhaps catalyzed by some impurities. To avoid explosions, a paraffin oil heel was used during distillations. The once-distilled product could be redistilled at reduced pressure.

Triethynylarsine and triethynylstibine were prepared by the same technique. Isolation was easier, because these products are less volatile. They are volatile enough to be sublimed, and leave no explosive residues. The stibine is hydrolyzed by water, so treatment with water during work-up must be done quickly.

The products are colorless crystalline solids with strong odors, which are probably poisonous; they are volatile and sublime easily, are stable on melting, very explosive upon strong friction and soluble in common organic solvents, solubility decreasing from the phosphine to the stibine.

Water does not hydrolyze triethynylphosphine or arsine, but alkali hydrolyzes them to give acetylene. Water does hydrolyze triethynylstibine. The products are not very sensitive to air. They can be stored under nitrogen and slowly turn brown. One sample of triethynylphosphine became black and exploded spontaneously. Samples can be stored under nitrogen at $-20°$ for months.

Infrared absorption spectra are simple, and the PMR spectrum shows only one signal. The properties of these unusual acetylenic compounds are listed in Table 4-37.

TABLE 4-37
Properties of Triethynylphosphine, Triethynylarsine and Triethynylstibine[22]

Product	% Yield	Constants	IR Absorption (cm^{-1})
$P(C{\equiv}CH)_3$	51.4	b.p. 52°, @ 30 mm Hg	3291, 2054, 1382, 1269, 694 and 640, 711 and 651 (shoulders)
$As(C{\equiv}CH)_3$	62.6	m.p. 49–50°	3291, 2045, 1351, 1290, 681 and 650
$Sb(C{\equiv}CH)_3$	63.1	m.p. 71–72°	3291, 2025, 1358, 1320, 681 and 663

2.4. Tertiary Acetylenic Phosphine Sulfides

Tertiary phosphine sulfides form when excess acetylenic Grignard is refluxed in ether or benzene for several hours with PSX_3 (Table 4-38).[36]

TABLE 4-38
Tertiary Acetylenic Phosphine Sulfides[36]

$$PSX_3 + 3MgBrC{\equiv}CR''' \longrightarrow RR'R''PS$$

R	R'	R''	% Yield	m.p. (°C)
$PhC{\equiv}C$	$PhC{\equiv}C$	$PhC{\equiv}C$	50	138.4–138.8
$MeC{\equiv}C$	$MeC{\equiv}C$	$MeC{\equiv}C$	35	198.2–198.8
Ph[a]	$PhC{\equiv}C$	$PhC{\equiv}C$	85	129.6–130
Ph[a]	$CH_2{=}CHC{\equiv}C$	$CH_2{=}CHC{\equiv}C$	30	67.8–68.4

[a] $PhSCl_2$ + Grignard.

Tri(phenylethynyl)phosphine heated for 5 minutes with $PSCl_3$ gives tri-(phenylethynyl)phosphine sulfide (the first product in Table 4-38).

2.5. Acetylenic Phosphites

Trimethyl phosphite reacts with 1-bromoacetylenes to form acetylenic phosphites:[37]

$$CH_2{=}CHC{\equiv}CBr + P(OMe)_3 \longrightarrow (MeO)_2PC{\equiv}CCH{=}CH_2$$

Sodium dialkylphosphites react similarly:[38,39]

$$(RO)_3P(O)Na + BrC{\equiv}CR' \longrightarrow (RO)_3P(O){-}C{\equiv}CR'$$
$$(35–87\%)$$

If R' contains a hydroxyl group, as in $-CH_2OH$, the products are propargyl phosphites:

$$(RO)_3P(O)Na + BrC\equiv CCH_2OH \longrightarrow (RO)_3P(O)OCH_2C\equiv CH$$
$$(70\%)$$

The 1-acetylenic phosphites hydrate normally:

$$(RO)_3P(O)C\equiv CR' + H_3O^+ \xrightarrow{Hg^{++}} (RO)_3P(O)CH_2\overset{\displaystyle O}{\overset{\displaystyle \|}{C}}R'$$

Tertiary phosphines and 1-bromoacetylenes form phosphonium salts.[39] Phosphines reduce bromoacetylenes to acetylenes if water is present.[28]

3. ACETYLENIC β-PHOSPHINES

Perveev[20] prepared some acetylenic epoxides and reacted them with phosphine:

$$\underset{O}{\overset{\displaystyle Me}{CH_2-\underset{\diagdown\diagup}{C}-C\equiv CMe}} + PH_3 + NaNH_2-NH_3 \xrightarrow[-50°]{2\ days} MeC\equiv C\overset{\displaystyle Me}{\underset{\displaystyle OH}{C}}-CH_2PH_2$$
$$(73\%)$$

These phosphines do not hydrogenate over Raney nickel or platinum. They do not react with p-toluenesulfonyl chloride or phenyl isocyanate.

4. PROPARGYLPHOSPHONATES AND ALLENYLPHOSPHONATES

Propargylphosphonates are made by reacting propargyl alcohol with dialkyl-phosphonium chlorides in triethylamine-ether.[40] These products rearrange to allenylphosphonates on standing at room temperature in ether. Allenylphosphonates isomerize to 1-propynylphosphonates on standing at room temperature without solvent:

$$(RO)_2PCl + HOCH_2C\equiv CH \xrightarrow[ether]{Et_3N} (RO)_2\overset{\displaystyle O}{\overset{\displaystyle \uparrow}{P}}CH_2C\equiv CH \text{ (b.p. 35° at 0.03 mm)} \xrightarrow[15\cdot20\ hr]{ether\ soln.}$$
$$(46\%)$$

$$(RO)_2\overset{\displaystyle O}{\overset{\displaystyle \uparrow}{P}}CH=C=CH_2 \xrightarrow[no\ solvent]{room\ temperature} (RO)_2\overset{\displaystyle O}{\overset{\displaystyle \uparrow}{P}}C\equiv CCH_3$$
$$(60-70\%)$$

where $R = Et$, Pr or i-Pr.

Mixed allenyl-propargylphosphonates have also been prepared:[40]

$$\text{EtPCl}_2 + \text{HOCH}_2\text{C}{\equiv}\text{CH} \longrightarrow \underset{\underset{(53\%)}{\overset{|}{\text{O}-\text{CH}_2\text{C}{\equiv}\text{CH}}}}{\overset{\overset{\text{O}}{\uparrow}}{\text{EtP}-\text{CH}{=}\text{C}{=}\text{CH}_2}} \xrightarrow[\text{3 hrs. 145°}]{\text{dry NaOET}} \underset{\underset{(64\%)}{\overset{|}{\text{OCH}_2\text{C}{\equiv}\text{CH}}}}{\overset{\overset{\text{O}}{\uparrow}}{\text{EtPC}{\equiv}\text{CMe}}}$$

Sodium dimethylphosphonate and propargyl bromide give only the rearranged product $\text{MeC}{\equiv}\text{CP(O)(OMe)}_2$ and none of the expected propargylphosphonate.[41]

5. ACETYLENIC TELLURIUM COMPOUNDS

Acetylenic sulfur and selenium compounds are usually made by elimination reactions (Chapter 3). Olefinic and acetylenic tellurium compounds are prepared by reacting Grignards with 2-naphthyl-tellurenyl iodide:[42]

where R = PhCH=CH— or PhC≡C—.

Acetylenic Grignard reagents and tellurium tetrachloride give a diacetylenic telluride:

$$5\text{PhC}{\equiv}\text{CMgBr} + \text{TeCl}_4 \longrightarrow \text{PhC}{\equiv}\text{C}-\text{Te}-\text{C}{\equiv}\text{CPh} + 4\text{MgBrCl}$$

$$\Big\downarrow +\text{I}_2$$

$$\text{PhC}{\equiv}\text{C}-\text{Te}-\text{C}{\equiv}\text{CPh} \text{ (isolated as diiodide)}$$

$$\text{I}_2$$

References

1. Wolf, V., and Kowiz, F., *Ann. Chem.*, **638**, 33 (1960).
2. Viehe, H. G., *Angew. Chem.*, **75**, 638 (1963).
3. Viehe, H. G., and Reinstein, M., *Angew. Chem.*, **76**, 537 (1964).
4. Montijn, P. P., Harryvan, E., and Brandsma, L., *Rec. Trav. Chim.*, **83**, 1211 (1964).
5. Ficini, J., and Barbara, C., *Bull. Soc. Chim. France*, 2787 (1965).
6. Speziale, A. J., et al., *J. Am. Chem. Soc.*, **82**, 903 (1960); **84**, 1868 (1962).
7. Sladkov, A. M., and Ukhin, L. Yu., *Izv. Akad. Nauk SSSR, Ser. Khim.*, 1552 (1964); *Chem. Abstr.*, **64**, 14116 (1966).
8. Wolf, V., Block, W., and Piater, H., *Ann. Chem.*, **682**, 112 (1965).
9. Wolf, V., and Piater, H., *Ann. Chem.*, **696**, 90 (1966).

10. Viehe, H. G., et al., *Angew. Chem.*, **76**, 571, 572 (1964).
10a. Viehe, H. G., et al., *Angew. Chem., Intern. Ed.*, **6**, 77 (1967).
11. Union Carbide Corp., *Netherlands Application* 6, 507, 867 (Dec. 20, 1965); *Chem. Abstr.*, **64**, 19773 (1966).
12. van Mourik, A. S., Harryvan, E., and Arens, J. F., *Rec. Trav. Chim.*, **84**, 1344 (1965).
13. de Mahler, E., *Bull. Soc. Chim. France*, **29**, 1071 (1921).
14. Bergmann, E., and Bondi, A., *Chem. Ber.*, **66**, 278 (1933).
15. Hartmann, H., Beermann, C., and Czempik, H., *Z. Anorg. Allgem. Chem.*, **287**, 261 (1956).
16. Hartmann, H., Reiss, W., and Karbstein, B., *Naturwissenschaften*, **46**, 321 (1959).
17. Hartmann, H., *Angew. Chem.*, **73**, 173 (1961).
18. Hartmann, H., and Meixner, A., *Naturwissenschaften*, **50**, 403 (1963).
19. Hartmann, H., and Fratzcher, H., *Naturwissenschaften*, **51**, 213 (1964).
20. Perveev, F. Ya., and Rikhter, K., *Zh. Obshch. Khim.*, **30**, 784 (1960); *Chem. Abstr.*, **55**, 1580 (1961).
21. Voskuil, W., and Arens, J. F., *Rec. Trav. Chim.*, **81**, 993 (1962).
22. *Ibid.*, **83**, 1301 (1964).
23. Cherbuliez, E., et al., *Helv. Chim. Acta*, **48**, 632 (1965).
24. Ionin, B., Petrov, A. A., and Lebedev, L., *Dokl. Akad. Nauk SSSR*, **156**, 1354 (1963).
25. Ionin, B., and Petrov, A. A., *Zh. Obshch. Khim.*, **34**, 1174 (1964).
26. Maretina, I. A., and Petrov, A. A., *Z. Obshch. Khim.*, **34**, 1685 (1964).
27. Viehe, H. G., and Franchimont, E., *Chem. Ber.*, **95**, 319 (1962).
28. Hoffmann, H., and Foerster, H., *Tetrahedron Letters*, **17**, 983 (1964).
29. Sturtz, G., and Charrier, C., *Compt. Rend.*, **261**, 1019 (1965).
30. Charrier, C., Chodkiewicz, W., and Cadiot, P., *Bull. Soc. Chim. France*, 1002 (1966).
31. Charrier, C., et al., *Compt. Rend.*, **258**, 1537 (1964).
32. Chodkiewicz, W., Cadiot, P., and Willemart, A., *Compt. Rend.*, **250**, 866 (1960).
33. Hartmann, H., Beerman, C., and Czempik, H., *Z. Anorg. Allgem. Chem.*, **287**, 261 (1956).
34. Gilman, H., and Aoki, D., *Chem. Ind. (London)*, 1619 (1961).
35. Skatteb⊘l, L., Jones, E. R. H., and Whiting, M. C., *Org. Syn.*, **39**, 56 (1959).
36. Bogolyubov, G. M., and Petrov, A. A., *Zh. Obshch. Khim.*, **35**, 704 (1965); *Chem. Abstr.*, **63**, 4330 (1965).
37. Mashlyakovskii, L. N., and Ionin, B. I., *Zh. Obshch. Khim.*, **35**, 1577 (1965); *Chem. Abstr.*, **63**, 18143 (1965).
38. Sturtz, G., Charrier, C., and Normant, H., *Bull. Soc. Chim. France*, 1707 (1966).
39. Miller, B., in "Topics in Phosphorus Chemistry," Vol. 2, p. 176, New York, Interscience Publishers, 1965.
40. Pudovik, A. N., Aladzheva, I. M., and Yakovenko, L. N., *Zh. Obshch. Khim.*, **35**, 1210 (1965); *Chem. Abstr.*, **63**, 11609 (1965).
41. Gordon, M., and Griffin, C. E., *J. Org. Chem.*, **31**, 333 (1966).
42. Campos, M. deM., and Petragnani, N., *Tetrahedron*, **18**, 521 (1962).

PART SIX

1-Haloacetylenes

Introduction

The 1-haloacetylenes, $-C\equiv C-X$, have no industrial importance and are interesting in the laboratory mainly as examples of positive halogen compounds which undergo some atypical reactions. The 1-bromoacetylenes are most important as one reagent in the Chodkiewicz-Cadiot coupling reaction (see Chapter 6).

1. PREPARATION OF 1-HALOACETYLENES

1.1. Chloroacetylene

$HC\equiv CCl$ boils at $-31°$, is explosive and spontaneously flammable in air, and is highly toxic.[1] The most convenient laboratory synthesis is the reaction of 1,2-dichloroethylene with KOH-water-mercuric cyanide.[2]

1.2. Dichloroacetylene

Dichloroacetylene, $ClC\equiv CCl$, melts at $-65°$ and boils at $29°$ at 743 mm of Hg. It is also spontaneously flammable in air and is toxic.[1] Generally, reactions of dichloroacetylene are carried out with the 1 : 1 complex with diethyl ether. The complex is relatively stable and is not spontaneously flammable at low temperature. At high temperature or in strong light, it trimerizes to hexachlorobenzene and forms 1,2-dichloro-1-ethoxy-1-butene and other products. The known preparative methods are:[3]

(1) Trichloroethylene method: Trichloroethylene and ether vapor are swept over hot KOH in a stream of nitrogen. This is the most convenient laboratory method. It is difficult to remove the ether from the 1 : 1 complex. When Riemschneider[4] did the reaction over KOH at 115–125°, he had several explosions. Pure or low-ether dichloroacetylene explodes with traces of oxygen and spontaneously flashes above 130° to form carbon and chlorine. Most of the ether can be removed in a special apparatus for water washing.

(2) Hypochlorite method: Acetylene is passed into alkaline hypochlorite. This synthesis has doubtful value.[3]

(3) Calcium carbide method: Water vapor and chlorine in nitrogen are passed over calcium carbide. Riemschneider[3] was able to isolate only hexachlorobenzene from this reaction.

(4) Barium trichloroacrylate method: This salt decomposes at 250° to give dichloroacetylene. No other salt which will pyrolyze at lower temperature is known.[3]

When Riemschneider[3] passed moist chlorine over calcium carbide and KOH, he collected a solution of 58% dichloroacetylene in ether. The solution burned spontaneously and filled the laboratory with phosgene. When the head was removed from a steel bomb used for one of the experiments, contact with air caused an explosion which drove the base of the bomb through the floor. Obviously, dichloroacetylene must be handled with extreme caution.

1.3. Fluoroacetylene

In 1959, Middleton[5] reported the first preparation of fluoroacetylene:

$$\begin{array}{c} FC-C=O \\ \parallel \qquad \diagdown \\ \qquad \qquad O \xrightarrow[5-7\ mm]{650°} HC\equiv CF + CO + CO_2 \\ \parallel \qquad \diagup \\ FC-C=O \qquad \qquad (100\%) \end{array}$$

Middleton obtained complete IR and NMR spectra.

Fluoroacetylene is a colorless gas, freezing at $-196°$ to a white solid which melts to a liquid whose boiling point is a little below $-80°$. The liquid is treacherous and sometimes detonates with great force. The gas is not explosive or spontaneously flammable in air. The mercury and silver salts are not shock sensitive. The silver salt detonates when warmed, and the mercury salt decomposes violently without detonation when warmed.

When fluoroacetylene is passed into bromine in carbon tetrachloride, a pyrophoric reaction gives a flash of light as each bubble of fluoroacetylene enters. The product is mostly the tetrabromide.

Viehe[6] prepared fluoroacetylene by two other reactions:

$$BrFC=CFBr + Mg \xrightarrow{THF} HC\equiv CF$$
$$(80\%)$$

$$Br_2FCCHBr_2 + KOH \xrightarrow[reflux]{EtOH} HC\equiv CF + C_2H_2$$
$$(66\%) \qquad (10\%)$$

The infrared spectra and the potential constants of monofluoro-, chloro- and bromoacetylene, and of deuteroacetylene halides have been obtained.[7]

1.4. Bromoacetylene

Bromoacetylene is made by the 1,2-dibromoethylene-KOH-water-mercuric cyanide method.[2]

1.5. Difluoroacetylene

Difluoroacetylene has not been made.

1.6. Other Haloacetylene Compounds

Gladshtein[8] added sulfuryl chloride to acetylene mono-Grignard and obtained 10% yield of $ClC{\equiv}CSO_2Cl$ (b.p. 91° at 10 mm of Hg).

Diethylaminochloroacetylene was made by the reaction:[9]

$$Et_2N\overset{\overset{\displaystyle O}{\|}}{C}CH_2Cl + PCl_5 \xrightarrow[\text{heat}]{\text{inert diluent}} Et_2NC{\equiv}CCl$$

Kloster-Jensen[10] prepared iodocyanoacetylene (m.p. 152°) by reacting cyanoacetylene with iodine in KI. It is only moderately sensitive to air and light. Its dipole moment is 4.59 D.

2. 1-BROMO-SUBSTITUTED ACETYLENES

The 1-bromo-substituted acetylenes are important because they are one reagent in Chodkiewicz-Cadiot coupling (Chapter 6). Eglinton detailed the preparation and coupling reactions involving 1-bromoacetylenes in his extensive review on coupling of acetylenic compounds.[11] Two methods of preparing 1-bromoacetylenes are most widely used in the laboratory:

(1) The hypobromite method is simplest: The acetylenic compound is agitated with a strongly basic hypobromite solution. The 1-bromoacetylene (density greater than one) settles out in a few minutes or hours. The more strongly acidic the acetylenic hydrogen, the faster is the reaction. The order of reactivity is: $RC{\equiv}CC{\equiv}CH > RCH{=}CHC{\equiv}CH$, $RCH(OH)C{\equiv}CH$, $PhC{\equiv}CH \gg RC{\equiv}CH$. Efficient agitation, emulsifiers or co-solvents are used for water-insoluble acetylenes. 1-Bromoacetylenes should not be distilled. They sometimes explode, even when distilled at reduced pressure. They are used crude, after checking the infrared spectrum to make sure the ethynyl hydrogen absorption (around $3300\ cm^{-1}$) is gone. The lower-boiling 1-bromoacetylenes have disagreeable odors, are probably toxic and should be stored in stoppered bottles in a refrigerator.

(2) In the other method, the acetylenic compound is reacted with K_2HgI_4 or with mercuric acetate in butylamine to form $RC{\equiv}CHgC{\equiv}CR$. The crystalline mercury derivative is isolated and added to bromine in carbon tetrachloride. Mercury is precipitated as the bromide.

3. MONO- AND DIHALODIACETYLENES

Sodium alkynylides react with iodine in ammonia to form 1-iodoalkynes.[12] Kloster-Jensen[13] extended this reaction to diacetylenes. He reacted monolithium diacetylide in ether at $-55°$ with chlorine, bromine and iodine. The

TABLE 4-39
Halodiacetylenes[13]

Halodiacetylene	m.p. (°C)	% Yield
Monochloro	−41	25–30
Monobromo	−18	15–18
monoiodo	−30	59
Dichloro	1	
Dibromo	52	
Diodo	*ca.* 100	

reaction requires only two steps and is easy to control. The unstable products were isolated by GLC on "Apiezon" L (Table 4-39). All of the monohalodiacetylenes polymerize at room temperature, even in the dark. The polymers are insoluble. Iododiacetylene detonates on scratching in light. Kept at −80°, the compounds are stable, and numerous preparations have been made without any difficulty.

Other 1-haloacetylenes have been made recently by several methods. These are summarized in Table 4-40.

TABLE 4-40
Other Preparations of 1-Haloacetylenes

Acetylenic Compound	Reagent and Conditions	% Yield	Reference
1-Hexyne	$KOH-Br_2-H_2O, 0°, 18$ hr	72	14
ω-Fluoroalkynes	$NaOBr-H_2O$ or dioxane	67–87	15
$F-(CH_2)_6C\equiv CLi$	*p*-Toluenesulfonyl chloride	42	15
$EtSC\equiv CH$	$KOCl-2N$ KOH	—	16
$R'NHC(RR'')C\equiv CNa$	*p*-Toluenesulfonyl chloride	—	17
⬡O—$C\equiv CMgBr$	I_2-ether	48	18

4. REACTIONS OF 1-HALOACETYLENES

4.1. Cyclizations

Dichloroacetylene trimerizes to hexachlorobenzene,[3] and fluoroacetylene gives 1,2,4-trifluorobenzene.[5] Dichloroacetylene does not undergo a Diels-Alder reaction with cyclopentadiene, hexachloropentadiene or furan.[4] Tars were the only products from these attempted reactions.

4.2. Nucleophilic Displacement of Halogen

The study of halo-alkyne reactivity dates back at least to Nef in 1899. Nef got no reaction between phenyliodoethyne and cyanide, ethoxide or amines.[19] Haloalkynes and organometallic compounds give coupled products (Grignard coupling). Haloalkynes also couple in the Chodkiewicz-Cadiot system. They exchange halogen for metal from alkyllithiums.[20] 1-Phenyl-2-chloroacetylene reacts rapidly with n-butyllithium to give 93% yield of phenylacetylene (after hydrolysis).[20] Viehe[6] reacted fluoroacetylene with n-butyllithium and obtained 1-hexyne. This is an example of direct substitution of halogen by an alkyl.

The halogen in 1-haloalkynes is positive, and thus the 1-haloalkynes are oxidants. In protonic solvents, the reaction used to prepare haloalkynes can be reversed:

$$R'C\equiv CX + ROH \underset{}{\overset{RO^-}{\rightleftharpoons}} R'C\equiv CH + ROX$$

Haloalkynes also disproportionate in basic media:

$$HC\equiv CI \underset{}{\overset{OH^-}{\rightleftharpoons}} {}^-C\equiv CI \xrightarrow{HC\equiv CI} IC\equiv CI + HC\equiv C^-$$

Nucleophilic displacements in benzene and ethylene halogen compounds are well known, but negative reports in the literature show that haloalkynes in general were formerly believed to be inert:[21-23]

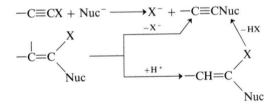

The examples of formation of $-C\equiv CNuc$ in the literature are usually the result of dehydrohalogenation reactions. These reactions are done in the presence of a proton donor, and the substitution becomes uncertain.[24,25]

Miller[28] found that sodium thiolates react with haloalkynes in dimethylformamide by direct substitution to give the acetylenic thioethers. Like other nucleophilic substitutions, this reaction probably involves a carbanion. 1-Phenyl-2-phenylthioethyne formed in 65% yield. 1-Phenyl-2-p-t-butylphenylthioethyne and 1-phenyl-2-pentachlorophenylethyne were also obtained. Similarly, triphenylphosphine reacts with phenylbromoacetylene to form the

phosphonium salt which contains a $-\overset{|}{\underset{|}{P}}-C\equiv C$ bond.

Acetylenic thioethers are usually made from aldehydes, 1-alkynes or polyhaloalkenes in about four steps.[27] In an improved synthesis which starts with haloacetylenes, only two steps are required.[25] Ziegler[19] developed this two-step synthesis based on the nucleophilic displacement reaction of 1-haloalkynes:

$$RC\equiv CH + X_2 + NaOH \longrightarrow RC\equiv CX \xrightarrow[\text{DMF}]{R'S^-} RC\equiv CSR'$$

The displacement reaction is usually fast even below 0°, and aprotic dimethyl-formamide is a key factor. Dimethyl sulfoxide is more aprotic and might be better. Both alkyl- and arylthiolates react. Pentachlorophenylthiolate reacts more slowly than other thiolates, indicating that reactivity may depend on base strength. Ziegler[19] reacted various thiolates with several 1-bromo- and 1-chloroacetylenes, and obtained 30–70% yields. Bromoacetylene and p-tolyl-thiolate gave bis(p-tolylthio)acetylene:

$$HC\equiv CBr + TS^- \longrightarrow HC\equiv CST \xrightarrow{+TS^-} {}^-C\equiv CST \xrightarrow{+HC\equiv CBr}$$
$$BrC\equiv CST \xrightarrow{+TS^-} TSC\equiv CST$$

Dichloroacetylene and sodium p-toluenethiolate in dimethylformamide gave some p,p'-ditoluenedisulfone. The haloalkyne was probably the oxidizing agent.

In 1-haloacetylenic-3-carbinols, the hydroxyl group can act as a proton donor, and this allows ketonic fission in the reaction with TS⁻:

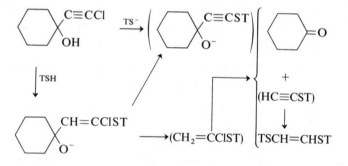

4.3. Discussion of Nucleophilic Substitution at Acetylenic Carbon (or Halogen)

Miller[28] obtained kinetic data for the reaction of phenyl-chloroacetylene with p-toluenethiolate in dimethylformamide. The reaction is first order on halo-acetylene and on thiolate (see also reference 29). The rates are comparable to alkyl halide-thiolate reactions—an unprecedented reactivity for a halo un-saturate.

$$RC\equiv CX + R'S^- \longrightarrow R\bar{C}=C\overset{\displaystyle X}{\underset{\displaystyle SR'}{\Big\langle}} \xrightarrow{-X^-} RC\equiv CSR'$$

Miller concluded that this reaction is nucleophilic substitution at the acetylenic carbon.

Arens[30] examined this, and other, reactions and concluded that the reactions of haloacetylenes with nucleophiles may just as well be substitutions at *halogen* rather than at *carbon*. Dichloroacetylene reacts with alcoholic KOH to give chloroacetylene and KOCl, and the reaction of hypochlorites with acetylene is the reverse. These reactions, and the reaction of alkali metal acetylides with arylsulfonyl chlorides, can also be nucleophilic substitutions at halogen:

$$ClC{\equiv}CCl + OH^- \rightleftharpoons ClC{\equiv}C^- + HOCl$$

$$ClC{\equiv}C^- + H_2O \rightleftharpoons ClC{\equiv}CH + OH^-$$

$$RC{\equiv}C^- + ArSO_2Cl \longrightarrow RC{\equiv}CCl + ArSO_2^+$$

$$RC{\equiv}C^- + BrCN \longrightarrow RC{\equiv}CBr + CN^-$$

Dehydrohalogenation of highly halogenated ethanes gives acetylene and haloacetylenes. This may be the result of loss of HX and then nucleophilic dehalogenation of the intermediate haloacetylenes:

$$Br_2CHCHBr_2 + KOH \xrightarrow{-2HBr} BrC{\equiv}CBr \xrightarrow{KOH} HC{\equiv}CBr \xrightarrow{KOH} HC{\equiv}CH$$

Grignard reagents and organolithium compounds which can be considered to be carbanions react with haloacetylenes to form the metallo derivatives. The halogen from the haloacetylene becomes attached to the attacking carbanion. A nucleophilic substitution at halogen is reasonable:[30]

$$HC{\equiv}CBr + 2Et^- {}^+MgBr \longrightarrow BrMgC{\equiv}CMgBr + EtBr + C_2H_6$$

$$PhC{\equiv}CCl + Bu^- Li^+ \longrightarrow PhC{\equiv}CLi + n\text{-BuCl}$$

These are special cases of the known halogen-metal interconversion which generally is regarded as a nucleophilic substitution at halogen.

Diethyl sodiomalonate and 1-phenyl-2-bromoacetylene react to form phenylacetylene and tetraethyl ethanetetracarboxylate. If the malonate carbanion attacks the acetylenic halogen to give acetylenic anion and diethyl halomalonate, the latter can react with unreacted sodiomalonate to form the tetraester. This is probably nucleophilic substitution at acetylenic halogen.

Truce[21] reacted phenylbromoacetylene and sodium thiophenate in ethanol to form phenylacetylene and diphenyl disulfide. The reaction is explained as follows:[30]

$$PhC{\equiv}CBr + PhS^- \longrightarrow PhC{\equiv}C^- + PhSBr \xrightarrow{PhS^-} Ph_2S_2 + Br^-$$

$$\downarrow +EtOH$$

$$PhC{\equiv}CH + EtO^-$$

When phenyliodoacetylene is heated with morpholine, the product is ω-morpholinostyrene.[31] This is probably another nucleophilic substitution at iodine:[30]

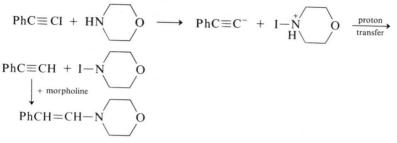

Acetylenic phosphines such as $HC \equiv CPBu_2$ react with EtSNa in ammonia to give insoluble $Bu_2PC \equiv CPBu_2$.[32] This is a nucleophilic substitution at phosphorus:[30]

$$HC \equiv CPR_2 + R'S^- \rightleftharpoons HC \equiv C^- + R'SPR_2$$

$$HC \equiv CPR_2 + HC \equiv C^- \rightleftharpoons {}^-C \equiv CPR_2 + C_2H_2$$

$$R'SPR_2 + {}^-C \equiv CPR_2 \rightleftharpoons RS^- + R_2PC \equiv CPR_2$$

The same general reactions occur when the acetylenic phosphine reacts with a little sodamide. The product is then attacked by its own anion. Alkylseleno-acetylenes behave similarly.

Thus, the reaction of phenylchloroacetylene with p-toluenethiolate anion is probably:[30]

$$PhC \equiv CCl + RS^- \longrightarrow PhC \equiv C^- + RSCl \longrightarrow PhC \equiv CSR + Cl^-$$

The first step is nucleophilic substitution at chlorine, giving a sulfenyl chloride. Sulfenyl chlorides are known to react with carbanions to form sulfides. Some of the sulfenyl chloride can react with thiolate to form disulfide, which also is an alkyl-thiolating agent.[25]

According to Arens,[30] the interpretation of reactions as nucleophilic substitu-tions at atoms other than carbon has received too little attention from organic chemists. This is especially so for reactions of compounds which contain positive halogen. Abstraction of hydrogen atoms can be regarded as nucleophilic substitution at hydrogen. Nucleophilic substitutions at atoms other than carbon are especially likely when stable carbanions can be removed.

5. ACETYLENIC AND ETHYLENIC IODONIUM SALTS

The properties and reactions of diaryliodonium salts are well known.[33,34] Some vinyliodonium salts are also known. Beringer and Galton[33] reacted lithium phenylacetylide with iodosobenzene dichloride and obtained the first reported acetylenic iodonium salt, phenyl(β-phenylethynyl)iodonium chloride (1).

$$PhC\equiv CH + n\text{-}BuLi \xrightarrow[0-5°]{\text{ether, hexane}} PhC\equiv CLi \xrightarrow[0-5°]{PhICl_2}$$

$$PhC\equiv C-\overset{+}{I}-Ph-Cl^- + PhI + PhC\equiv CCl$$

(1)

(12–20%)

Salt (1) decomposes at room temperature after a few hours to form iodobenzene and phenylchloroacetylene. The decomposition is probably a nucleophilic displacement, in one or two steps, by chloride ion on the acetylenic α-carbon, and is one of the few known examples of this reaction:

$$PhC\equiv \underset{\underset{Cl^-}{\uparrow}}{\overset{+}{C}}-I-Ph \longrightarrow PhC\equiv CCl + PhI$$

Salt (1) with aqueous sodium fluoroborate gives a new iodonium salt, phenyl-(α-chlorostyryl)iodonium fluoroborate:

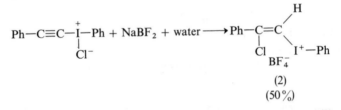

(2)

(50%)

Thus, the acetylenic bond of salt (1) is very susceptible to nucleophilic addition.

The anion of 2-phenyl-1,3-indandione reacts with (1) in refluxing t-butanol (potassium t-butoxide catalyst) to form 2-phenyl-2-phenylethynyl-1,3-indandione, 73% yield:

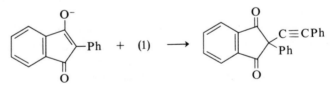

References

1. Hardie, D. W. F., in "Kirk-Othmer Encyclopedia of Chemical Technology," Second ed., Vol. 5, p. 203, New York, Interscience Publishers, 1964.
2. Bashford, L. A., Emeleus, H. J., and Briscoe, H. V. A., *J. Chem. Soc.*, 1358 (1938).
3. Riemschneider, R., and Brendel, K., *Ann. Chem.*, **640**, 5 (1961).
4. *Ibid.*, **640**, 1 (1961).
5. Middleton, W. J., and Sharkey, W. H., *J. Am. Chem. Soc.*, **81**, 803 (1959).
6. Viehe, H. G., and Franchimont, E., *Chem. Ber.*, **95**, 319 (1962).

7. Hunt, G. R., and Wilson, M. K., *J. Chem. Phys.*, **34**, 1301 (1961).
8. Gladshtein, B. M., and Soborobskii, L. Z., *Zh. Obshch. Khim.*, **30**, 1574 (1960); *Chem. Abstr.*, **55**, 1496 (1961).
9. Tsmur, Yu. Yu., U.S.S.R. Patent 166,357 (Nov. 19, 1964); *Chem. Abstr.*, **62**, 10335 (1965).
10. Kloster-Jensen, E., *Chem. Ind. (London)*, 658 (1962).
11. Eglinton, G., and McCrae, W., *Advan. Org. Chem.*, **4**, 225 (1963).
12. Vaughn, T. H., and Nieuwland, J. A., *J. Am. Chem. Soc.*, **55**, 2150 (1933).
13. Kloster-Jensen, E., *Tetrahedron*, **22**, 965 (1966).
14. Schulte, K. E., and Goes, M., *Arch. Pharm.*, **290**, 118 (1957); *Chem. Abstr.*, **51**, 12817 (1957).
15. Pattison, F. L. M., and Dear, R. E. A., *Can. J. Chem.*, **41**, 2600 (1963).
16. Nooi, J. R., and Arens, J. F., *Rec. Trav. Chim.*, **81**, 533 (1962).
17. Easton, N. R., and Ryan, C. W. (to Eli Lily Co.), U.S. Patent 3,172,912 (Mar. 9, 1965); *Chem. Abstr.*, **62**, 14527 (1965).
18. Gouin, L., *Ann. Chim. (Paris)*, **5**, 529 (1960); *Chem. Abstr.*, **55**, 8399 (1961).
19. Ziegler, G. R., *et al.*, *J. Am. Chem. Soc.*, **85**, 1648 (1963).
20. Viehe, H. G., *Chem. Ber.*, **92**, 3064 (1959).
21. Truce, W. E., Hill, H. E., and Boudakian, M. M., *J. Am. Chem. Soc.*, **78**, 2760 (1956).
22. Wolf, V., and Kowiz, F., *Ann. Chem.*, **638**, 33 (1960).
23. Wolf, V., and Block, W., *Ann. Chem.*, **637**, 119 (1960).
24. Boonstra, H. J., and Arens, J. F., *Rec. Trav. Chim.*, **79**, 866 (1960).
25. Nooi, J. R., and Arens, J. F., *Rec. Trav. Chim.*, **80**, 244 (1961).
26. Mironov, V. F., and Gar, T. K., *Izv. Akad. Nauk SSSR, Ser. Khim.*, 291 (1965); *Chem. Abstr.*, **62**, 14715 (1965).
27. Arens, J. F., *Advan. Org. Chem.*, **2**, 117 (1960).
28. Miller, S. I., *et al.*, *J. Am. Chem. Soc.*, **84**, 2020 (1962).
29. Kuriakase, A. K., and Miller, S. I., *Tetrahedron Letters*, 905 (1962).
30. Arens, J. F., *Rec. Trav. Chim.*, **82**, 183 (1963).
31. Southwick, P. L., and Kirchner, J. R., *J. Org. Chem.*, **27**, 3305 (1962).
32. Voskuil, W., and Arens, J. F., *Rec. Trav. Chim.*, **81**, 993 (1962).
33. Beringer, F. M., and Galton, S. A., *J. Org. Chem.*, **30**, 1930 (1965).
34. Beringer, F. M., Dehn, J. W., Jr., and Winicov, M., *J. Am. Chem. Soc.*, **82**, 2948 (1960).
35. Beringer, F. M., Galton, S. A., and Huang, S. J., *J. Am. Chem. Soc.*, **84**, 2819 (1962).

Chapter Five

ETHYNYLATION AND ALKYNYLATION

Introduction

Ethynylation is the addition of acetylene or an acetylene reagent across the double bonded atoms in another molecule to form a different acetylenic compound. Alkynylation is the same reaction starting with an acetylenic hydrocarbon or other substituted acetylene:

$$RC\equiv CY + \overset{\diagdown}{\underset{\diagup}{C}}=Z \longrightarrow RC\equiv C\overset{|}{\underset{|}{C}}ZY$$

Y is usually H, alkali metal, or Mg halogen (Grignard reagent). Z is usually O, but can be $=NH$ or $=CNR'_2$. Reppe first used the word "ethynylation" (*Äthinierung*) to describe the addition of methine hydrogen to carbonyl groups of aldehydes and ketones, or to vinyl-amines, and the elimination of water from methine hydrogen and a reactive hydroxyl group (as in N-methylolamines). Today, ethynylation and alkynylation are general terms which describe addition of metal acetylides, acetylenic Grignard reagents and free acetylenic compounds across unsaturated bonds, usually carbonyl. The terms are sometimes used interchangeably in the literature. Strictly speaking, alkynylation describes the reaction of an alkyne with an unsaturated group, but "alkynylation" is generally used to describe the reaction of any substituted acetylene with the unsaturate.

Ethynylation and alkynylation are discussed here according to the reaction system involved. Reactions are classified as stoichiometric, semicatalytic and catalytic, depending on the quantity of "catalyst" used. The most important reaction systems are acetylene compound-KOH, metal acetylides and alkynylides, Grignard reagents, and cuprous catalysts. Most reactions have been done with monocarbonyl compounds. The ethynylation and alkynylation of dicarbonyl compounds are discussed separately.

Comparison of Ethynylation Systems

Ethynylation on acetophenone by different systems illustrates the point that it is sometimes difficult to predict which ethynylation system will give the best results with a given carbonyl compound (Table 5-1).

TABLE 5-1
Ethynylation of Acetophenone in Different Systems

| Ethynylating Agent | Solvent | Product | | Reference |
		Carbinol (%)	Glycol (%)	
NaC$_2$H	NH$_3$	11	35	11
	Dioxane	90	0	12
LiC$_2$H·ethylenediamine	Dimethylacetamide	75	—	13
C$_2$H$_2$·KOH	Ether	5	19	14
C$_2$H$_2$·KOH (pressure)	Ether	91	—	15
C$_2$H$_2$·KOH (semicatalytic)	Ethylenediamine	57	—	16
C$_2$H$_2$·KOH (semicatalytic; pressure)	Ammonia	58[a]	—	17
Acetylene Grignard reagents	Not reported	—	—	—

[a] Yield on KOH, 463 %.

This chapter is divided into six parts, and pertinent references are appended to each part:
(1) Ethynylation and alkynylation using stoichiometric amounts of base as condensing agent.
(2) Ethynylation and alkynylation by alkali metal acetylides.
(3) Ethynylation and alkynylation by acetylenic Grignard reagents.
(4) Catalytic ethynylation reactions.
(5) Ethynylation and alkynylation of dicarbonyl compounds.
(6) The Mannich reaction with acetylenes.

Books and Reviews

This important branch of acetylene chemistry has been the subject of several recent books and reviews:

Books:

Ziegenbein,[2] 1963, on ethynylation and alkynylation by metal acetylides and acetylenic Grignard reagents.

Johnson,[3] 1946, on the preparation of acetylenic carbinols and glycols.

Raphael,[4] 1955, on the use of acetylenic compounds in organic synthesis, including ethynylation and alkynylation reactions.

Copenhaver and Bigelow,[5] 1949, on propargyl alcohol, butynediol and their derivatives.

Reviews:

Beller and Wilkinson,[6] 1963, include some ethynylations in their review on properties, manufacture, analysis, economics and uses of acetylene.

Dalton,[7] 1963, on butynediol, butenediol and propargyl alcohol.

Leeds,[8] 1963, secondary and tertiary acetylenic and ethylenic glycols.

Ried,[9] 1964, ethynylation and alkynylation of unusual carbonyl compounds.

Ziegenbein,[10] 1963, ethynylation and alkynylation.

PART ONE

Ethynylation and Alkynylation Using Stoichiometric Amounts of Base as Condensing Agent

1. STOICHIOMETRIC KOH ETHYNYLATIONS AND ALKYNYLATIONS

1.1. Atmospheric Pressure

In 1900 Favorskii reported the reaction of aldehydes and ketones with acetylene in the presence of a large amount of solid powdered KOH.[18] Reaction below 5–10° gives mostly ethynylcarbinol, but reaction at 25–35° gives mostly the glycol:

$$RR'C{=}O + C_2H_2 \underset{}{\overset{\text{excess KOH}}{\rightleftarrows}} RR'C(OH)C{\equiv}CH + RR'C(OH)C{\equiv}CC(OH)RR'$$

Various modifications of the Favorskii ethynylation reaction have been reported.[3,19] Major changes have involved solvents: Ethers, acetals and amines give the best results in the atmospheric pressure Favorskii reactions.[20] Sodium hydroxide cannot be used instead of KOH. KOH can be reacted with the carbonyl compound before acetylene is added.[21] Some workers have used highly polar solvents to minimize KOH requirements.[16,22] Others have used catalysts, such as Reppe's heavy metal acetylides.[23] and basic ion exchange resins,[24] or have operated continuously at elevated pressures.[25] The ethynylation reaction is most "catalytic" on KOH if highly polar solvents such as ammonia, dimethyl sulfoxide, N-methylpyrrolidone, ethylenediamine or hexamethylphosphoramide, are used.

No single KOH system is applicable to all kinds of carbonyl compounds. Low conversions, aldolization of base-sensitive carbonyl compounds and isolation problems are complications. Polar solvents boiling at 80–200° tend to form stable hydrogen-bonded complexes with product carbinols, making isolation by distillation difficult in many cases, and impossible in extreme cases. Low-boiling polar solvents such as acetonitrile, dioxane and ethylenediamine frequently azeotrope with the carbinols.

1.2. Stoichiometric KOH Ethynylation under Pressure

Nazarov[15] reacted numerous aldehydes and ketones with acetylene-KOH in ether under pressure. A typical procedure involved stirring 50 grams of powdered KOH, 300 ml of ether and 3 ml of ethanol (to improve yield) at 10° in an autoclave; this mixture was then flushed with nitrogen, and acetylene pressed in to 10 atmospheres. The addition of acetylene and the carbonyl compound was continued for 1–2 hours, and then the mix was stirred for another 1–2 hours. Acetylenic carbinols were the main products. Only traces of the corresponding glycols were formed unless acetylene pressure was lowered to 4–5 atmospheres. The post-addition stirring was necessary to obtain good yields.

Table 5–2 summarizes the results from this study and subsequent work with aryl carbonyl compounds.[26] Nazarov[27] reacted the arylethynylcarbinols with acrylonitrile in the presence of 40% aqueous KOH to form the β-cyanoethyl ethers. β-Cyanoethyl ethers hydrolyzed to amides in the presence of hydrogen peroxide, KOH and acetone.

1.3. Ethynylation of Aldehydes

Aldehydes other than formaldehyde are usually ethynylated by lithium acetylide or sodium acetylide in ammonia. The usual Favorskii conditions cause extensive aldol condensation of most aldehydes, and yields of ethynylcarbinols are low, even when acetals and glycol ethers are used as solvents. KOH presumably forms less basic complexes with these solvents. Nazarov[15] found that the reaction of carbonyls with acetylene-KOH in ether is improved by adding a little alcohol. At 20 atmospheres acetylene pressure, acetaldehyde ethynylates to form 1-butyn-3-ol in 40% yield.

In 1962, Stansbury[30] reported a system which avoids the hazards of operating with acetylene under pressure and gives better yields of secondary carbinols from aldehydes and acetylene. He made a stable, mobile suspension of KOH in a diluent (usually 1,2-dimethoxyethane) by grinding in a cooled "Waring Blendor." He then added additional diluent and ethanol (an essential ingredient), 4 mole % based on KOH. The reaction of acetylene at atmospheric

TABLE 5-2
Ethynylation of Carbonyl Compounds in the Presence of KOH under 8–10 atm C_2H_2 Pressure

Carbonyl Compound	Product	% Yield	b.p. (°C, @ mm Hg)
Isobutyraldehyde	4-Methyl-1-pentyn-3-ol	68	133–134
Crotonaldehyde	2-Hexen-5-yn-4-ol	1.2	57–59, @ 13
MEK	3-Methyl-1-pentyn-3-ol	86	121.5
Diethyl ketone	3-Ethyl-1-pentyn-3-ol	90	137–138
Isopropyl methyl ketone	2,3-Dimethyl-4-pentyn-3-ol	82	133
n-Propyl methyl ketone	3-Methyl-1-hexyn-3-ol	84	138–140
Di-n-propyl ketone	3-Propyl-1-hexyn-3-ol	86	173
Di-isopropyl ketone	3-Isopropyl-4-methyl-1-pentyn-3-ol	86	165
Methyl hexyl ketone	3-Hexyl-1-butyn-3-ol	92	78, @ 5
Methyl nonyl ketone	3-Methyl-1-dodecyn-3-ol	94	127–128, @ 11
Mesityl oxide	3,5-Dimethyl-4-hexen-1-yn-3-ol	11	65–66, @ 17
1,2,5-Trimethyl-piperidone	1,2,5-Trimethyl-4-ethynyl-4-piperidonol	Isomers	110 (m.p.) 177 (m.p.)
2-Methylcyclohexanone	2-Methyl-1-ethynyl-1-cyclohexanol	96	72, @ 8
2,2-Dimethyl-tetrahydro-4-pyrone	2,2-Dimethyl-4-ethynyl-tetrahydro-4-pyranol	82	77, @ 3
cis-2-Oxodecahydronaphthalene	cis-2-Ethynyl-2-hydroxy-decahydronaphthalene	94	92–93, @ 3
trans-2-Oxodecahydronaphthalene	trans-2-Ethynyl-2-hydroxy-decahydronaphthalene	90	98–99, @ 2
Cyclopentanone	1-Ethynyl-1-cyclopentanol		157
5-Hydroxypentanone-2	3-Methyl-1-hexyne-3,6-diol	57	110–113, @ 5
3-Hydroxy-3-methyl-butanone-2	2,3-Dimethyl-4-pentyne-2,3-diol	84	79–80, @ 10
Acetophenone	3-Phenyl-1-butyn-3-ol	91	82–83, @ 4
p-Tolyl methyl ketone	3-p-Tolyl-1-butyn-3-ol	80	103–104, @ 4
p-Methoxyphenyl methyl ketone	3-p-Methoxyphenyl-1-butyn-3-ol	86	108–109, @ 1
p-Chlorophenyl methyl ketone	3-p-Chlorophenyl-1-butyn-3-ol	95	113–114, @ 5
3,4-Dichlorophenyl methyl ketone	3-(3,4-Dichlorophenyl)-1-butyn-3-ol	91	122–123, @ 3
p-Bromophenyl methyl ketone	3-p-Bromophenyl-1-butyn-3-ol	80	120–121, @ 3
Phenyl ethyl ketone	3-Phenyl-1-pentyn-3-ol	85	86–87, @ 2
Diphenyl ketone	Diphenylethynylcarbinol	93.5	125–126, @ 1
Methyl heptenone	3,7-Dimethyl-1-octyn-6-en-3-ol	90[28,29]	

TABLE 5-3
KOH Ethynylation of Aldehydes[30]

Aldehyde	% Yield, Carbinol
Acetaldehyde	51 (81% KOH, reagent grade)
	61 (91.5% KOH, technical grade)
Propionaldehyde	81
Butyraldehyde	82
3-Cyclohexenecarboxaldehyde	92
3,4-Dihydro-2,5-dimethyl-2-formyl-2H-pyran	56
2-Ethyl-2-hexenal	37
Crotonaldehyde	22 (Nazarov's system[15,26] gives 1.2% yield)

pressure in KOH-1,2-dimethoxyethane at 0° gave good yields of secondary ethynylcarbinols (Table 5-3). Methacrolein, phenylacetaldehyde, cinnamaldehyde and 2,4-hexadienal gave only polymers.

Stansbury's method is simple, safe and easy, and therefore is a very useful technique for ethynylating aldehydes and (probably) ketones also

In 1959, Herbertz[14] reinvestigated several reactions reported earlier. Hess[31] had written in 1918 that sodium acetylide in ether at −5° reacted with benzaldehyde to give benzyl benzoate as the sole product. Herbertz changed the procedure and passed acetylene into a suspension of powdered KOH in ether while adding benzaldehyde. He got 22% yield of phenyl*allyl* alcohol (not phenyl*propargyl* alcohol).

1.4. Ethynylation of Ketene

Ketene reacts with acetylene in ether in the presence of KOH at −25° to form methyl vinyl ketone in 5% yield. The first-formed vinyl alcohol

$$(CH_2{=}C{-}C{\equiv}CH)$$ with OH attached, probably rearranges to methyl vinyl ketone.[32]

1.5. Ethynylation of Tropinone

Micovic *et al.*[33] ethynylated tropinone in ether-benzene, using KO-*t*-C$_5$H$_{11}$ as catalyst. He got 13% yield of 3-ethynyltropan-3-ol:

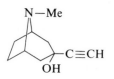

1.6. Tetraarylbutynediols and Their Reduction to Cumulenes

Diaryl ketones react easily with acetylene-KOH in tetrahydrofuran to give 90% yields of carbinols. The methyl or pyranyl ethers of the carbinols react with another mole of diaryl ketone to form unsymmetrical or symmetrical tetraarylbutynediols. Reduction of tetraarylbutynediols by PBr_3 in pyridine, or by $SnCl_2$-H_2SO_4 in ether, gives good yields of tetraaryl-1,2,3-butatrienes, the so-called 3-cumulenes (three cumulative double bonds):[34]

$$ArAr'C(OH)C{\equiv}C(OH)Ar''Ar''' \longrightarrow ArAr'C{=}C{=}C{=}CAr''Ar'''$$

1.7. Liquid Phase Ethynylation System

Nedwick[35] described in detail a special reactor for conducting liquid phase acetylene reactions. In the equipment, acetylene is dissolved in a solvent at low temperature and moderate pressure, and then mixed with other reactants and with catalysts; the resulting solution is passed through a tubular reactor at high enough pressure to keep acetylene in solution. There is no gas phase. The safety advantage is that acetylene gas is not heated under pressure.

Other advantages are higher yields, higher productivity and greater selectivity than in conventional batch operations. The system was used for vinylations and for ethynylation of cyclohexanone. For the ethynylation, methanol (27 weight %) was the solvent, and KOH (1–2 weight %) was the catalyst. The following is a comparison between this procedure and a conventional batch KOH ethynylation:

	Batch	Liquid Full
Temperature, °C	90	135
Time, min	1182	10
% Conversion to carbinol	54	51
% Yield of carbinol	73	72
% Conversion to glycol	11	7.5
% Yield of glycol	15	11
Carbinol production rate, moles/liter/hr	0.08	16.0

The liquid phase process also improves the rate of production of ethyl β-ethoxyacrylate from the base-catalyzed reaction of acetylene with diethyl carbonate.

1.8. Stereochemistry of KOH Ethynylation

Little is known about the stereochemistry of KOH ethynylation. Nazarov[36] observed that both stereoisomers of substituted piperidones react with acetylene and the proportion of stereoisomeric ethynylcarbinols depends mostly on acetylene pressure. Unkovskii[37,38] ethynylated 1,3-dimethyl-4-piperidone with acetylene-KOH in ether at 0°. The product ethynylcarbinol was 88% *cis*-2e,4a epimer; the rest was *trans*. Acetylene entered the reaction axially:

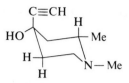

2-Methylcyclohexanone ethynylated non-stereoselectively. The product carbinol was an equal mixture of the *cis* and *trans* isomers.[39]

1.9. Ketone Exchange Reactions

Meister[40] in 1965 reported two interesting reactions. First, he reacted diacetylenic carbinols with ketones to obtain dioxolanes.

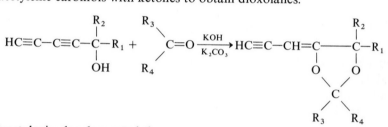

Diacetylenic glycols reacted the same way.

Acetylenic carbinols can be reversibly split by warming in the presence of alkali. Meister's second reaction was a ketone exchange between diacetylenic glycol or diacetylenic dioxolane to form a different compound. This exchange worked well with ketones boiling higher than the one exchanged:

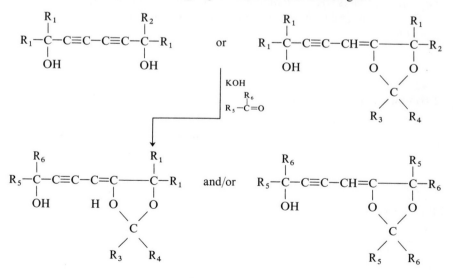

Thus, the diacetylene-ketone reaction is reversible and so is the addition reaction which forms dioxolanes.

1.10. Alkynylations Using Diynes—Skipped Diynes

1,3-Pentadiyne is a component of arc acetylene. Herbertz[14] reported several alkynylations with this potentially important diacetylene:

$$HC\equiv CCH_2C\equiv CH \xrightarrow[\text{(2) acetone, 0°, 8 hr.}]{\text{(1) NaNH}_2\text{-benzene}} Me_2C(OH)C\equiv CCH_2C\equiv CH$$
$$(55\%)$$

$$HC\equiv CCH_2C\equiv CH \xrightarrow[\text{(high temperature for a KOH reaction)}]{\text{KOH-benzene, 80°, acetone}} 70\% \text{ yield}$$

$$HC\equiv CCH_2C\equiv CH \xrightarrow[\text{MEK}]{\text{KOH-benzene}} EtMeC(OH)C\equiv CCH_2C\equiv CH$$
$$(57\%)$$

$$HC\equiv CCH_2C\equiv CH \xrightarrow[\text{isobutyraldehyde}]{\text{KOH-benzene}} i\text{-PrHC(OH)}C\equiv CCH_2C\equiv CH$$
$$(90\%)$$

Pent-1-en-4-yne (allylacetylene) is another component of arc acetylene. It reacted poorly with acetone in the presence of sodamide. 1,3-Hexadiyne is yet another component. It reacted with acetone in the presence of sodium amide to give 70% yield of 2-methyl-3,5-octadiyn-2-ol.[11]

1.10.1. DIACETYLENE

Diacetylene gives much better yields than acetylene in reactions with aldehydes and ketones under Favorskii (KOH-diluent) conditions[41] (Table 5-4). Diacetylene reacts well even at $-70°$. Acetylene usually reacts best around $0°$. Note that temperature plays a large part in determining whether carbinol or glycol forms.

TABLE 5-4
KOH-Diacetylene Alkynylations

Carbonyl Compound	T (°C)	Diluent	Product	% Yield
Acetone	−70	Ether	Carbinol	80
	−30	Ether	Glycol	90
Paraformaldehyde	−70	MeOH	Carbinol	77
	−30	MeOH	Glycol	72
Butyraldehyde	−70	Ether	Carbinol	62
Acetaldehyde	−70	THF	Carbinol	46
Acetophenone	−30	Ether	Glycol	42

1.11. Alkynylations Using Other Acetylenic Hydrocarbons

A few examples illustrating the reactions obtained with other acetylenic hydrocarbons show that alkynylation reactions at atmospheric pressure usually give good yields of carbinols (Table 5-5).

TABLE 5-5
Alkynylation of Monoketones in the Presence of KOH

Acetylenic	Ketone	Solvent	Product	% Yield	Reference
Vinylacetylene	Acetone	Xylene	Carbinol	74	42
Propyne	MEK	Ether	Carbinol	80	14
t-Butylacetylene	Diisopropyl ketone	Ether	Carbinol	75	43
Phenylacetylene	Acetophenone	Ether	No reaction	—	44
	Acetone	Ether	Carbinol	63	44
(PhC≡CLi)	Acetophenone	Ether	Carbinol	72	44
p-Diethynylbenzene	Benzophenone	Amide	p-$(C_6H_4)[C{\equiv}CC$-$(OH)Ph_2]_2$	90	45
4,4'-Diethynyl-diphenylmethane	Acetone	Ether	$CH_2[C_6H_4C{\equiv}CC$-$(OH)Me_2]_2$	80	46

1.12. "Alkynylations" Using Acetylenic Carbinols

In 1956, Robert[47] described KOH condensation of propargyl alcohol and 3-butyn-1-ol with aromatic ketones. Tetrahydrofuran, dimethylacetamide, dimethylformamide and N-methylpyrrolidone are useful solvents. The solubility of the potassium alcoholates in the solvents is:

K Alcoholate	Solvent	Solubility (moles/liter)
Propargyl alcohol	THF	Trace
	DMA	0.16
	NMP	0.18
	DMF	0.3
3-butyn-1-ol	THF	>1
	DMA	>1

When dimethylacetamide or dimethylformamide is used as the solvent, the temperature can be kept lower, because the reaction takes place much faster. The yield of mixed diol is usually 80–90%:

Mixed Diol	% Yield	m.p. (°C)
$Ph_2C(OH)C{\equiv}CCH_2OH$	94	150
$(p\text{-}BrPh)_2C(OH)C{\equiv}CCH_2OH$	88	153
$Ph_2C(OH)C{\equiv}CCH_2CH_2OH$	83	112

Methyl butenynyl ether reacts with acetone in the presence of KOH-MeOH at 60° to form the tertiary alkoxyenynol in 28% yield:[48]

$$HC{\equiv}CCH{=}CHOMe + acetone \longrightarrow Me_2C(OH)C{\equiv}CCH{=}CHOMe$$

The methyl ether of 3-methyl-1-butyn-3-ol reacts with 2-methyl-2-methoxy-3-butanone in the presence of KOH in ether at 15° to give 41% yield of

$$\overset{\displaystyle Me}{\underset{\displaystyle |}{}} \overset{\displaystyle OMe}{\underset{\displaystyle |}{}}$$

$Me_2C(OH)C{\equiv}CC(OH)CMe_2.$[49]

Tedeschi[50] could not make a mixed primary-tertiary glycol by reacting acetone with methylbutynol. Apparently primary acetylenic alcohols react better with ketones than tertiary alcohols do. However, Zakharova[51] stirred methylbutynol, benzophenone and KOH in ether and isolated all three possible acetylenic glycols. This again confirms the reversibility of the ethynylation reaction.

Some other KOH alkynylations using acetylenic alcohols are (see table on page 155).

2. "SEMICATALYTIC" KOH ETHYNYLATION AND ALKYNYLATION

The main disadvantage of the Favorskii KOH ethynylation system for large-scale manufacture of acetylenic carbinols is the requirement of stoichiometric (or larger) amounts of KOH. One way to avoid the added expense of the base is to recover and recycle it. This method has not been reported. An inherently better approach is to find economical systems in which a base can function "semicatalytically" or catalytically to give significantly more than 1 mole of product per mole of base. Some progress has been made in this direction. Certain polar organic solvents, special reactors and the use of ammonia as a solvent are three partial answers to the problems of obtaining catalytic reactions.

2.1. Polar Organic Solvents

Blumenthal[16] found that KOH can be used in semicatalytic amount for the ethynylation of carbonyl compounds in solvents such as sulfoxides and ethylenediamine. He used 0.38–0.5 mole of alkali metal hydroxide or alcoholate and 5.0–6.25 moles of carbonyl compound per liter of solvent. Below 40°,

Acetylenic Compound	Carbonyl Compound	Solvent	Product	% Yield	Reference
3-Butyn-1-ol	Acetone	Ether (5°)	Mixed glycol	46	52
		(20°)	Mixed glycol	76	
Propargyl alcohol	Benzophenone	DMF		94	47
	Acetone	THF		62	53
$\overset{\displaystyle CH_3}{\underset{\displaystyle \vert}{BuOCH}}-O-CH_2C{\equiv}CH$	Acetone	Et_2O	$\overset{\displaystyle CH_3}{\underset{\displaystyle \vert}{BuOCH}}-O-CH_2C{\equiv}C-\overset{\displaystyle OH}{\underset{\displaystyle \vert}{C}}-Me_2$ $\xrightarrow{\text{dilute acid}}$ $HOCH_2C{\equiv}CCMe_2$ $\vert$ OH		55
$Ph_2AsC{\equiv}CH$	$RR'C{=}O$	THF	$Ph_2AsC{\equiv}CC(OH)RR'$	60–87	54

ethynylcarbinol is the major product. At 40–70°, the acetylenic glycol can be the main product. Although NaOH cannot be used in regular Favorskii reactions, it is fairly active in this system (Table 5-6).

TABLE 5-6
Semicatalytic KOH Ethynylations

Carbonyl Compound	Base	Mole % Conversion to Carbinol on:	
		Carbonyl Compound	Base
Acetone	KOH (90%)	71	647
Acetone	NaOH (95%)	47	470
Acetaldehyde	KOH	10	200
Cyclohexanone	KOH	90	450
Methyl ethyl ketone	KOH	66	660
Propionaldehyde	KOH	11	170

Blumenthal also ethynylated acetophenone, isobutyraldehyde, 3-methyl-3-hydroxy-2-butanone, butyraldehyde, acetophenone and paraformaldehyde. Paraformaldehyde gave 40% conversion to propargyl alcohol (240% on KOH) and 9% conversion to butynediol.

2.2. Ammonia as Solvent

2.2.1. SEMICATALYTIC ETHYNYLATION AND ALKYNYLATION

Tedeschi[17] thought that liquid ammonia should be a good solvent for semi-catalytic KOH ethynylation reactions because:

(1) Ammonia boils at −33°, so separation of solvent and products should be simple.

(2) The solubility of acetylene in liquid ammonia from −40° to +30° is fairly constant, and is about 1 mole/mole: This indicates a hydrogen-bond complex between ammonia and acetylene: $HC \equiv CH \leftarrow NH_3$.

Tedeschi did a series of reactions in liquid ammonia under about 200-psig acetylene to check these predictions. Acetone reacted to form 3-methyl-1-butyn-3-ol as the only acetylenic product. Conversions based on KOH were high, and the productivity (grams of carbinol from 500 ml of liquid ammonia) was also high (Table 5-7). These experiments demonstrate some important points:

(1) *Loading:* More than 18 moles of acetone in 500 cc of liquid ammonia decreases the conversion of acetone (and the conversion based on KOH) and is therefore uneconomical.

TABLE 5-7

Semicatalytic Favorskii Ethynylation of Acetone[17]

Acetone (moles/500 ml solvent)	Solvent	% Conversion[a] of Acetone	on KOH	Carbinol (g/500 ml of solvent)
1	Ammonia	95	95	80
12	Ammonia	82	660	830
12 (NaOH)	Ammonia	81	647	815
18	Ammonia	75	902	1138
24	Ammonia	52	835	1050
1	Methylal	90	60	76
18	Methylal	32	388	487
1	Diisopropyl ether	80	53	67
18	Dimethyl sulfoxide	42	497	635[b]

[a] Conversion, mole $\% = \dfrac{\text{moles product}}{\text{moles acetone (or KOH) charged}} \times 100$

[b] Based on analysis[56] since this could not be purified by distillation

(2) *Base:* In the one experiment using NaOH instead of KOH, NaOH gave essentially the same results.

(3) *Solvent:* Liquid ammonia gave the most product per mole of base. Methylal was about one-half as effective. Dimethyl sulfoxide was better than methylal, but could not be separated from the product by distillation.

Reaction of carbonyl compounds with vinylacetylene (VA) and with iso-propenylacetylene (IPA) gave the results shown in Table 5-8.

The enynes were not as reactive as acetylene, but still gave semicatalytic alkynylation (on KOH). The competitive experiment with IPA and acetylene gave 21% conversion of acetone to IPA-derived carbinol, and 60% conversion to the acetylene carbinol.

TABLE 5-8

Semicatalytic Alkynylation Using Enynes in Liquid Ammonia[17]

Carbonyl Compound	Moles Carbonyl	Enyne	Moles Enyne	% Conversion of Carbonyl Compound	on KOH
Acetone	6	VA	6	62	249
Acetone	12	VA	6	54	217
MEK	18	VA	18	46	554
1-Butyraldehyde	6	VA	6	52	209
Acetone	6	IPA	6	69	274
Acetone	12	IPA		21	982
	12	Acetylene	18	60	

Experiments with other carbonyl compounds and acetylene gave variable results (Table 5-9). Reaction times were 2–5 hours, and acetylene pressure was 100–300 psig in most reactions. In all reactions, distillation (15–20 plate column) gave 93–99% pure carbinols. The only aldehyde tried which did not work was formaldehyde.

Potassium acetylide, prepared *in situ*, was only half as effective as KOH under the same conditions. Potassium acetylide probably is not the active

TABLE 5-9
Semicatalytic Ethynylation of Carbonyl Compounds in Liquid Ammonia[17]

Carbonyl Compound	Moles per 500 ml of Ammonia	% Conversion of Carbonyl	on KOH
Acetone	18	75	900
MEK	18	67	800
Diethyl ketone	6	66	264
Methyl isobutyl ketone	17	47	524
Acetophenone	12	58	463
Acetaldehyde	6	31	178
Propionaldehyde	5	46	587
Butyraldehyde	6	53	206
Isobutyraldehyde	12	72	615
2-Ethylhexanal	7.3	75	650
Cyclohexanone	18	71	846
Cyclohexanone	10.3	52	1560[a]

[a] Results obtained by Nedwick and Watanabe in a liquid–full pressure reactor.[25]

catalyst for ethynylation in the presence of KOH. Only 4% of the acetone ethynylated to carbinol in an experiment in which KOH was left out. The NH_3-C_2H_2 complex is obviously not a highly active ethynylating agent.

2.2.2. REACTION OF ALKALI METAL HYDROXIDES WITH TERTIARY ACETYLENIC CARBINOLS AND GLYCOLS

The Favorskii synthesis of acetylenic carbinols and glycols is reversible.[40,51] The glycol goes to the carbinol and a mole of carbonyl compound, and the carbinol then decomposes to carbonyl compound and acetylene.[3] Glycol decomposes in the presence of base at lower temperature than carbinol does:

$$R_1R_2C{=}O + C_2H_2 \underset{\Delta}{\overset{KOH}{\rightleftharpoons}} R_1R_2\overset{\overset{OH}{|}}{C}{-}C{\equiv}CH \underset{\Delta}{\overset{KOH}{\rightleftharpoons}} R_1R_2\overset{\overset{OH}{|}}{C}{-}C{\equiv}C{-}\overset{\overset{OH}{|}}{C}{-}R_1R_2$$
$$+$$
$$R_1R_2C{=}O$$

Tedeschi[50] was the first to react pure alkali metal hydroxides with tertiary acetylenic carbinols and glycols and then isolate the products. He found that 3-methyl-1-butyn-3-ol and 2,5-dimethyl-3-hexyne-3,5-diol formed crystalline 1:1 molar adducts. The reaction is fast even at $-30°$, is not very exothermic and goes in 15–30 minutes even at $-50°$ to $-60°$ in liquid ammonia. Some hydroxides formed adducts better than others did:

| | Conversion to Adduct (%) | |
Hydroxide	Methylbutynol	Dimethylhexynediol
Li	0	0
Na	3.5	0
K	100	100
Rb	100	76
Cs	52	72

The KOH adducts are very stable but do not survive prolonged storage. One sample of dry methylbutynol adduct was unchanged in appearance after $2\frac{1}{2}$ years, but analysis could detect no methylbutynol. A solid state reaction slowly occurred to give dimethylhexynediol·KOH + KOH:

$$MB \cdot KOH \rightleftharpoons acetone + acetylene + KOH$$

$$MB \cdot KOH + acetone \rightleftharpoons [Me_2C(OH)C \equiv C - C(OH)Me_2] \cdot KOH$$

When Tedeschi added methylbutynol·KOH to acetone under Favorskii conditions for glycol, he could detect no glycol. This means the solid state reaction was not a simple condensation. He could not form a 1:2 adduct. The solid state reaction was faster at 35–40° in isopropyl ether. Above 60°, the reaction reversed to form acetone, KOH and acetylene.

MB·KOH formed directly by the stoichiometric reaction of acetone, acetylene and powdered KOH in isopropyl ether at 0° (87% conversion).

Tedeschi prepared 1:1 adducts from other tertiary acetylenic carbinols and glycols. Most carbinols reacted rapidly to form heavy, crystalline products.

The characteristic $C \equiv C$ stretching at 4.68–4.76 μ is missing from the infrared spectrum of MB·KOH. There is no strong absorption at 2.96–3.08 μ for $\equiv CH$, and instead of the characteristic $-OH$ absorption of methylbutynol at 3.00–3.07 μ, a broad weak band at about 3.0–4.0 μ appeared. The usual $C-O$ stretching absorption of tertiary acetylenic carbinols and glycols at 8.7 μ is still detected.

The dimethylhexynediol-KOH adduct has infrared absorption similar to the glycol, but the normal $-OH$ band at 3.0 μ is gone. A fairly strong absorption is noted at 4.0 μ, similar to that found in chelated or hydrogen-bonded groups. The usual $C-O$ stretching band is still at 8.7 μ, but the $C \equiv C$ band at 4.7 μ is gone. This is not unexpected since internal triple bonds generally absorb weakly in the infrared.

The absence of acetylene group absorption indicates that KOH interacts with both the cylindrical π-shell of the acetylenic bond and with the hydroxyl group. This confirms the fact that a true complex is formed and not simply an alkoxide with a tightly held water molecule.

2.2.3. MECHANISM OF BASE-CATALYZED ETHYNYLATION IN DONOR SOLVENTS

2.2.3.1. *Evidence.* Favorskii proposed this mechanism:

$$RR'C{=}O + KOH \longrightarrow RR'\underset{\underset{OH}{|}}{C}{-}OK \xrightarrow{HC\equiv CH} RR'\underset{\underset{OH}{|}}{C}{-}C\equiv CH + KOH$$

The base forms a salt with the carbonyl compound.[57] Alkali hydroxide–carbonyl adducts of this sort have never been found in reaction mixtures.[3,58] Acetone or methyl ethyl ketone and equimolar amount of powdered 98–99% KOH in methylal or diisopropyl ether did not form KOH-ketone adducts.[58] Tertiary acetylenic carbinols and glycols react rapidly and nearly quantitatively with KOH and with RbOH to give 1:1 mole adducts.[50] These experiments prove that free base cannot be present in the reaction mixture.

An enolate intermediate is not essential. Benzophenone, which cannot enolize, ethynylates readily. Ketones that can enolize give very low concentrations of enolate, which could not react fast enough to account for the rapid rates of ethynylation.

Bergmann[59] proposed that potassium acetylide forms and that it is the ethynylating reagent. The excess KOH required in the Favorskii ethynylation merely removes the water from contact with the potassium acetylide:

$$KOH + C_2H_2 \rightleftarrows KC\equiv CH + H_2O$$

$$H_2O + KOH \rightleftarrows KOH{\cdot}H_2O$$

$$RR'C{=}O + KC\equiv CH \rightleftarrows RR'C(OK)C\equiv CH$$

Bergmann also proposed the formation of molecular complexes between KOH and solvents such as acetals and glycol dialkyl ethers. He used these to account for reports that the Favorskii synthesis goes best in such solvents.

Tedeschi's[58] results indicate that the mechanism is completely different. In both stoichiometric and semicatalytic ethynylation, the intermediates are probably alkali hydroxide-acetylene adducts. Formation of these essential adducts is strongly favored by donor solvents which solvate acetylene. Tedeschi's results and arguments can be summarized as follows:

(1) Potassium acetylide formed in liquid ammonia is inferior to KOH in the ethynylation of ketones with acetylene. Thus, metal acetylide *per se* plays at most a very minor part in ethynylations in $KOH-NH_3$. If acetylides were involved, then NaOH would be active in the usual Favorskii reaction, but it is not.

(2) 1:1 KOH-acetylene complexes can be formed (up to 44% conversion) by treating KOH in ammonia with acetylene. The complexes can be dried by pumping at less than 1 mm of Hg at room temperature. They lose all their acetylene at 1 mm and 110° after 4 hours. In contrast, sodium acetylide prepared in dioxane at 65–75° does not change on identical treatment.[60] This is good evidence that the acetylene-alkali hydroxides are complexes, not true acetylides.

(3) The infrared spectrum of the KOH-acetylene adduct in Nujol (or KBr disc) shows that the $C\equiv C$ and $\equiv CH$ stretching bands at 4.68–4.76 μ and 2.96–3.08 μ are gone. Thus, acetylene complexes with the KOH through the π-cylinder electrons and the ethynyl hydrogen. The complex associates strongly with solvents such as ammonia, methylal and isopropyl ether.

(4) The very rapid reaction of acetylenic carbinols, such as 3-methyl-1-butyn-3-ol, with KOH to form 1:1 adducts is similar. The methylbutynol-KOH complex can also be made directly by reaction of acetone and acetylene with KOH. This complex, either freshly made or after several months storage, is very active in the semicatalytic ethynylation of acetone in ammonia. The methylbutynol-KOH adduct forms dimethylhexynediol-KOH adduct slowly on standing, or rapidly when heated. The diol-KOH adduct is also an active catalyst in the semicatalytic liquid ammonia ethynylation reaction, since no glycol is formed in this system. In addition, the carbinol-KOH adduct does not react with acetone in ether solvents to form the glycol.

(5) Sodium hydroxide does not form the adducts with carbinols and glycols. This explains why sodium hydroxide in catalytic or excess amounts is not effective in atmospheric pressure ethynylations in usual organic solvents.[16] However, the adduct of NaOH and methylbutynol forms easily in liquid ammonia and is isolated in 83% conversion as a fluffy white crystalline 1:1 complex. It disproportionates to dimethylhexynediol, acetylene and free base, just as the KOH complex does. The carbinol-NaOH complex does not absorb water from the air. This indicates a chelate or clathrate bonding, and even the free sodium hydroxide cannot adsorb water. Infrared absorption shows that the complex is the same type as the KOH-carbinol complex.

(6) The dried NaOH-methylbutynol complex is a good catalyst in the liquid ammonia semicatalytic ethynylation reaction. So is the methylbutynol-RbOH complex. Lithium hydroxide is not active in this ethynylation system; it does not form a complex with methylbutynol. Lithium acetylide in ammonia is well known as a good ethynylating reagent.

2.2.3.2. *Mechanism of Carbinol Formation.* All of these facts led Tedeschi[58] to conclude that the actual intermediate in ethynylations in donor solvents such as ammonia is a hydrogen-bonded solvent-acetylene complex, which in turn forms an ionized complex with KOH. Tedeschi's mechanism is:

$$C_2H_2 + NH_3 \rightleftarrows H_3N \rightarrow H-C\equiv CH \rightleftarrows \tag{1}$$

$$H_3N \rightarrow H-C\equiv C\cdots H \overset{NH_3}{\rightleftarrows} H_3N \rightarrow H-C\equiv C^- NH_4^+$$
$$\text{(A)}$$

$$KOH + A \rightleftarrows [H_3N \rightarrow H-C\equiv C^-] \cdot KOH \tag{2}$$
$$\text{(B)}$$

$$+ \text{acetone} \updownarrow$$

$$[Me_2-\underset{\underset{O^-}{|}}{C}-C\equiv CH \leftarrow NH_3] \cdot KOH \tag{3}$$

$$+A \updownarrow$$

$$B + Me_2\underset{\underset{O^-}{|}}{C}-C\equiv CH \leftarrow NH_3 \tag{4}$$

$$+ NH_4 \updownarrow$$

$$NH_3 + Me_2\underset{\underset{OH}{|}}{C}-C\equiv CH \leftarrow NH_3 \tag{5}$$

Reaction (3) is practically nonreversible at 25° and becomes significantly reversible only above 60°, where decomposition to acetylene, ketone and KOH is noted. The decomposition can also go through the dimethylhexynediol-KOH complex, which is also an effective ethynylation catalyst.

The catalytic activity of the diol-KOH complex is explained by assuming that the diol complex exchanges with solvated acetylene to form the active KOH-acetylene complex:

$$H_3N \rightarrow H-C\equiv C^- + \text{diol} \cdot KOH \rightleftarrows [NH_3 \rightarrow H-C\equiv C^- \cdot KOH] + \text{diol}$$

Reactions (3), (4) and (5) are the usual catalytic cycle, and the diol becomes inert material. The exchange between diol-KOH and methylbutynol to form free diol and methylbutynol-KOH would be important only after a fair amount of methylbutynol has formed.

2.2.4. MECHANISM OF GLYCOL FORMATION

Glycols are not formed in the semicatalytic ammonia system. The carbinol-KOH-adduct does not react with acetone in ether or liquid ammonia to form glycol. The usual assumption that glycol is formed via carbinol must, therefore, be discarded. The glycols are best made at 30–40° using 10–20% (molar) excess of KOH. The water content of the KOH determines how much excess is required. Acetal or ether solvents are best, and the more reactive ketones give 85–95% conversion to diol. The reaction requires at least 1 mole of KOH, is not catalytic, and cannot be done with NaOH.

If glycol does not form via carbinol, it must be formed by simultaneous bimolecular attack of ketone on the KOH-acetylene complex. Above 30–35°, the carbinol-KOH complex does not form. With less active ketones, however, this reaction does compete, and conversions to carbinol are frequently relatively high (30–35%) under glycol-forming conditions.[58]

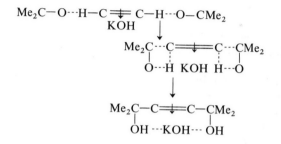

2.3. Semicatalytic Reaction of Diacetylene with Ketones in Aqueous NaOH

Acetone (6.9 moles) and diacetylene (0.5 mole) react in the presence of 0.2 mole of NaOH and 400 ml of water at 55° to form 0.29 mole of dimethyloctadiynediol (1) and 0.185 mole of methylhexadiynol (2).[61] KOH is not as good. Barium hydroxide gives 47% of (1) and 28% of (2), while trisodium phosphate gives 14% of (1) and 53% of (2). Thus, diacetylene alkynylates acetone much more easily than acetylene ethynylates it. Acetylene would not ethynylate acetone under these conditions.

References

1. Copenhaver, J. W., and Bigelow, M. H., "Acetylene and Carbon Monoxide Chemistry," p. 915, New York, Reinhold Publishing Corp., 1949.
2. Ziegenbein, W., "Einführung der Äthinyl- und Alkinyl-Gruppe in organische Verbindungen," Weinheim/Bergstr., Germany, Verlag Chemie, 1963.
3. Johnson, A. W., "Acetylenic Compounds," Vol. 1, "The Acetylenic Alcohols," London, Ed. Arnold Co., 1946.
4. Raphael, R. A., "Acetylenic Compounds in Organic Synthesis." pp. 134–139, London, Butterworths, 1955.
5. Copenhaver, J. W., and Bigelow, M. H., "Acetylene and Carbon Monoxide Chemistry," p. 98, New York, Reinhold Publishing Corp., 1949.
6. Beller, H., and Wilkinson, J. M., Jr., "Kirk-Othmer Encyclopedia of Chemical Technology," Second ed., Vol. 1, p. 171, New York, Interscience Publishers, 1963.

7. Dalton, P. B., *et al.*, "Kirk-Othmer Encyclopedia of Chemical Technology, Second ed., Vol. 1, p. 598, New York, Interscience Publishers, 1963.
8. Leeds, M. W., *et al.*, "Kirk-Othmer Encyclopedia of Chemical Technology, Second ed., Vol. 1, p. 598, New York, Interscience Publishers, 1963.
9. Ried, W., *Angew. Chem.*, **76**, 933, 973 (1964).
10. Ziegenbein, W., Hüls A.G.-Chem. Werke, *Ger. Nachr. Chem. Techn.*, **1963**(79), 1–187; *Chem. Abstr.*, **60**, 13105 (1964).
11. Hess, K., and Munderloh, H., *Chem. Ber.*, **51**, 377 (1918).
12. Rutledge, T. F. (to Air Reduction Co.), U.S. Patent 2,910,510 (Oct. 27, 1959); *Chem. Abstr.*, **54**, 4499 (1960).
13. Beumel, O. F., Jr., and Harris, R. F., *J. Org. Chem.*, **29**, 1872 (1964).
14. Herbertz, T., *Chem. Ber.*, **92**, 541 (1959).
15. Nazarov, I. N., Kotlyarevskii, I. L., and Ryabchenko, V. F., *Izv. Akad. Nauk SSSR, Otd. Khim. Nauk*, 960 (1956); *Chem. Abstr.*, **51**, 5019 (1957).
16. Blumenthal, J. H. (to Air Reduction Co.), U.S. Patent 2,996,552 (Aug. 15, 1961).
17. Tedeschi, R. J., *et al.*, *J. Org. Chem.*, **28**, 1740 (1963).
18. Favorskii, A. E., and Skossarewsky, M., *Russ. J. Phys. Chem. Soc.*, **32**, 652 (1900); *Bull. Soc. Chim.*, **26**, 284 (1901); *J. Gen. Chem. USSR*, **32**, 356, 362 (1902).
19. BASF, A.-G., British Patent 771,708 (Apr. 3, 1957); *Chem. Abstr.*, **51**, 18510 (1957).
20. Chodroff, S., and Dunkel, M. (to Norda Essential Oil and Chem. Co.), U.S. Patent 2,919,281 (Dec. 29, 1959); *Chem. Abstr.*, **54**, 9849 (1960).
21. Zeltner, J., and Genas, M. (to Pechiney-Compaigne), German Patent 862,005 (Jan. 8, 1953); *Chem. Abstr.*, **53**, 2090 (1959).
22. Schachat, N., and Bagnell, J. J., Jr., *J. Org. Chem.*, **27**, 1498 (1962).
23. Reppe, W., *et al.*, *Ann. Chem.*, **596**, 1 (1955); *ibid.*, **601**, 81 (1956).
24. Whitfield, G. H. (to Imperial Chemical Industries, Ltd.), British Patent 735,118 (Aug. 17, 1955); U.S. Patent 2,826,614 (Mar. 11, 1958); *Chem. Abstr.*, **50**, 8721 (1956).
25. Nedwick, J. J., and Watanabe, W. H. (to Rohm and Haas Co.), U.S. Patent 2,973,390 (Feb. 28, 1961); *Chem. Abstr.*, **55**, 17543 (1961).
26. Nazarov, I. N., and Rabchenko, V. F., *Izv. Akad. Nauk SSSR. Otd. Khim. Nauk*, 1370 (1956); *Chem. Abstr.*, **51**, 8046 (1957).
27. Nazarov, I. N., and Shvekhgeimer, G. A., *ibid.*, 1378 (1956); *Chem. Abstr.*, **51**, 8046 (1957).
28. Nazarov, I. N., *et al.*, *Dokl. Akad. Nauk SSSR*, **114**, 796 (1957); *Chem. Abstr.*, **52**, 4481 (1958).
29. Nazarov, I. N., *et al.*, *Dokl. Akad. Nauk SSSR*, **114**, 579 (1958); English translation.
30. Stansbury, H. A., Jr., and Proops, W. R., *J. Org. Chem.*, **27**, 279 (1962).
31. Hess, K., and Munderloh, H., *Chem. Ber.*, **51**, 384 (1918).
32. Svetkin, Yu. V., *Uchenye Zapiski Kishinev. Univ.*, **14**, 71 (1954); *Chem. Abstr.*, **52**, 2745 (1958).
33. Micovic, V. M., Mladenvic, S., and Stefanovic, M., *Glasnik Hem. Drustva, Beograd*, **28**, 285 (1963); *Chem. Abstr.*, **63**, 3007 (1965).
34. Godineau, J., Cadiot, P., and Willemart, A., *Compt. Rend.*, **246**. 2499 (1958).
35. Nedwick, J. J., *Ind. Eng. Chem., Process Design Develop.*, **1**, 137 (1962).
36. Nazarov, I. N., *et al.*, *Zh. Obshch. Khim.*, **29**, 1867 (1959); *Chem. Abstr.*, **54**, 8810 (1960).
37. Unkovskii, B. V., Mokhis, I. A., and Urinovich, E. M., *Zh. Obshch. Khim.*, **33**, 1808 (1963); *Chem. Abstr.*, **59**, 7473 (1963).

38. Unkovskii, B. V., Malina, Yu. F., and Sokolova, T. D., *Zh. Organ. Khim.*, **1**, 699 (1965); *Chem. Abstr.*, **63**, 5594 (1965).
39. Nazarov, I. N., Kamernitskii, A. V., and Akhrem, A. A., *Zh. Obshch. Khim.*, **28**, 1458 (1958); *Chem. Abstr.*, **53**, 1178 (1959).
40. Meister, H., *Chem. Ber.*, **98**, 2862 (1965).
41. Bogdanova, A. V., *et al.*, *Izv. Akad. Nauk SSSR, Ser. Khim.*, 174 (1964); *Chem. Abstr.*, **60**, 9133 (1964).
42. Happel, J., and Marsel, C. J., U.S. Patent 2,922,765 (Jan. 26, 1960); *Chem. Abstr.*, **54**, 10249 (1960).
43. Zakharova, A. I., and Murashov, G. M., *Zh. Obshch. Khim.*, **26**, 3328 (1956); *Chem. Abstr.*, **51**, 8639 (1957).
44. Pittman, C. U., Jr., and Olah, G. A., *J. Am. Chem. Soc.*, **87**, 5632 (1965).
45. Chodkiewicz, W., Cadiot, P., and Willemart, A., *Compt. Rend.* **245**, 206 (1957).
46. Shergina, S. I., *et al.*, *Izv. Akad. Nauk SSSR, Ser. Khim.*, 574 (1965); *Chem. Abstr.*, **63**, 522 (1965).
47. Robert, N., Chodkiewicz, W., and Cadiot, P., *Bull. Soc. Chim. France*, 1575 (1956).
48. Bogdanova, A. V., Dolgikh, A. N., and Shostakovskii, M. F., *Izv. Akad. Nauk SSSR, Ser. Khim.*, 363 (1965); *Chem. Abstr.*, **62**, 14484 (1965).
49. Sabirov, S. S., Grigina, I. N., and Glazunova, E. M., *Dokl. Akad. Nauk-Tadzh. SSR*, **9**, 19 (1966); *Chem. Abstr.*, **65**, 3730 (1966).
50. Tedeschi, R. J., *et al.*, *J. Org. Chem.*, **28**, 2480 (1963).
51. Zakharova, A. I., *J. Gen. Chem. USSR*, **11**, 939 (1941); *Chem. Abstr.*, **37**, 3556 (1943).
52. Shostakovskii, M. F., *et al.*, *Izv. Akad. Nauk SSSR, Ser. Khim.*, 709 (1965); *Chem. Abstr.*, **63**, 2889 (1965).
53. Vlasov, V. M., Vasil'eva, A. A., and Semenova, E. F., *Zh. Organ. Khim.*, **2**, 595 (1966); *Chem. Abstr.*, **65**, 8744 (1966).
54. Benaim, J., *Compt. Rend.*, **261** (group 8), 1996 (1965).
55. Shostakovskii, M. F., *et al.*, *Zh. Organ. Khim.*, **2**, 953 (1966); *Chem. Abstr.*, **65**, 16849 (1966).
56. Barnes, L., Jr., and Molinini, L. J., *Anal. Chem.*, **27**, 1025 (1955).
57. Favorskii, A. E., *J. Russ. Phys. Chem. Soc.*, **37**, 643 (1905).
58. Tedeschi, R. J., *J. Org. Chem.*, **30**, 3045 (1965).
59. Bergmann, E. D., "The Chemistry of Acetylene and Related Compounds," New York, Interscience Publishers, 1948.
60. Rutledge, T. F., *J. Org. Chem.*, **22**, 649 (1957).
61. Franke, W. (to Chemische Werke Hüls A.-G.), German Patent 895,596 (1958); *Chem. Abstr.*, **52**, 7344 (1958).

PART TWO

Ethynylation and Alkynylation by Alkali Metal Acetylides

1. BACKGROUND

In 1897, Matignon reported the first attempts to react disodium acetylide (sodium carbide) with aldehydes and ketones.[1] He wrote that the violent reactions liberated free acetylene. A 1915 German patent[2] claimed the first successful reaction of sodium acetylide and sodium carbide with simple ketones. The patent showed the use of inert solvents for the reaction of sodium acetylide and carbide with acetone, methyl ethyl ketone and diethyl ketone.

The sodium alkynylide or lithium alkynylide method is probably the most widely used ethynylation and alkynylation reaction. For laboratory work, liquid ammonia is the usual solvent. Ammonia has recently been used in processes claimed to have industrial economics. The preparation of alkali metal acetylides and some of their other reactions are described in Chapter 4.

The reactions included here are recent ones selected to illustrate the very broad utility of the alkali metal acetylide ethynylation and alkynylation systems. No attempt is made to list the myriad ethynylation and alkynylation reactions reported in the literature.

2. ETHYNYLATION BY SODIUM ACETYLIDE AND LITHIUM ACETYLIDE IN AMMONIA

2.1. Aldehydes

Jones[3] in 1942 described the reaction of a series of α,β-unsaturated aldehydes with sodium acetylide in ammonia saturated with acetylene. This technique gave good yields of ethynylcarbinols from many aldehydes (Table 5-10).

Note that benzaldehyde reacted normally. In 1906, Klages[4] had reported that benzaldehyde reacted with sodium acetylide in ammonia to give α-phenyl-allyl alcohol and cinnamic acid. In 1959, Herbertz[5] repeated Klages' work, using substantially the same conditions as Jones,[3] and obtained 25% yield of each of the products found by Klages. This discrepancy cannot be easily explained. There may have been subtle differences in the reaction systems which caused the different reactions.

TABLE 5-10
Ethynylation of Aldehydes by Sodium Acetylide in Ammonia

Aldehyde	Carbinol
Crotonaldehyde	60
Acrylaldehyde	35
2-Methylcrotonaldehyde	50
Tiglic aldehyde	75
2-Ethylhex-2-enal	80
Furfural	65
Cinnamaldehyde	2
Benzaldehyde	82.5

2.2. Cyclopropyl Alkyl Ketones

Julia[6] used cyclopropylethynylcarbinols as starting materials for the synthesis of some conjugated trienic acids:

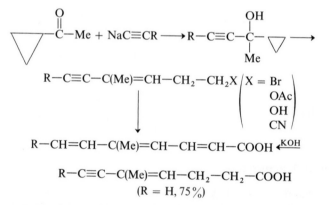

He also used these carbinols, or the diol from cyclopropyl methyl ketone and diacetylene, to prepare hexaenic acids (see structure on page 168).

2.3. Methylheptenone

6-Methyl-5-hepten-2-one reacts with sodium acetylide in ammonia to form the sodioethynylcarbinol which reacts with halogen compounds to give perfume products. Alkylation with MeBr gives the methyl ether, with the odor of bergamot. Semihydrogenation to the octadiene derivative by Pd-CaCO$_3$ (poisoned by lead) also gives a bergamot odor. The ethoxy derivative is like bergamot, the amyloxy derivative is jasmine, as are the alkyloxy and the diene. The propargyl ether is *bois de rose*, and the n-butyl ether is cinnamon.[7]

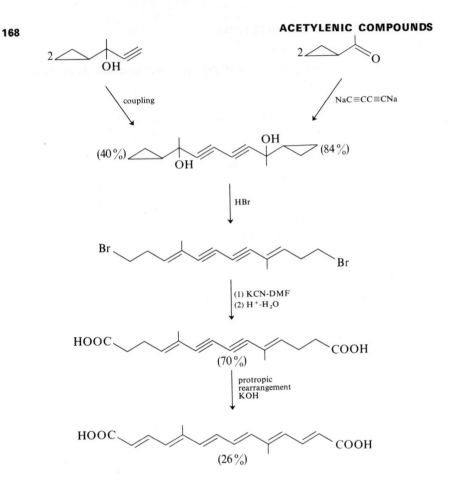

2.4. Terpene Ketones

Keto acid salts and esters can be ethynylated at the carbonyl group.[8]

Sodium acetylide reacts with sodium pinonate (1) in ammonia to give 92 % yield of the ethynylcarbinol (2), which is hydrated by mercuric sulfate-formic acid to the acetyl derivative (3) in 81 % yield. Homoterpenyl methyl ketone reacts with sodium acetylide in ammonia to give 69 % yield of a carbinol.[9]

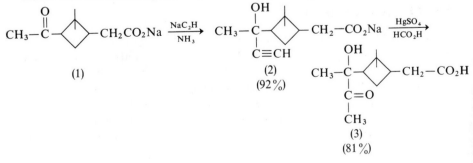

2.5. Bicyclic Terpene Ketones

Görlich[10] ethynylated bicyclic ketones with sodium acetylide in ammonia.

TABLE 5-11
Ethynylation of Bicyclic Terpene Ketones[10]

Ketone	Product	b.p. (°C, @ mm Hg)	% Yield
Norcamphor		195–196	90–93
3-Methylnorcamphor		90–91, @ 15	67
Camphenilan (3,3-dimethylnorcamphor)		78–81, @ 13	40
d-Fenchone		74–76, @ 13	55
d-Camphor		88–90, @ 13	73
π-Bromo-d-camphor		m.p. 81–81.5	43–47

2.6. Pyridyl Ketones

Gautier[11] ethynylated three types of pyridyl ketones to ethynylcarbinols:

(1) $(C_5H_4N)COR$ in which the carbonyl is adjacent to the ring (see also reference 12).

(2) $(C_5H_4N)CH_2COR$ in which carbonyl is separated from the ring by one methylene group.

(3) $(C_5H_4N)(CH_2)_4COR$ in which carbonyl is separated from the ring by four methylene groups.

Examples of ethynylation of type 1 ketones are:

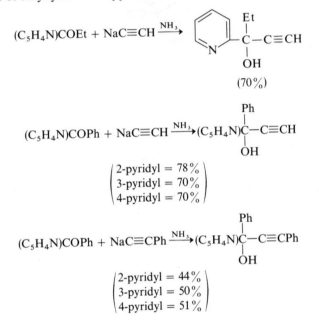

$$(C_5H_4N)COEt + NaC{\equiv}CH \xrightarrow{NH_3}$$

(70%)

$$(C_5H_4N)COPh + NaC{\equiv}CH \xrightarrow{NH_3} (C_5H_4N)\overset{Ph}{\underset{OH}{C}}-C{\equiv}CH$$

$$\begin{pmatrix} 2\text{-pyridyl} = 78\% \\ 3\text{-pyridyl} = 70\% \\ 4\text{-pyridyl} = 70\% \end{pmatrix}$$

$$(C_5H_4N)COPh + NaC{\equiv}CPh \xrightarrow{NH_3} (C_5H_4N)\overset{Ph}{\underset{OH}{C}}-C{\equiv}CPh$$

$$\begin{pmatrix} 2\text{-pyridyl} = 44\% \\ 3\text{-pyridyl} = 50\% \\ 4\text{-pyridyl} = 51\% \end{pmatrix}$$

Type 1 ethynylcarbinols can be made by alternate reactions:

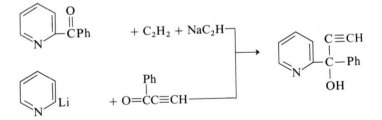

(Note that benzophenone also reacts well with sodium acetylide in ammonia to give 85% yield of carbinol.[13]

The pyridyl acetylenic carbinols might have anomalous properties if hydrogen bonding were strong.

The infrared absorption of the ethynyl group is normal, however.

2.7. Spiroketones

When spiroketones in tetrahydrofuran are added to lithium acetylide in ammonia; the expected carbinols form[14] (Table 5-12).

TABLE 5-12
2-Ethynyl-2-hydroxycyclohexane-1-spiro-2'-
(1',3'-dioxolanes)

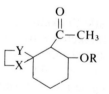

X	Y	m.p. (°C)	Time (hr)	% Yield
O	O	b.p. 95–100	20	25
O	S	68	48	30
S	S	79.5	20	55

The ethynylcarbinols were hydrated to the ketones by refluxing with mer-

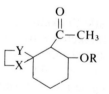

curiacetamide in 95 % ethanol for 6 hours (yields were 12–30 %).

The ethynylcarbinols in collidine were dehydrated by POCl₃ at 120° to form enynes. Dehydration left ring double bonds at different positions:

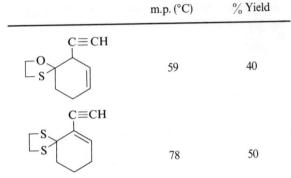

	m.p. (°C)	% Yield
	59	40
	78	50

Treatment of the oxathiolane with mercuric oxide, trichloroacetic acid, boron trifluoride etherate and methanol caused a hydration-addition reaction:

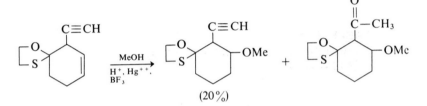

From this, it appears that the products from the mercuriacetamide reaction may form via the enyne dehydration product.

2.8. Benzotropones

Ried and Müller[15,16] ethynylated benzotropones with lithium acetylide in ammonia. Because the charges on benzotropones are delocalized by the aromaticity of the rings, some ring "ethynylation" occurred (see structure on page 173).

2.9. Thioketones

Aliphatic and aliphatic-aromatic thioketones are unstable. Ried and Klug[17] tried to ethynylate aromatic thioketones by means of the reagents which are so useful for other unusual carbonyl compounds. Sodium acetylide and sodium phenylacetylide in ammonia at −35° did not ethynylate or alkynylate thioketones. Instead, an interesting series of episulfides, dithianes and trithianes were formed. The dithianes and trithianes were desulfurized by Raney nickel in benzene to form tetrasubstituted ethylenes in quantitative yield. Preparations of some of the episulfides, cyclobuta-1,3-dithianes and cyclohexa-1,3,5-trithianes are listed in Table 5-13.

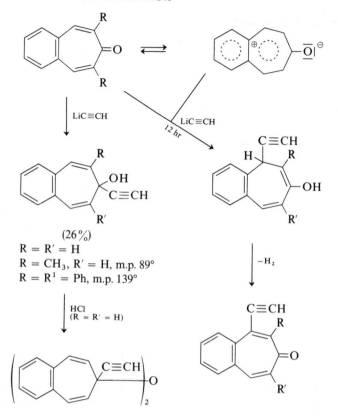

(26%)

R = R' = H
R = CH₃, R' = H, m.p. 89°
R = R¹ = Ph, m.p. 139°

TABLE 5-13
Reaction of Thioketones with Sodium Acetylides in Ammonia

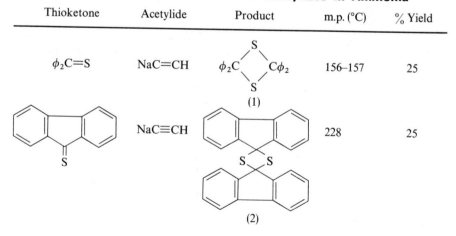

Thioketone	Acetylide	Product	m.p. (°C)	% Yield
$\phi_2C{=}S$	$NaC{\equiv}CH$	(1)	156–157	25
	$NaC{\equiv}CH$	(2)	228	25

TABLE 5-13—(continued)

Thioketone	Acetylide	Product	m.p. (°C)	% Yield

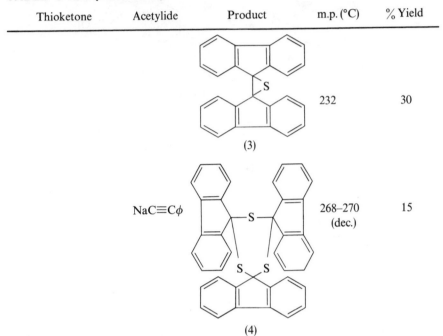

| | | (3) | 232 | 30 |
| | NaC≡Cφ | (4) | 268–270 (dec.) | 15 |

Some of the desulfurization products are shown in the scheme below. Note that the same desulfurized products are obtained from more than one of the sulfides.

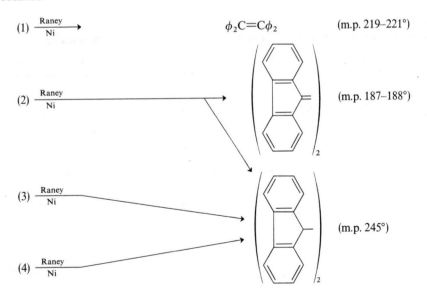

(1) $\xrightarrow[\text{Ni}]{\text{Raney}}$ φ$_2$C=Cφ$_2$ (m.p. 219–221°)

(2) $\xrightarrow[\text{Ni}]{\text{Raney}}$ (m.p. 187–188°)

(3) $\xrightarrow[\text{Ni}]{\text{Raney}}$

                                                                        (m.p. 245°)

(4) $\xrightarrow[\text{Ni}]{\text{Raney}}$

2.10. Stereochemistry of Sodium Acetylide Ethynylations

Hennion[18] ethynylated 4-*t*-butylcyclohexanone with sodium acetylide in ammonia and found that the *trans:cis* ratio in the product ethynylcarbinol was 8:

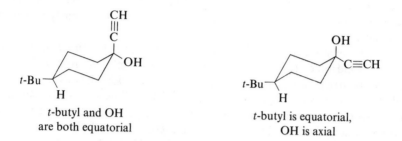

t-butyl and OH
are both equatorial

t-butyl is equatorial,
OH is axial

The *t*-butyl group prefers the equatorial position. Cyclohexyl esters with equatorial ester groups saponify faster than axial esters. The esters of the equatorial *t*-acetylenic carbinols also saponify faster than the axial.

cis-6-Methoxy-1-oxo-Δ^6-octahydronaphthalene and sodium acetylide in ammonia form three isomeric carbinols. The main product is the *cis*- ethynyl-carbinol.[19]

Lithium ethoxyethynylide reacts with 3β-acetoxyandrost-5-en-17-one in a highly stereospecific manner:[20]

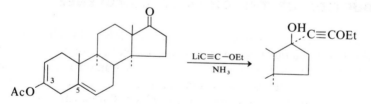

3. SEMICATALYTIC ETHYNYLATION OF ACETONE BY SODIUM ACETYLIDE-ACETYLENE

In 1962, deMalde and co-workers[21] claimed catalytic ethynylation of acetone in liquid ammonia, using metal acetylide catalysts. In one example, 0.0177 mole of sodium metal in 300 ml of liquid ammonia at $-40°$ was treated with acetylene. The temperature was raised to $0°$, acetylene was added to a total pressure of 6.5 atmospheres, and acetone (0.69 mole) was slowly added. After 2 hours more, the yield of methylbutynol was 71% based on acetone. One mole of catalyst made 28 moles of methylbutynol. Cesium was better. With it, the methylbutynol yield was 100%, and each mole of cesium made 79 moles of methylbutynol. Barium was relatively poor.

In 1964, this group[22] described the new Societa Nazionale Metanodotti (SNAM) process for isoprene, starting with methylbutynol. Acetone is cheap and plentiful. Although acetylene is relatively expensive, consumption is near the theoretical 38.5 kg per 100 kg of isoprene, so this is not a serious factor. Furthermore, they felt that new developments in synthetic acetylene promise to bring the price down ultimately to near 5 cents/lb. An advantage of the SNAM process is that the isoprene can be distilled in a simple way to make polymerization grade monomer. SNAM believes its isoprene will be nearly as cheap as butadiene.

The ethynylation apparently is similar to the one described in deMalde's patent.[21] One mole of catalyst makes 50–60 moles of methylbutynol. Conditions need not be strictly anhydrous. At the end of the reaction, the mix is hydrolyzed, and the ammonia is evaporated for reuse. Methylbutynol is distilled as the 74% azeotrope with water and is purified by a further distillation. The methylbutynol is selectively hydrogenated over a colloidal palladium catalyst with "an appropriate support in the presence of a suitable inhibitor." The conversion to methylbutenol is quantitative. The catalyst has a long life because the feed is quite pure. The recyclable catalyst is removed, and the methylbutenol-water azeotrope is passed over commercial high-purity alumina at 260–300° to give fairly pure isoprene. The isoprene is washed with water, and then distilled. Isoprene is polymerization grade, at least 98.5% pure.

4. PREPARATION OF ACETYLENIC DIOLS AND REDUCTION OF THE DIOLS TO CUMULENES

Ried and co-workers[23] prepared a series of alkynediols and studied the reduction of the diols to cumulenes. To prepare the alkynols, a solution of ketone in ether or toluene was added to sodium acetylide in ammonia, and reacted for 6–10 hours. To prepare the alkynediols in ammonia, alkynol in ether was added to sodium amide in ammonia and stirred for 20 hours at −35°.

Some of the alkynols were oxidatively coupled to form alkadiynediols (Chapter 6 discusses coupling in detail):

Alkynol in methanol or dioxane was stirred at room temperature with cuprous chloride. Pyridine, or ammonium chloride plus ammonium hydroxide was added, and oxygen was bubbled through for 2–3 hours (vigorous stirring). The products were extracted with methylene chloride or ether.

Alkadiynediols were also prepared from disodiodiacetylene and ketone:

Dichlorobutyne in ether was added to sodium amide in ammonia. After stirring for an hour at −35°, the solution of disodiodiacetylene was cooled to −70°, and the ketone in ether or toluene was added dropwise over 15 minutes. After another 10 minutes, ammonium chloride was added to neutralize and liberate free diol. The ammonia was evaporated off, and the residues were dissolved in ether. The product precipitated first as ether was evaporated. If much polymer precipitated along with product, treatment with active carbon in hot ether removed the polymer. If excess dichlorobutyne was used, diacetylene-carbinols were the major products.

Diols were reduced to cumulenes by stannous chloride or chromous chloride:

Stannous chloride in concentrated HCl and acetic acid was stirred with diol in dioxane. The yellow or red products formed rapidly and precipitated. In the chromous chloride reduction, chromous acetate was dissolved in HCl-saturated ether and the diol in HCl-saturated ether was added. After $1\frac{1}{2}$ hours during which HCl was introduced, the mixture was hydrolyzed with water. The solid was washed with water, alcohol and ether, and recrystallized.

Suberones, benzophenones, fluorenones, cyclopentanone and cyclohexanone were used in this extensive work. The product from 2,3,6,7-dibenzosuberone was put through the following series of transformations:

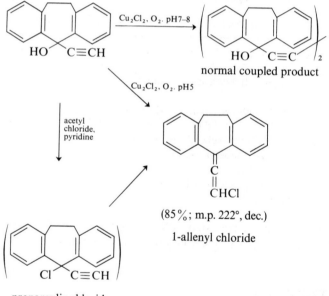

These reactions confirm observations that oxidative coupling is sensitive to pH. Different products can result from relatively small changes in pH (see Chapter 6).

The ethynyl- and diethynylcarbinols prepared by the methods described are listed in Table 5-14.

Alkynediols were prepared from alkynols and carbonyl compounds (Table 5-15).

TABLE 5-14
Preparation of Acetylenic Carbinols[23]

Acetylenic Carbinols	m.p. (°C)	% Yield
4,4'-Dimethylethynylbenzhydrol	87–88	86
4-Chlorophenylethynylbenzhydrol	94–96	70
1-Ethynyl-2,3,6,7-dibenzsuberol-1	72–74	85
1-Ethynyl-2,3,6,7-dibenzsuberenol-1	115–116	75
1-Butadiynyl-2,3,6,7-dibenzsuberol-1	105–115	70 (crude)
1-Butadiynyl-2,3,6,7-dibenzsuberenol-1	125–126 (dec.)	70 (crude)

TABLE 5-15
Alkynediols from Alkynols and Ketones[23]

Alkynediol	m.p. (°C)	% Yield
1,2-Bis[9-hydroxyfluorenyl-(9)]acetylene	238	78
1,1,4,4-Tetraphenylbutyne-2-diol-1,4	194–195	81
1-Phenyl-1-(4-chlorophenyl)-3-(9-hydroxyfluorenyl-9)propyn-2-ol-1	135–136	75
1,1-Bis(4-chlorophenyl)-3-(9-hydroxyfluorenyl-9)propyn-2-ol-1	148–149	76
1,1-Diphenyl-3-(1-hydroxy-2,3,6,7-dibenzsuberyl-1)propyn-2-ol-1	137–139	67
1,2-Bis(1-hydroxy-2,3,6,7-dibenzsuberyl-1)acetylene	Broad	70
1-(1-Hydroxy-2,3,6,7-dibenzsuberyl-1)-2-(9-hydroxyfluorenyl-9)acetylene	237–242	80
1-(1-Hydroxy-2,3,6,7-dibenzsuberenyl-1)-2-(9-hydroxyfluorenyl-9)acetylene	227–229	85

Some butadiynediols are listed in Table 5-16.[23] Table 5-17 lists some hexadiynediols made by reacting ketones with disodium diacetylide.

TABLE 5-16
Butadiynediols (R—C≡C—C≡C—R)

R	m.p. (°C)	Method[a]	% Yield
	136	2	82
	166–167	2	80

TABLE 5-16—(continued)

R	m.p. (°C)	Method[a]	% Yield
	167–168	2	72
	150–151	2	64
	165–167	2	84
	184–186	2	80
	146–148	2	62
	232–235	1 (pH 7–8) 2	85
	249 (dec.)	1 2	73

[a] (1) Coupling.
(2) From disodium diacetylide.

TABLE 5-17
Hexadiynediols from Disodium Diacetylide and Carbonyl Compounds

$$\underset{\substack{| \\ R_1R_2C}}{OH} - C \equiv C - C \equiv C - \underset{\substack{| \\ CR_3R_4}}{OH}$$

R_1	R_2	R_3	R_4	m.p. (°C)	% Yield
$\phi-$	$\phi-$	$\phi-$	$\phi-$	150–151	84
Me$\phi-$	Me$\phi-$	Me$\phi-$	Me$\phi-$	205–206	72
$\phi-$	$\phi-$	4-Cl$\phi-$	4-Cl$\phi-$	161–162	65
$\phi-$	H—	$\phi-$	H—	106–107	80[a]
Et—	Et—	Et—	Et—	119–120	78

[a] According to Armitage[24] (section 5.5), benzaldehyde reacts poorly with disodium diacetylide in ammonia.

The cumulenes prepared by reducing diols are listed in Table 5-18.

TABLE 5-18
Cumulenes

Cumulene	m.p. (°C)	% Yield
	440 (dec.)	60
	298	80
	318–320	60
	222–223	66

Cumulene	m.p. (°C)	% Yield

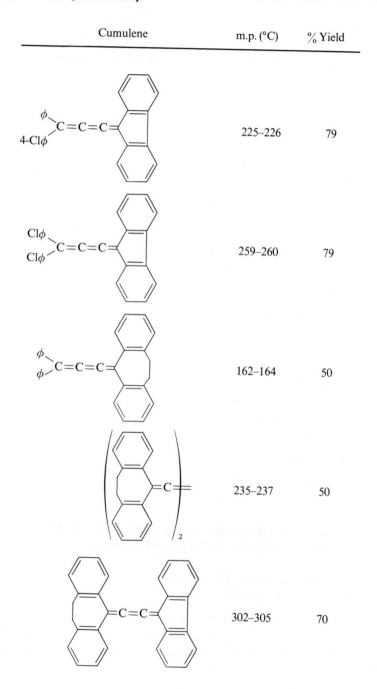

	225–226	79
	259–260	79
	162–164	50
	235–237	50
	302–305	70

TABLE 5-18—(continued)

Cumulene	m.p. (°C)	% Yield
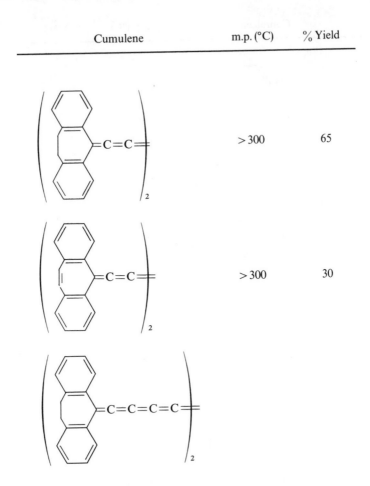	> 300	65
	> 300	30

5. REACTIONS OF SODIUM AND LITHIUM ALKYNYLIDES WITH SIMPLE CARBONYL COMPOUNDS

5.1. Lithium Propynylide (Preparation of Vitamin A Aldehyde)

As the first step in a new synthesis of vitamin A aldehyde, Jacobs[25] reacted lithium propynylide with ketobutyraldehyde dimethyl acetal in tetrahydrofuran. Either propyne or allene reacted with lithium amide to form lithium propynylide.

$$CH_3C\equiv CH$$

or $\quad + LiNH_2 \xrightarrow[\text{NH}_3]{\text{liquid}} CH_3C\equiv CLi$

$$CH_2=C=CH_2$$

$$CH_3C\equiv CLi + CH_3COCH_2CH(OCH_3)_2 \xrightarrow[20-30°]{\text{THF}}$$

$$\begin{array}{c} CH_3 \\ | \\ CH_3C\equiv C-C-CH_2CH(OCH_3)_2 \\ | \\ OH \\ (90\%) \end{array}$$

The hydroxyl group was "protected" by reaction with ethyl vinyl ether, and the product was rearranged in the presence of 3 equivalents of KNH_2 in ammonia:

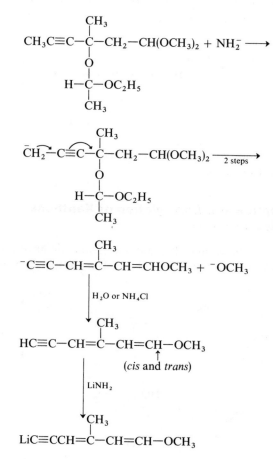

$CH_3C\equiv C-\overset{\overset{\displaystyle CH_3}{|}}{\underset{\underset{\displaystyle H-\overset{\overset{\displaystyle |}{|}}{\underset{\displaystyle CH_3}{C}}-OC_2H_5}{O}}{C}}-CH_2-CH(OCH_3)_2 + NH_2^- \longrightarrow$

$\bar{C}H_2-C\equiv C-\overset{\overset{\displaystyle CH_3}{|}}{\underset{\underset{\displaystyle H-\overset{\overset{\displaystyle |}{|}}{\underset{\displaystyle CH_3}{C}}-OC_2H_5}{O}}{C}}-CH_2-CH(OCH_3)_2 \xrightarrow{\text{2 steps}}$

$^-C\equiv C-CH=\overset{\overset{\displaystyle CH_3}{|}}{C}-CH=CHOCH_3 + ^-OCH_3$

$\downarrow$ H$_2$O or NH$_4$Cl

$HC\equiv C-CH=\overset{\overset{\displaystyle CH_3}{|}}{C}-CH=CH-OCH_3$

(*cis* and *trans*)

$\downarrow$ LiNH$_2$

$LiC\equiv CCH=\overset{\overset{\displaystyle CH_3}{|}}{C}-CH=CH-OCH_3$

Finally, the lithium alkynylide was reacted with β-ionone, semihydrogenated, and hydrolyzed:

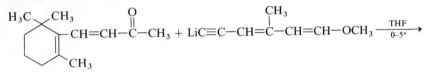

β-ionone

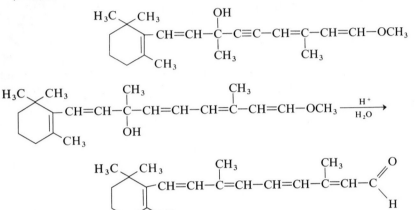

(55–60% yield on β-ionone)

The lithium aluminum hydride reduction is an example of semihydrogenation in a homogeneous system.

5.2. Ethynylation and Alkynylation of Xanthone and Thioxanthones

Xanthone, thioxanthone, and thioxanthone-S-dioxide have been reacted with lithium acetylide and lithium alkynylides.[26] The product (1) from xanthone and

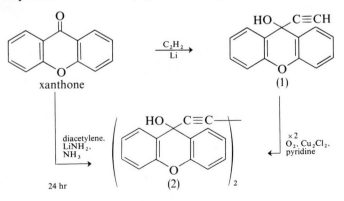

lithium acetylide oxidatively coupled to form the same diacetylenic glycol (2) as obtained from reaction of dilithiodiacetylene.

9-Phenylethynylxanthydrol from lithium phenylacetylide hydrated to the vinyl ketone (3) and formed an explosive perchlorate:

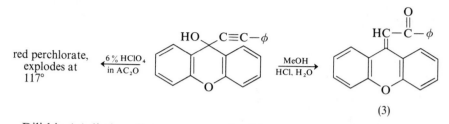

(3)

Dilithio-1,4-diethynylbenzene reacted with xanthone to form (4). (Some reactions of sodio-p-diethynylbenzene with ketones are described in reference 27.)

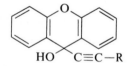

TABLE 5-19
Ethynylation and Alkynylation of Xanthone and Thioxanthones[26]

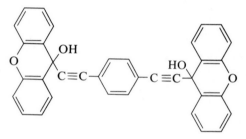

R	Method[a]	Time (hr)	% Yield	m.p. (°C)
—H	1	8	59	67–68
—φ	2	16	55	121–122
	3 (Et₂O)	24	83	122
—CH=CH₂	2	24	44	79–81
$\overset{\text{CH}_3}{\underset{}{-\text{C}=\text{CH}_2}}$	2	24	51	64–65
—CH₂—O—CH₃	2	24	70	83–85
—CH₂—O—φ	2	24	24	146–148
—CH=CH—OCH₃		Polymer		
—CH₂N(CH₃)₂	2	12	51	202–203

TABLE 5-19—(continued)

R	Method[a]	Time (hr)	% Yield	m.p. (°C)
	3 (dioxane)	6	74	202–204
	2	1	78	203–204
—CH$_2$OH	2	12	73	191–192
	2	4	30	136–138

—H	1	8	50	98–99
—ϕ	2	24	34	86–88
	3 (Et$_2$O)	24	40	87–88
—CH$_2$N(CH$_3$)$_2$	2	1	45	189–191

—H	1	24	62	250–252 (dec.)
—ϕ	2	24	40	206–207

[a] (1) Reaction with lithium acetylide in ammonia.
(2) Acetylenic compound was added to lithium amide in ammonia, and then the carbonyl compound was added.
(3) Lithium amide in an organic diluent was refluxed for 2 hr with the acetylenic compound and then the ketone was added.
(4) To lithium amide in N-methylpyrrolidone, first the acetylenic compound, and then the carbonyl compound, were added.

5.3. Reaction of Sodium Vinylacetylide with Hydroxyketones

Sodium vinylacetylide in ammonia reacts with hydroxyketones:

$$CH_2{=}CHC{\equiv}CH + Na \text{ in } NH_3 + Fe(NO_3)_3 + Me_2C(OH)\overset{\displaystyle O}{\overset{\|}{C}}{-}Ph, \xrightarrow[\text{R.T.}]{12 \text{ hr}}$$
$$\text{(trace amount)}$$

$$HOC(Me)_2C{\equiv}C{-}CH{=}CH_2 + Ph\overset{\displaystyle H}{\underset{\displaystyle OH}{C}}{-}C{\equiv}C{-}CH{=}CH_2 \text{ or}$$
$$\text{(small amount)}$$
$$PhCH(OH)CH{=}CH{-}C{\equiv}CH$$

The hydroxyketone apparently disproportionates to acetone and benzaldehyde, which is alkynylated to give the observed products.

In some α-hydroxyketones, however, the carbonyl group ethynylates normally to give acetylenic *vic*-diols.[29]

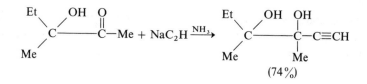

(74%)

5.4. Reaction of Sodium Methoxyvinyl Acetylide with Carbonyl Compounds

Herbertz[30] prepared methoxyvinylacetylene by reacting methanol with diacetylene at 75° for 4 hours (relatively mild conditions for a vinylation). He used this acetylenic compound as a starting material for several syntheses:

(1) Reaction of the sodium methoxyvinylacetylide derivative with acetone: He suspended sodamide in ether, and at 10° added methoxyvinylacetylene and the acetone, stirred for 12 hours at 10° and isolated 84% yield of the carbinol:

$$MeOCH=CH-C{\equiv}C-Na + Me_2C=O \longrightarrow MeO-CH=CH-C{\equiv}C-C(OH)Me_2$$

(2) Reaction with methyl ethyl ketone in the same way at 0° gave 68% yield of carbinol, b.p. 147° at 105 mm of Hg.

(3) Reaction with acetophenone at 0° gave 70% yield of carbinol, b.p. 102° at 37 mm.

(4) Reaction with propionaldehyde at 10° gave 30% yield of carbinol, b.p. 120° at 15 mm.

(5) Reaction with benzaldehyde was unusual. After reaction as above, the product was hydrolyzed to the aldehyde during acidification, and the aldehyde was oxidized to give a 24% yield of acid:

$$PhCH(OH)C{\equiv}CCH_2CHO \xrightarrow{\text{air}} PhCH(OH)C{\equiv}CCH_2CO_2H$$
(m.p. 116.5°, b.p. 102° at 37 mm)

5.5. Preparation and Reactions of Disodium Diacetylide

Armitage detailed a very convenient laboratory technique for preparing products from diacetylene.[24] Four equivalents of sodamide in ammonia reacted with 1,4-dichlorobutyne-2 in just 1 minute to give disodiodiacetylene in quantitative yield. The ammonia solution was used to prepare products according to these equations:

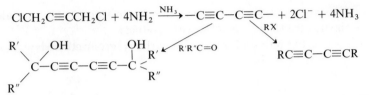

When large batches of the diacetylenic hydrocarbons were distilled at atmospheric pressure or at 100 mm, explosive decompositions occurred. The products are listed in Table 5-20.

TABLE 5-20
Products from Disodiodiacetylene in Ammonia[24]

From	Product Name	% Yield	m.p. (°C)
MeI	2,4-Hexadiyne	65	67
EtI	3,5-Octadiyne	43	b.p. 69°, @ 17 mm
BuBr	5,7-Decadiyne	50	b.p. 83°, @ 0.5 mm
HCHO (*para*)	Hexa-2,4-diyne-1,6-diol	88	112
Acetaldehyde	Octa-3,5-diyne-4,8-diol	71	65–66
Butyraldehyde	Dodeca-5,7-diyne-4,8-diol		b.p. 147, @ 0.5 mm
Benzaldehyde	1,6-Diphenylhexa-2,4-diyne-1,6-diol	7	131–133
Acetone	2,7-Dimethylocta-3,5-diyne-2,7-diol	87	129
MEK	3,8-Dimethyldeca-4,6-diyne-3,8-diol	90	89
Methyl nonyl ketone	10,15-Dimethyltetracosa-11,13-diyne-10,15-diol	36	45–46
Pinacone	2,2,3,8,9,9-Hexamethyldeca-4,6-diyne-3,8-diol	90	248–251
Cyclohexanone	Di(1-hydroxycyclohexyl)butadiyne	83	174
Acetophenone	1,1,6,6-Tetraphenylhexa-2,4-diyne-1,6-diol	48	140–141
Benzylideneacetone	3,8-Dimethyl-1,10-diphenyldeca-1,9-diene-4,6-diyne-3,8-diol	52	Syrup

This synthesis of diacetylenes complements oxidative coupling and is usually better for small-scale work. In some cases, the ethynyl alcohols are hard to prepare, and the diacetylene method becomes even more attractive. Aliphatic ketones react well. Aldehydes require longer time, and the water content of the ammonia is more critical. Aromatic ketones require a long time and react best in a 1:3 mixture of ether and ammonia. The low yield from benzaldehyde is not improved by reaction at $-70°$ or by using lithium or calcium instead of sodium. α,β-Unsaturated aldehydes are not alkynylated: Mesityl oxide gives the ammonia adduct; β-ionone is 84% unreacted after one day. The product from benzylideneacetone is a mixture of the *meso-* and racemic glycols.

Sodium acetylide and disodiodiacetylene do not have the same kind of reactivity. For example, ethylene oxide, propylene oxide and epichlorohydrin react well with sodium acetylide, but not with disodiodiacetylene. Acetophenone reacts better with disodiodiacetylene in ammonia (but see reference 31). Benzaldehyde reacts better with sodium acetylide (see reference 5). Armitage explains the difference: The greater acidity of diacetylene reduces its reactivity as an anion in nucleophilic attacks on relatively inert carbonyls, such as β-ionone but, on the other hand, also decreases its tendency to react with enolizable ketones like acetophenone by proton transfer.

5.6. Alkali Metal Chloroacetylides

Straus and co-workers[32] prepared some chloroethynylcarbinols

$$R_1R_2C(OH)C \equiv C - Cl$$

in 1930. In 1959, Viehe[33] reported the first preparation of lithium, sodium and calcium chloroacetylides, which were used to prepare a series of chloro-acetylenic products. Viehe prepared his chloroacetylides by adding *cis-* or *trans-*1,2-dichloroethylene in ether to metal amide in ammonia at -35 to $70°$. He let the mixture reflux for 15–60 minutes, and then added the other reagent:

$$ClCH = CHCl + 2MNH_2 \longrightarrow MCl + 2NH_3 + MC \equiv C - Cl$$

Lithium amide reacted best, sodium amide reacted well, but calcium amide was less desirable.

Viehe[33] recorded the following infrared absorptions:

Compound	cm^{-1}
NaC≡CCl (in paraffin)	1986
ClC≡CH	2119
NaCN	2083
HCN	2212

Sodium chloroacetylide is a very sensitive, high-brisance explosive. It forms carbon and sodium chloride when it detonates.

The presence of the Cl increases the ionic character of the M—C bond in M—C≡CCl, and makes the chloroacetylide more reactive than sodium acetylide in ammonia:

$$M - C \equiv C - Cl \rightleftarrows M - \bar{C} = C = \overset{+}{C}l$$

The products from reactions of M—C≡CCl are listed in Table 5-21.

TABLE 5-21
Products^a from M—C≡CCl in Ammonia^{33}

Reagent	M	% Yield
Cyclohexanone	Na	86
	Li	72
	Ca	50
Acetone	Na	80
1-Pentanal	Na	62
Propionaldehyde	Li	—
n-Hexanal	Na	50
Crotonaldehyde	Na	45
Ethylene oxide	Na	Low
Br(CH$_2$)$_6$Br	Na	81
Br(CH$_2$)$_4$Br	Na	82.5
Cl(CH$_2$)$_4$Br	Na	49
C$_6$H$_5$SnCl	Na	84

^{a} Products from carbonyl compounds are:

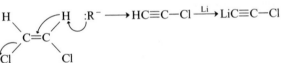

The reaction with ethylene oxide gave: HOCH$_2$CH$_2$C≡C—Cl.
The dihalides gave: ClC≡C(CH$_2$)$_m$C≡C—Cl.
Triphenyltin chloride gave: C$_6$H$_5$SnC≡C—Cl.

Viehe^{34} also developed an alternate synthesis of MC≡CCl. He avoided the problems of liquid ammonia by reacting 1,2-dichloroethylene with 2 moles of butyllithium in ether. This method also avoids the formation of dichloroacetylene:

HC≡C—Cl $\xrightarrow{\text{Li}}$ LiC≡C—Cl

The details of the reaction are:

To 200 cc of 1.89N MeLi in 200 cc of ether, add over a period of 1 hour at 0° 18.5 grams of *trans*-dichloroethylene in 50 cc of ether. Stir for 1½ hours at room temperature, and then add ketone, or other reagent.

The polar character of the Li—C bond in LiR makes it a much stronger proton acceptor than the corresponding covalent Grignard reagent. Thus, when EtMgBr is used instead of LiR and cyclohexanone is added, no chloroethynylcarbinol is formed. With LiC≡CCl in ether, the yield of carbinol is 82%.

All dichloroethylenes are not equivalent. When MeLi was reacted with three different halides at 0° in ether, the amount of chloride ion formed after 5 minutes gave this relative reactivity:

cis-1,2-dichloroethylene > trans-1,2-dichloroethylene > vinylidene chloride
Yield: 76.5%   61%   7.3%

The products prepared in ether are summarized in Table 5-22.

TABLE 5-22
Products from LiC≡CCl in Ether[34]

Reagent	Product	% Yield	b.p. (°C, @ mm Hg)
Cyclohexanone	![cyclohexanol structure] OH, C≡C—Cl	82	
MEK	Et, Me—C—C≡C—Cl, OH	88	86–89, @ 53
Propionaldehyde	H, EtC—C≡C—Cl, OH	79	62–65, @ 12
1-Hexanal	H, $CH_3(CH_2)_4$—C—C≡C—Cl, OH	78	103–106, @ 14
HCHO	$HOCH_2C≡C$—Cl	76	96–98, @ 142
CO_2	$ClC≡CCO_2H$	41	m.p. 68–70
Propionic anhydride	{ O, EtC—C≡C—Cl + , $EtC(C≡CCl)_2$, OH }	—	70–75, @ 101
Naphthyl isocyanate	![naphthyl] H O, —N—C—C≡C—Cl	77	m.p. 158
Ethyl chloroformate	HO—$C(C≡C$—$Cl)_3$	—	90
Diethyl carbonate	Cl—$C≡C$—CO_2Et	—	82.5, @ 95

An interesting reaction was òbserved during this study. When Viehe added 66 grams of trichloroethylene in 5 cc of ether to 1 mole of sodium amide in ammonia, over a period of 75 minutes, and stirred for 1 hour, he obtained a black, unstirrable mass. He isolated 49 grams of high surface area carbon which contained 1.3 % Cl. Thus, trichloroethylene cannot be used instead of dichloroethylene in the MNH_2 system for making $MC≡CCl$.

6. ETHYNYLATION AND ALKYNYLATION IN ORGANIC DILUENTS

6.1. Ethynylation by Sodium Acetylide

Sodium acetylide has been reacted with alkyl aryl ketones in some organic diluents.[31] Sodium acetylide was made in xylene, dried and suspended in the second diluent. Dioxane was the best diluent for preparing arylalkyl acetylenic carbinols. Acetophenone reacted to give 3-phenyl-1-butyn-3-ol in 90% yield. Dioxane has the effect of making the reaction specific to carbinol, but it does not necessarily have the same effect when used as a diluent for ethynylating other types of ketones. Thus, dioxane probably forms a "complex" with the ketone, and probably also with sodium acetylide.

Blumenthal[35] later reported reactions of the same kind with sodium acetylide in dimethyl sulfoxide or thiophene-1-oxide. Acetaldehyde gave 89% yield (based on the acetylide) of 3-butyn-2-ol.

Sodium acetylide prepared from acetylene and sodium naphthalene in tetrahydrofuran reacts well with aldehydes and ketones to give carbinols.[36]

Carbonyl	Carbinol	% Yield
MEK	3-methylpent-1-yn-3-ol	80
Cyclohexanone	Ethynylcyclohexanol	90
Acetaldehyde	But-1-yn-3-ol	50
Propionaldehyde	Pent-1-yn-3-ol	55

6.2. Ethynylation by Lithium Acetylide–Ethylenediamine

Beumel and Harris[37] prepared ethynylcarbinols by reacting a wide variety of carbonyl compounds with ethylenediamine-lithium acetylide complex (see Chapter 4). In low-dielectric solvents such as benzene, the conversion was low mainly because of base-catalyzed enolization.

Base-catalyzed Enolization Constant $(K_{40°} \times 10^7)$		% Yield in Benzene-C_2H_2
Acetophenone	2200	55
Cyclohexanone	100	89
Cycloheptanone	19	96
Diisopropyl ketone	0.6	100

The addition of water gives all the charged carbonyl as ethynylcarbinol or as unchanged carbonyl compound. Two ketones which cannot enolize (fluorenone and benzophenone) showed even more dramatic drop in yield in low-dielectric

TABLE 5-23

Yields of Ethynylcarbinols from Lithium Acetylide–Ethylenediamine[a] and Ketones[37]

Ketone	Benzene[b]		Tetrahydrofuran-Benzene[c]		Tetrahydrofuran[c]		N,N-Dimethyl Acetamide–Benzene[b]		N,N-Dimethyl Acetamide[d]	
	C_2H_2[e]	Ar	C_2H_2[e]	Ar	C_2H_2[e]	Ar	C_2H_2[e]	Ar	C_2H_2[e]	Ar
Cyclopentanone	76	65	88–89[f]	76	82–86[f]	72	81	68	74	16
Cyclohexanone	89	91	98	90	90	84	100	84	89	73
Cycloheptanone		98			100	99		97	98	85
Acetone	62	55	92	69	75–86[f]	74	99	78	75	50
2-Butanone	89	76	99	81	98	83	100	96	87	61
3-Pentanone	94	87	99	96	96	94	100	87	95	66
2-Octanone	96	82	98	90	95	90		100	90	69
3-Octanone	97	91	100	98	97	94	100	92	92	63
Diisopropyl ketone		100		99	100	100				100
2-Cyclohexylcyclohexanone[g]		91		92	64	91				
2-Cyclohexylcyclohexanone		69							79	
Methyl vinyl ketone	27	20	75	61	86–98[f]	75	68	45	41	34
Methyl vinyl ketone		13			53	43				
Isophorone[g]	81	78	87–93[f]	86	58	46	32	11	0	0
Isophorone		74		73	41	44		9	8	0
Mesityl oxide		80		93	97	99		63	25	25
Benzal acetone		99		100	100	100		100	93	79
Dibenzal acetone		97		97		97				95
Acetophenone	55	46	64	53	57–79[f]	57	75–80[f]	60	64	37
Propiophenone	81	73	88	84	80–98[f]	78	76	67	47	37
Benzophenone	47	46		50	62	58	81	71	92–96[f]	77
9-Fluorenone		33		40	42–56[f]	47	77	82	82–90[f]	76
1-Indanone	66	45	74	69	82–83[f]	70	76	41	63	39

[a] 1:1 (volume) mixed solvents.
[b] 35°, 1¾ hr.
[c] 35°, 2¾ hr.
[d] 25°, 1¾ hr.
[e] Presaturated with acetylene; acetylene bubbled in during the reaction.
[f] 10% excess lithium acetylide–ethylenediamine.
[g] 45°, 6 hr.

solvents. This, and the effects noted in high-dielectric solvents, are due to metalation:

$$RR'C(OLi)C\equiv CH + LiC\equiv CH\cdot ethylenediamine \rightleftharpoons$$

$$RR'C(OLi)C\equiv CLi\cdot ethylenediamine + acetylene$$

In an acetylene atmosphere (instead of argon), the yields were higher because the metalation reaction was reversed.

Beumel and Harris[37] conducted enough experiments to show that ethylenediamine-lithium acetylide is an excellent and convenient reagent for laboratory scale ethynylation of ketones (Table 5-23). The yields varied from 50–100%, and generally were greater than 70%, based on the analysis of reaction mixtures. Product isolation was difficult in some cases.

6.3. Reaction of Lithium Alkynylides with Paraformaldehyde

Schaap[38] showed that organolithium compounds in ether react easily with dry paraformaldehyde in refluxing ether to give good yields of primary alcohols. This makes it unnecessary to generate gaseous formaldehyde. Results with acetylenic and allenic compounds show that lithium alkynylides react with formaldehyde better than lithium acetylide does (Table 5-24). Paraformaldehyde is much more reactive than trioxane.

TABLE 5-24
Reaction of Lithium Alkynylides with Formaldehyde[38]

Lithium Derivative of	Product	b.p. (°C, @ mm Hg)	% Yield
$C_4H_9-C\equiv CH$	$C_4H_9-C\equiv C-CH_2OH$	84, @ 16	80
$C_4H_9-CH=CH-C\equiv CH$	$C_4H_9-CH=CH-C\equiv C-CH_2OH$	116, @ 15	75
$C_4H_9-C\equiv C-C\equiv CH$	$C_4H_9-C\equiv C-C\equiv C-CH_2OH$	96, @ 0.22	77
$C_4H_9-CH=C=CH-S-C_2H_5$	$CH_3-CH(CH_2OH)-C\equiv C-S-C_2H_5$	62–63, @ 0.11	75
	$CH_3-CH=C=C(CH_2OH)-S-C_2H_5$ (mixture 3:2)		

6.4. Lithium Chloropropynylides

Methyllithium reacts with propargylic chlorides at ordinary temperature to form allene carbene, but at -20 to $-50°$ in ether, the acetylenic hydrogen is replaced. The lithium alkynylides react normally[39]

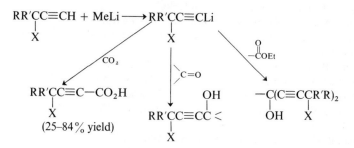

7. COMPLEX ALUMINUM ALKYNYLIDES AS ALKYNYLATING REAGENTS

Zakharkin[40] prepared sodium (or lithium) aluminum alkynylides and found that they had normal alkynylating activity:

$$NaAl(C≡CBu)_4 + EtCHO \xrightarrow[\text{room temperature}]{\text{THF}} BuC≡CCH(OH)Et$$
$$(70\%)$$

$$NaAl(C≡CBu)_4 + \text{crotonaldehyde} \longrightarrow MeCH=CHCH(OH)C≡CBu$$
$$(80\%)$$

$$LiAl(C≡CBu)_4 + PhCHO \longrightarrow BuC≡CCH(OH)Ph$$
$$(70\%)$$

$$NaAl(C≡CPh)_4 + PhCHO \longrightarrow PhC≡CCH(OH)Ph$$
$$(70\%)$$

$$LiAl(C≡CPh)_4 + PhCHO \longrightarrow PhC≡CCH(OH)Ph$$
$$(74\%)$$

Chini, however, noted that $Al(C≡CH)_3$ and acetone gave only a trace of methylbutynol.

References

1. Matignon, C., *Compt. Rend.*, **124**, 775 (1897); *ibid.*, **125**, 1033 (1897).
2. Bayer and Co., German Patent 285,770 (July 9, 1915); *Chem. Zentr.*, 508 (1915).
3. Jones, E. R. H., and McCombie, J. T., *J. Chem. Soc.*, 773 (1942).
4. Klages, A., and Klenk, K., *Chem. Ber.*, **39**, 2553 (1906).
5. Herbertz, T., *Chem. Ber.*, **92**, 541 (1959).
6. Julia, M., and Descoins, C., *Bull. Soc. Chim. France*, 1933 (1962).

7. Colaianni, L. J., and Tanzer, M. L. (to Hoffmann-LaRoche, Inc.), U.S. Patent 2,841,620 (July 1, 1958); *Chem. Abstr.*, **53**, 2090 (1959).
8. Riemer, A. C., and Rigby, W., *J. Chem. Soc. (C)*, 764 (1966).
9. Lewis, J. B., and Hedrick, G. W., *J. Chem. Eng. Data*, **9**, 100 (1964); *Chem. Abstr.*, **60**, 8064 (1964).
10. Görlich, B., and Hildebrandt, G., *Chem. Ber.*, **91**, 2388 (1958).
11. Gautier, J. A., Miocque, M., and Lafontaine, Cl., *Bull. Soc. Chim. France*, 1117 (1960).
12. Dabrowski, Z., and Wrobel, J. T., *Chem. Ind. (London)*, 1758 (1964).
13. Venus-Danilova, E. D., Serkova, V. I., and El'tsov, A. V., *Zh. Obshch. Khim.*, **27**, 334 (1957); *Chem. Abstr.*, **51**, 15467 (1957).
14. Jaeger, R. H., and Smith, H., *J. Chem. Soc.*, 646 (1955).
15. Ried, W., and Müller, H., *Chem. Ber.*, **94**, 1046 (1961).
16. Ried, W., and Müller, H., *Angew. Chem.*, **70**, 271 (1958).
17. Ried, W., and Klug, H., *Chem. Ber.*, **94**, 368 (1961).
18. Hennion, G. F., and O'Shea, F. X., *J. Am. Chem. Soc.*, **80**, 614 (1958).
19. Nazarov, I. N., *et al.*, *Zh. Obshch. Khim.*, **29**, 753 (1959); *Chem. Abstr.*, **54**, 1455 (1960).
20. Weiland, J. H. S., and Arens, J. F., *Rec. Trav. Chim.*, **79**, 1293 (1960).
21. Turner, L., Dolci, M., and deMalde, M. (to Ente Naz. Idrocarburi-E.N.I.), German Patent 1,125,909 (Mar. 22, 1962); *Chem. Abstr.*, **57**, 11020 (1962).
22. deMalde, M., *et al.*, *Hydrocarbon Process. Petrol. Refiner*, **43**, 149 (1964); *Chem. Abstr.*, **61**, 6906 (1964).
23. Ried, W., Schlegelmilch, W., and Piesch, S., *Chem. Ber.*, **96**, 1221 (1963).
24. Armitage, J. B., Jones, E. R. H., and Whiting, M. C., *J. Chem. Soc.*, 44 (1951).
25. Jacobs, H. A. M., *et al.*, *Rec. Trav. Chim.*, **84**, 1113 (1965).
26. Ried, W., and Schonherr, J., *Chem. Ber.*, **93**, 1870 (1960).
27. Jacobsen, G., and Spaethe, H. (to Farbwerke Hoechst A.-G.), German Patent 1,138,760 (Oct. 31, 1962); *Chem. Abstr.*, **58**, 6699 (1963).
28. Antanova, A. A., Venus-Danilova, E. D., *Zh. Obshch. Khim.*, **30**, 3263 (1960); *Chem. Abstr.*, **55**, 25836 (1961).
29. Favorskaya, T. A., Tolstopyatov, C. M., and Gal'ding, M. R.. *Zh. Obshch. Khim.*, **35**, 593 (1965); *Chem. Abstr.*, **63**, 2889 (1965).
30. Herbertz, T., *Chem. Ber.*, **85**, 475 (1952).
31. Rutledge, T. F. (to Air Reduction Co.), U.S. Patent 2,910,510 (Oct. 27, 1959); *Chem. Abstr.*, **54**, 4499 (1960).
32. Strauss, F., Kollek, L., and Heyn, W., *Chem. Ber.*, **63**, 1868 (1930).
33. Viehe, H. G., *Chem. Ber.*, **92**, 1270 (1959).
34. *Ibid.*, **92**, 1950 (1959).
35. Blumenthal, J. H. (to Air Reduction Co.), U.S. Patent 3,028,423 (Apr. 3, 1962); *Chem. Abstr.*, **57**, 8442 (1962).
36. Normant, J. F., and Angelo, B., *Bull. Soc. Chim. France*, 354 (1960).
37. Beumel, O. F., Jr., and Harris, R. F., *J. Org. Chem.*, **29**, 1872 (1964).
38. Schaap, A., Brandsma, L., and Arens, J. F., *Rec. Trav. Chim.*, **84**, 1200 (1965).
39. Battioni, J.-P., and Chodkiewicz, W., *Compt. Rend.*, **263**(C), 761 (1966).
40. Zakharkin, L. I., *et al.*, *Izv. Akad. Nauk SSSR, Otd. Khim. Nauk*, 1146 (1963); *Chem. Abstr.*, **59**, 8772 (1963); *Izv. Akad. Nauk. SSSR, Ser. Khim.*, 180 (1965); *Chem. Abstr.*, **63**, 5665 (1965).
41. Chini, P., *et al.*, *Chim. Ind. (Milan)*, **44**, 1220 (1962); *Chem. Abstr.*, **58**, 13973 (1963).

PART THREE

Ethynylation and Alkynylation by Acetylenic Grignard Reagents

1. BACKGROUND

Iotsitch[1] discovered the reaction of acetylenic Grignard reagents with aldehydes and ketones to form acetylenic carbinols (1906). The reaction is still frequently one of the best laboratory methods employed. Johnson[2] pointed out that Iotsitch was an outstanding pioneer in acetylene chemistry, but his work was not generally known by his contemporaries because he published in the early volumes of *Journal of the Russian Physical and Chemical Society*.

Grignard reagents of monosubstituted acetylenes generally give clean reactions. The Grignard reagent of acetylene is a mixture of acetylene-magnesium halide and acetylenedimagnesium dihalide, so the products are not as clean. Both carbinols and glycols frequently form, and sometimes there are separation problems.

Gaylord[3] in 1951 reviewed the reactions of acetylenic Grignard reagents with ethylene oxide and other oxiranes. He included some reactions of sodio-acetylenes with oxiranes. Yields in the Grignard reaction are usually 30–50%.

2. ACETYLENE MONOGRIGNARD REAGENT

Acetylene reacts with ethylmagnesium bromide in ether to form a dark, dense, viscous layer of acetylenedimagnesium dibromide (acetylene diGrignard). Excess acetylene presumably would give mostly acetylene monoGrignard, but this is a touchy reaction even if acetylene is used under pressure.[4] If dibutyl ether-benzene (1:2) is used as the solvent, the acetylene diGrignard is powdery and easy to stir, and reacts with carbonyl compounds to give ethynylation products which in one case were 85% glycol and 15% carbinol.[5] Acetylene and ethylmagnesium bromide in tetrahydrofuran give a solution of a Grignard which ethynylates ketones to carbinols, and which disproportionates to form acetylene and acetylene diGrignard.[6]

Jacobs[7] quotes examples which show that Grignards can be made to give carbonation and alkylation products which are mainly monosubstituted acetylenes and therefore presumably involved reactions of acetylene mono-Grignard. He also points out that the results should not be taken too literally, because equilibria between products and unreacted monoGrignard can lead to disubstituted products. Further, acetylene diGrignard can be made to give mostly monosubstituted products.[8]

The literature apparently has no reference to an easy and efficient way to make acetylene monoGrignard of known purity. Since acetylene diGrignard is easy to make, and since alkali metal acetylides are also easy to make, the two complement each other: Acetylene diGrignard is useful for making disubstituted acetylenes, and metal acetylides give good yields of monosubstituted acetylenes.

3. ACETYLENE DIGRIGNARD REAGENT

Acetylene diGrignard is frequently less reactive than alkynyl Grignards. The reaction with deoxyanisoin is an example:[9]

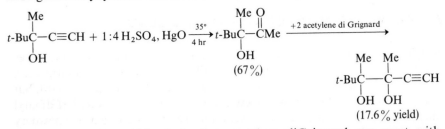

MeO—⟨ ⟩—CH$_2$C(=O)—⟨ ⟩—OMe + Grignard, refluxing ether ⟶ carbinol or glycol

$$\text{acetylene diGrignard} \longrightarrow \text{glycol } (4\% \text{ yield})$$
$$\text{1-hexyne Grignard} \longrightarrow \text{carbinol } (71\% \text{ yield})$$
$$\text{propyne Grignard} \longrightarrow \text{carbinol } (49.5\% \text{ yield})$$

Sodium acetylide and lithium acetylide in ether-ammonia give low yields of carbinol.

Favorskaya[8] carried out a series of reactions, one of which involved acetylene diGrignard ethynylation of a ketone to form an acetylenic carbinol:

$$t\text{-BuC}(\text{Me})(\text{OH})-\text{C}{\equiv}\text{CH} + 1:4\,\text{H}_2\text{SO}_4,\ \text{HgO} \xrightarrow[4\text{ hr}]{35°} t\text{-BuC}(\text{Me})(\text{OH})-\text{CMe}(=\text{O})$$
(67%)

+2 acetylene di Grignard ⟶

$$t\text{-BuC}(\text{Me})(\text{OH})-\text{C}(\text{Me})(\text{OH})-\text{C}{\equiv}\text{CH}$$
(17.6% yield)

Other examples which show that acetylene diGrignard can react with carbonyl compounds to give carbinols are: Crotonaldehyde reacts to form carbinol in 25% yield.[10a] 1,2,3,4-Di-O-isopropylidene-α-D-galactohexadialdo-1,5-pyranose and ethynyl Grignard reagent give 85% yield of carbinol.[11]

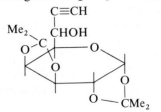

4. ALKYNYL GRIGNARD REAGENTS

An example illustrates the experimental ease of the Grignard alkynylations:
Grimmer[12] prepared 2-alkyn-1-ols by reacting alkyne Grignards with
formaldehyde.

Tetradecyne (0.35 mole) was added slowly to the Grignard from 0.40 mole of magnesium
and 0.43 mole of ethyl bromide in 200 cc of ether. After 2 hours reflux, the mixture was
cooled to −5°, and 0.53 mole of formaldehyde gas (by heating paraformaldehyde) was
carried in by a nitrogen stream over a period of 40 minutes. After standing for several
hours, the mixture was cooled to −30°, hydrolyzed, extracted with ether, and the carbinol
was distilled from the ether extract. The product 2-pentadecyn-1-ol was isolated in 79%
yield.

α-Bromoketones are alkynylated by alkynyl Grignard. Alkylation by reaction
with Br does not occur. The α-bromoalcohols are convenient starting materials
for α-acetylenic epoxides:[12a]

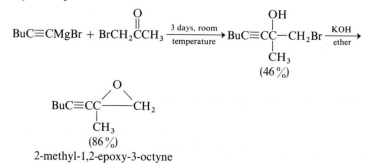

2-methyl-1,2-epoxy-3-octyne

Other examples of alkynylations via Grignards are shown in Table 5-25.
1-Chloro-2-alkylacetylene (RC≡CCl) reacts with magnesium in glycol ether
products or tetrahydrofuran to form alkynyl Grignard reagents, which react

TABLE 5-25
Alkynylation by Alkynyl Grignard Reagents

Alkyne	Carbonyl Reagent	Product	% Yield	Reference
Propyne	Ethylene oxide	Carbinol	—	13
1-Butyne	Formaldehyde	Carbinol	—	14
Isopropylacetylene	ClCH₂CH₂CHO	Carbinol	40	15
n-Butylacetylene	MeC(CH₂)₂CO₂Et (with C=O)	BuC≡CC=CHCH₂CO₂Et (with Me)	10	16
t-Butylacetylene	PhC—CMe (with Me, O, OH)	PhC—C—C≡C-t-Bu (with Me, Me, OH, OH)	70	17, 18

normally with aldehydes and ketones.[19] A few of the products made by this method are given in Table 5-26.

TABLE 5-26
Alkynylation by Grignard Reagents made from
1-Chloroacetylenes and Magnesium

Product	% Yield	b.p. (°C,@ mm Hg)
BuC≡CCH(OH)Me	75	84, @ 14
BuC≡CC(OH)MeEt	97	91, @ 16
$Me_2CH(CH_2)_2C≡CCH(OH)Me$	83	92, @ 17
BuC≡C—CH_2OMe	78	58, @ 15
PrC≡CCH_2CHOHMe	70	m.p. 55
		(from propylene oxide)

$$
\begin{array}{cc}
\text{H} & \text{H} \\
| & | \\
\text{Me}\overset{}{C}=\text{CC}\equiv\text{C}\overset{}{C}C_6H_{13} \\
| & | \\
\text{Me} & \text{O} \\
& | \\
& \text{H}
\end{array}
$$

	94	83, @ 0.1

5. ARALKYNYL GRIGNARD REAGENTS

Base-sensitive aldehydes react well with alkynyl or aralkynyl Grignards. For example, acrolein reacts well with phenylacetylene Grignard :[20]

$$PhC≡CH \xrightarrow[\text{(2) acrolein}]{\text{(1) Grignard}} PhC≡CCH(OH)CH=CH_2 \xrightarrow{PBr_3} PhC≡CCH=CHCH_2Br$$
$$(84\%)$$

| (1) Li-ether | PPh₃ |
| (2) $BrCH_2CH=CHCH_2Br$ | |

$$PhC≡CCH_2CH=CHCH_2C≡CPh \qquad\qquad PhC≡CCH=CHCH_2·PPh_3Br$$
$$(48\%)$$

| hot   MeOH-KOH | RLi |

$$PhC≡CCH=CHCH=CHCH=CHPh \xleftarrow{PhCH=CHCHO} PhC≡CCH=CHCH=PPh_3$$

This sequence illustrates two other interesting reactions: (1) the reaction of lithium phenylacetylide with 1,4-dibromo-2-butene, followed by protropic rearrangement in hot methanolic KOH, and (2) the reaction of cinnamaldehyde with phenylpentenynylidenephosphorane to give the diphenyloctatrienyne.

Aralkynyl Grignard reagents react with formaldehyde to form carbinols in 55–60% yield[21] and with epichlorohydrin to form β-chloroalkyl acetylenic carbinols.[22]

6. ARALKYNYLATION WITH ZINC "GRIGNARD" REAGENTS

Golse[23] reacted allyl bromide with zinc in tetrahydrofuran to make allylzinc bromide. He then added phenylacetylene, stirred at 50° for $\frac{1}{2}$ hour, cooled, and added carbonyl compound:

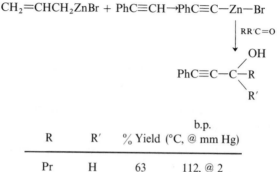

$$CH_2=CHCH_2ZnBr + PhC≡CH \rightarrow PhC≡C-Zn-Br$$

| | | b.p. |
R	R'	% Yield	(°C, @ mm Hg)
Pr	H	63	112, @ 2
Bu	H	56	132, @ 2
Me	Me	8	96, @ 1
Cyclohexyl		23	128, @ 2

Aldehydes reacted better than ketones.

7. ALUMINUM PROPARGYL "GRIGNARD" REAGENT

Bishop[24] found that propargylmagnesium Grignard reagent reacted with chloral to give mainly the propargylcarbinol, but some rearrangement occurred. With aluminum "Grignard," however, there is no rearrangement.[25]

$$HC≡C-CH_2MgGrignard + Cl_3CCHO \longrightarrow \begin{cases} \rightarrow 7 \text{ parts } Cl_3CH(OH)CH_2C≡CH \\ + \\ \rightarrow 1 \text{ part } Cl_3CH(OH)C≡C-CH_3 \end{cases}$$

$$HC≡C-CH_2AlGrignard + Cl_3CCHO \longrightarrow Cl_3CH(OH)CH_2C≡CH \text{ (exclusively)}$$

8. GRIGNARD REAGENTS OF HETEROCYCLIC COMPOUNDS

8.1. Reaction of Ethynylfuran and Tetrahydropyran Grignards

5-Bromo-2-ethynylfuran Grignard reacts with aldehydes to form 70% yields of carbinols[26]

The Grignard of 2-ethynyltetrahydropyran reacts with carbonyl compounds in refluxing ether to form the acetylenic carbinols. Both aldehydes and ketones give 50–86% yields.[27] Treatment of the ethynylcarbinols with alkali metals does not open the rings. Rings are opened by zinc chloride and acetic anhydride by heating at 250° for 15 hours in sealed ampules. Products are acetates of the straight-chain alcohols. Ring opening occurs at the 1,2-bond:

This is a potentially good synthesis for special straight-chain acetylenic diols.

8.2. Reaction of Thiophenemagnesium iodide with Tetrolaldehyde

Thiophenemagnesium iodide reacts with tetrolaldehyde to give 46% yield of carbinol.[28] The carbinol is oxidized by MnO_2 to give a ketone:

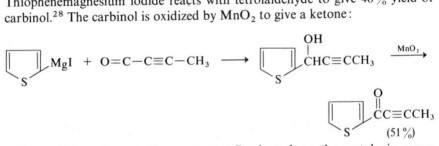

Furan Grignard reacts the same way. Products have the acetylenic group beta to the ring.

9. GRIGNARD REAGENTS OF ACETYLENIC ETHERS

Jacobs[29] reacted phenoxyethynylmagnesium bromide with a variety of reagents to prepare substituted phenoxyacetylenes. Alkyl p-toluenesulfonates give alkyl derivatives; aldehydes and ketones give the expected carbinols; water gives the free ether; aroyl halides give phenyl benzoate. Ethoxyacetylene and ethylmagnesium bromide in ether form ethoxyacetylenemagnesium bromide in 1 hour.[30] This Grignard reacts normally with ketones: Cyclohexanone, cyclopentanone and acetone give 50–73% yield of carbinol RR′C(OH)C≡COEt. Jordan[31] reported a violent explosion in one reaction. During preparation of a 20-gram batch of the Grignard, the agitator was stopped for alignment. The reaction mixture exploded during this manipulation.

Ethoxyacetylene Grignard does not react with aldehydes to form the expected secondary ethoxyethynylcarbinols. Aromatic aldehydes form products from

2 moles of aldehyde and 1 mole of ethoxyacetylene.[32] Aliphatic aldehydes give products from 3 moles of aldehyde and 1 mole of ethoxyacetylene. Benzaldehyde gives 30–50% yield of PhCH(OH)$\overset{\text{CO}_2\text{Et}}{\text{C}}$=CHPh, which also forms when a normal acetylenic carbinol from benzaldehyde and lithium ethoxyethynylide reacts with benzaldehyde in ether:

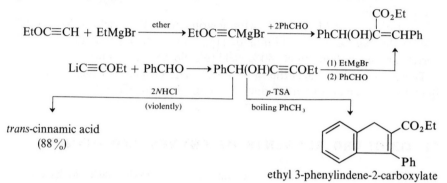

Acids rearrange secondary ethoxyethynylcarbinols to α,β-unsaturated esters, such as *trans*-cinnamic acid in the above equations. Newman[33] reacted the Grignard reagent of ethoxyethyne with 2,2,5,5-tetramethyl-3,4-hexanedione (dipivalyl) and obtained the monoalkynylation product. He rearranged the product to the allene and then to a substituted acrylate:

$$t\text{-BuC}\overset{\text{O}}{\underset{}{\|}}-\overset{\text{O}}{\underset{}{\|}}\text{C}-t\text{-Bu} + \text{EtOC}\equiv\text{CMgBr} \longrightarrow t\text{-BuC}\overset{\text{OH}}{\underset{t\text{-BuC}=\text{O}}{|}}\text{C}\equiv\text{COEt} \overset{\text{H}^+}{\longrightarrow}$$

$$t\text{-BuC}\overset{\text{OH}}{\underset{t\text{-BuC}=\text{O}}{|}}\text{C}=\text{C}-\text{COEt} \xrightarrow[\substack{\text{stereospecific}\\\text{rearrangement}}]{\text{H}^+} t\text{-BuC}=\text{CH}$$

these groups are *cis*

10. GRIGNARD REAGENTS OF ACETYLENIC THIOETHERS

Thioethyl vinylethynyl ether Grignard reagent reacts with aldehydes, ketones and ethylene oxide to give carbinols.[34] The Grignard reagent forms when the ether and ethylmagnesium bromide are mixed overnight. The other reagent is added the next day.

$$\text{BrMgC}\equiv\text{CCH}=\text{CHSEt} \xrightarrow[\text{or ethylene oxide}]{+\text{aldehyde, ketone,}} (\text{R})\text{C}\equiv\text{CCH}=\text{CHSEt}$$

Ethylene oxide, acetone, dipropyl ketone, methyl vinyl ketone, benzaldehyde, propionaldehyde, crotonaldehyde and methyl ethyl ketone react according to the above equation.

The Grignard of MeSC≡CH with acetone gives 48% yield of Me$_2$C(OH)-C≡CSMe (b.p. 92–95° at 17 mm of Hg). Ethyl ethynyl thioether gives the corresponding carbinol in 66–80% yield (b.p. 96–98° at 10 mm).[36]

The oxygen ether reacts the same way.[35] The Grignard reagent of alkoxybutenyne also gives similar products in about the same yields.

11. GRIGNARD REAGENTS OF ENYNES AND DIYNES

Enynes form Grignards easily, and these react normally with aldehydes and ketones. Aldehydes and substituted enyne Grignards form carbinols

$$\text{RCH(OH)C}\equiv\overset{\overset{\textstyle R'}{\textstyle |}}{\text{C}}\text{C}=\text{CR}''_2,$$ which are oxidized to ketones by MnO$_2$. The ketones are very powerful antifungal agents *in vitro*, but they are too irritating for topical application.[37] The Grignard of *trans*-pent-2-en-1-yne reacts with formaldehyde gas to form the carbinol in 80% yield.[21] It also reacts with acrolein to form the carbinol in 60% yield. The Grignard of 4-methoxybut-3-en-1-yne reacts with aldehydes and ketones to give carbinols.[38]

The Grignard of hexa-1,3-diyne reacts with acetone in tetrahydrofuran to give 62% yield of carbinol. Grignards of other 1,3-diynes react similarly.[39] Gusev[40] used the potassium carbonate decomposition of diacetylenic glycols to diacetylenic alcohols, followed by reaction of the carbinol Grignard with another ketone, to prepare mixed diacetylenic glycols. The potassium carbonate decomposition usually gave carbinols in 56–64% yield. For example, Gusev heated 2,7-dimethyl-3,5-octadiyne-2,7-diol rapidly to 185° at 25 mm in the presence of potassium carbonate, and distilled out 2-methyl-3,5-hexadiyn-2-ol. The Grignard of this carbinol reacted with ketones to form mixed diacetylenic glycols in 55–87% yield.

The Grignard of phenyldiacetylene reacts with cyclohexene oxide to give 100% yield of the β-carbinol[21]

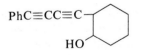

Nonconjugated diacetylenes form diGrignard reagents which react easily with carbonyl compounds. One step in the synthesis of lobelanine is an example:[41]

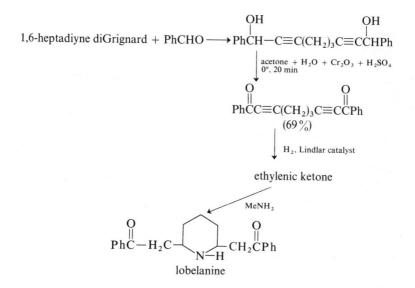

ethylenic ketone

lobelanine

References

1. Iotsitch, I., *J. Russ. Phys. Chem. Soc.*, **38**, 1040 (1906); *Chem. Abstr.*, **1**, 1271 (1907).
2. Johnson, A. W., "Acetylenic Compounds," Vol. I, "The Acetylenic Alcohols," London, Edward Arnold Co., 1946.
3. Gaylord, N. G., and Becker, E. J., *Chem. Rev.*, **49**, 413 (1951).
4. Raphael, R. A., "Acetylenic Compounds in Organic Synthesis," London, Butterworth, 1955.
5. Bachmann, W. E., and Controulis, J., *J. Am. Chem. Soc.*, **73**, 2639 (1951).
6. Skattebol, L., Jones, E. R. H., and Whiting, M. C., *Org. Syn.*, **39**, 56 (1959).
7. Jacobs, T. L., *Org. Reactions*, **5**, 1 (1949).
8. Favorskaya, T. A., and Tolstopyatov, G. M., *Zh. Obshch. Khim.*, **33**, 3160 (1963); *Chem. Abstr.*, **60**, 5320 (1964).
9. Cymerman-Craig, J., et al., *Australian J. Chem.*, **9**, 373 (1956); *Chem. Abstr.*, **51**, 1922 (1957).
10. Armitage, J. B., Jones, E. R. H., and Whiting, M. C., *J. Chem. Soc.*, **44** (1951).
10a. Lespiau, R., and Lombard, R., *Compt. Rend.*, **198**, 2179 (1934).
11. Horton, D., Hughes, J. B., and Tronchet, J. M. J., *Chem. Communications*, 481 (1965).
12. Grimmer, G., and Hildebrandt, A., *Ann. Chem.*, **685**, 154 (1965).
12a. Ilomets, T., *Zh. Obshch. Khim.*, **30**, 1194 (1960); *Chem. Abstr.*, **55**, 499 (1961).
13. Schulte, K. E., and Goes, M., *Arch. Pharm.*, **290**, 118 (1957); *Chem. Abstr.*, **51**, 12817 (1957).

14. Schulte, K. E., and Engelhardt, W., *Arch. Pharm.*, **287**, 495 (1954); *Chem. Abstr.*, **52**, 1920 (1958).

15. Favorskaya, T. A., and Portnyagin, Yu. M., *Zh. Obshch. Khim.*, **35**, 440 (1965); *Chem. Abstr.*, **63**, 1692 (1965).

16. Favorskaya, T. A., Samusik, B. N., and Moizhes, N. Yu., *Zh. Obshch. Khim.*, **35**, 255 (1965); *Chem. Abstr.*, **62**, 13040 (1965).

17. Venus-Danilova, E. D., and Serkova, V. I., *Zh. Obshch. Khim.*, **28**, 1477 (1958); *Chem. Abstr.*, **53**, 1221 (1957).

18. Venus-Danilova, E. D., Serkova, V. I., and El'tsov, A. V., *Zh. Obshch. Khim.*, **27**, 334 (1957); *Chem. Abstr.*, **51**, 15467 (1957).

19. Normant, H., and Cuvigny, T., *Bull. Soc. Chim. France*, 1447 (1957).

20. Akhtar, M., Richards, T. A., and Weedon, B. C. L., *J. Chem. Soc.*, 933 (1959).

21. Bohlmann, F., Enkelmann, R., and Plettner, W., *Chem. Ber.*, **97**, 2118 (1964).

22. Malinovskii, M. S., and Khmel, M. P., *Zh. Obshch. Khim.*, **35**, 960 (1965); *Chem. Abstr.*, **63**, 9895 (1965).

23. Golse, M. R., and Liermain, A., *Bull. Soc. Pharm. Bordeaux*, **101**, 3 (1962); *Chem. Abstr.*, **58**, 4451 (1963).

24. Bishop, D. C., Meacock, S. C. R., and Williamson, W. R. N., *J. Chem. Soc. (C)*, 670 (1966).

25. Sondheimer, F., Amiel, Y., and Gaoni, Y., *J. Am. Chem. Soc.*, **84**, 270 (1962).

26. Vereshchagin, L. I., and Korshunov, S. P., *Zh. Organ. Khim.*, **1**, 955, 960 (1965); *Chem. Abstr.*, **63**, 6943 (1965).

27. Gouin, L., *Ann. Chim. (Paris)*, **5**, 529 (1960); *Chem. Abstr.*, **55**, 8399 (1961).

28. Iwai, I., and Tomita, K. (to Sankyo Co., Ltd.), Japanese Patent 13,818-9 (1961); *Chem. Abstr.*, **56**, 10103 (1962).

29. Jacobs, T. L., Cramer, R., and Weiss, F. T., *J. Am. Chem. Soc.*, **62**, 1849 (1940).

30. Wieland, J. H. S., and Arens, J. F., *Rec. Trav. Chim.*, **75**, 1358 (1956).

31. Jordan, C. F., *Chem. Eng. News*, **44** (8), 40 (1966).

32. Postma, J. C. W., and Arens, J. F., *Rec. Trav. Chim.*, **75**, 1385 (1956).

33. Newman, M. S., and Kahle, G. R., *J. Org. Chem.*, **23**, 666 (1958).

34. Bogdanova, A. V., Dolgikh, A. N., and Shostakovskii, M. F., *Izv. Akad. Nauk SSSR, Ser. Khim.*, 363 (1965); *Chem. Abstr.*, **62**, 14484 (1965).

35. Bogdanova, A. V., Dolgikh, A. N., and Shostakovskii, M. F., *Izv. Akad. Nauk SSSR, Ser. Khim.*, 359 (1965); *Chem. Abstr.*, **62**, 14482 (1965).

36. Arens, J. F., et al., *Rec. Trav. Chim.*, **75**, 1459 (1956).

37. Nash, B. W., et al., *J. Chem. Soc.*, 2983 (1965).

38. Sorenson, T. S., *J. Am. Chem. Soc.*, **87**, 5075 (1965).

39. Labarre, J. R., *Compt. Rend.*, **252**, 1169 (1961).

40. Gusev, B. P., and Kucherov, V. F., *Izv. Akad. Nauk SSSR, Otd. Khim. Nauk*, 1062 (1962); *Chem. Abstr.*, **57**, 16383 (1962).

41. Parker, W., Raphael, R. A., and Wilkinson, D. I., *J. Chem. Soc.*, 2433 (1959).

PART FOUR

Catalytic Ethynylation Reactions

1. BACKGROUND

The only commercially important ethynylation catalyzed by cuprous acetylide is the acetylene-formaldehyde reaction to form propargyl alcohol and butynediol. On paper, the reaction is quite simple. Acetylene–nitrogen and aqueous formaldehyde are passed over a supported cuprous acetylide catalyst at 90–100° and 5–50 atmospheres pressure. Butynediol is usually the major product, and high ratios of propargyl alcohol to butynediol are hard to obtain. Reppe's discovery of this catalytic ethynylation reaction was important for several reasons: (1) The products are versatile intermediates. (2) The reaction system demonstrated that pressure acetylene reactions can be done safely on a large scale. (3) The required cuprous acetylide catalyst was prepared in a nonexplosive form. Although Reppe is usually credited with the discovery that acetylene reactions can be done safely at high pressure and temperature if an inert gas is used as diluent, Plauson and Vielle in 1921[2] reported the use of nitrogen or carbon monoxide as diluents for pressure reactions of acetylene.

Copenhaver and Bigelow[1] devoted a large portion of their book to discussion of the preparation and reactions of propargyl alcohol and butynediol. More recently (1963), Dalton reviewed the current status of this fascinating part of acetylene chemistry.[3]

Most of the literature is patents. Very few comprehensive studies of the effects of variables and of possible mechanisms have been published.

2. CUPROUS ACETYLIDE CATALYSTS

Preparation of supported cuprous acetylide is discussed briefly in Chapter 4.

Behn[4] prepared a catalyst which contained 15% copper and 2.1% bismuth deposited on magnesium silicate. This catalyst was so active for the ethynylation of formaldehyde that the pressure could be as low as 20 psig, instead of the usual 80. The yield of butynediol was 80% based on acetylene, and 90% on formaldehyde. A very small amount of cuprene formed and there was very little loss of copper into processing lines. The catalyst lasted for 8 months in a 19-cubic-foot bed in a continuous reactor. This improvement may be due to some peculiar property of the magnesium silicate carrier.

3. CATALYTIC ETHYNYLATION OF FORMALDEHYDE IN ORGANIC SOLVENTS

Chukhadzhyan[5] used bismuth-activated cuprous acetylide Reppe catalyst for the acetylene-formaldehyde reaction in various organic solvents, including DMF, butanol, cyclohexane, xylene and pyridine. In DMF, butynediol formed in 92% yield after 8 hours at 100° and atmospheric pressure. Dry para-formaldehyde was the source of formaldehyde. Atmospheric pressure reactions are reasonably fast only if a highly polar strong solvent for acetylene is used.

TABLE 5-27
Effect of Solvent
(15 grams paraformaldehyde, 100 cc of solvent, reaction for 8 hr at room temperature)

Solvent	Press (atm)	% Yield Propargyl Alcohol	% Yield Butynediol
Water	50	30	51
Methanol	48	52 (max)	30 (min)
Tetrahydrofuran	47	41	38
Acetone[a]	45	47	42
Methyl acetate	40	36	47
Benzene	45	31 (min)	60 (max)

[a] Acetone is unreactive.

TABLE 5-28
Effect of Temperature
(Methanol solvent, initial pressure 40 atm)

Temperature (°C)	% Yield Propargyl Alcohol	% Yield Butynediol
90–100	28	31
100–110 ⎬ increases	32 ⎬ increases	45 ⎬ decreases
110–120	36	49

TABLE 5-29
Effect of Pressure
(Methanol solvent, 110–120°, 6 hr)

Acetylene (g)	Initial Pressure (atm)	% Yield Propargyl Alcohol	% Yield Butynediol
28	40	41	37
14 ⎬ increases	26 ⎬ increases	32 ⎬ increases	43 ⎬ increases
78	15	10	62

TABLE 5-30

Effect of Paraformaldehyde Concentration

(110–120°, 8 hr, methanol solvent)

Concentration HCHO (%)		Initial Pressure (atm)	% Yield Propargyl Alcohol		% Yield Butynediol	
10		50	56		26	
20		45	41		37	
30	increases	43	32	increases	45	increases
50		50	24		52	

Oka[6] reported similar work. He investigated the effects of varying solvent, temperature, pressure and paraformaldehyde concentration (Tables 5-27 through 5-30). Methanol is the best solvent for propargyl alcohol. Benzene is a surprisingly good solvent for butynediol formation, the total yield being 90%. All of the effects are in the direction expected.

4. OTHER CUPROUS ACETYLIDE-CATALYZED ETHYNYLATION REACTIONS

Cuprous acetylide-catalyzed ethynylation of other compounds is summarized in Table 5-31.

5. VAPOR PHASE CATALYTIC ETHYNYLATION OF ACETONE OVER BASES

In 1965, Nogaideli[13] reported a very significant catalytic reaction. He was able to ethynylate acetone by passing acetone vapors and acetylene over a solid-supported sodium hydroxide catalyst. 3-Methyl-1-butyn-3-ol was the only product. He prepared the catalyst by mixing 25 grams of gumbrin clay with 75 grams of fused NaOH, moistening, and making 5-mm-diameter spheres which he dried at 130° for 3 hours. The best yield resulted at 120–125°, where the conversion was 13%. Recycle of the mixture over the catalyst increased the conversion to 20–23%.

The major advantages of this reaction are: No by-products form, sodium hydroxide is cheaper than KOH and no hydrolysis step is required in the work-up. The crude product is simply distilled.

Frantz[14] claimed that the cyanide form of an anion exchange resin was a good catalyst for ethynylations in the vapor phase. He passed acetylene at 100–250 psig through acetone to saturate the acetylene stream, and then passed the gas through the cyanide form of "Amberlite" IRA 400 resin. After 3–6 hours at 30–53°, the yield of 3-methyl-1-butyn-3-ol was 85–93%, based on acetone.

TABLE 5-31
Catalytic Ethynylation of Other Reagents

Reagent	Solvent	Catalyst	Conditions	Product	% Yield	Reference
Paraformaldehyde	DMF	Cu_2C_2-silica-alumina	85–120°, 255 psig	3 carbinol : 1 glycol	—	7
Benzaldehyde	MeOH	Cu_2C_2	100°, 20 atm	Carbinol	80	8
		Cu_2C_2-magnesium silicate	134°, 230 psig	Carbinol	—	9
Ethylene oxide	Dioxane-triethyl-amine	Cu_2C_2	160°, 50 psig	1-Butyn-3-ol	24	10
Epichlorohydrin	Dioxane-triethyl-amine	Cu_2C_2	160°, 50 psig	5-Chloro-1-pentyn-4-ol	4.6	10
Paraformaldehyde[a]	Methylal	Cu_2C_2-C	150°	$Me_2CC{\equiv}CCH_2OH$ $\underset{OH}{|}$	96	11
Formaldehyde[b]		Cu_2C_2	Atmospheric pressure	Propargyl alcohol	Low	12

[a] 3-Methyl-1-butyn-3-ol is the acetylenic reagent.
[b] Vinylacetylene is the acetylenic reagent.

6. CATALYTIC REACTION OF ORTHOESTERS WITH ACETYLENES

These reactions are not alkynylations, but are similar to them.

6.1. Synthesis of Acetals

One common method of preparing acetylenic acetals is the reaction of an acetylenic Grignard or sodium acetylide with an orthoformate ester. Howk and Sauer[15] described a one-step synthesis from available starting materials. The reaction of phenylacetylene with ethyl orthoformate illustrates the new reaction:

$$PhC\equiv CH + HC(OEt)_3 \xrightarrow[\text{heat}]{ZnCl_2} EtOH + PhC\equiv C\overset{\overset{\displaystyle H}{|}}{C}(OEt)_2$$

Equimolar amounts of the acetylene and orthoester are heated, and alcohol is removed as it forms. Ethanol starts to distill at about 135° (liquid) and is completely removed when the temperature reaches 200°. One-half mole reactions require 0.4–3.9 hours, and the yields are 15–80%. For low-boiling acetylenes such as 1-hexyne, the reaction is done in an autoclave under autogenous pressure. The best catalysts are zinc chloride, iodide or nitrate, or cadmium iodide.

Acetylene reacts under pressure with ethyl orthoformate to form acetylene-dicarboxaldehyde bis(diethylacetal) as the main product in yields up to 48%. A little propiolaldehyde diethylacetal is formed, and by-product malonaldehyde bis(diethylacetal)[3] is obtained in yields up to 28%.

An ionic mechanism explains the products:

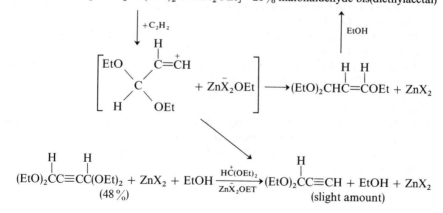

6.2. Synthesis of Ketals

The method is general, and Howk and Sauer extended it to several other orthoesters and other monosubstituted acetylenes.[15] Phenylacetylene reacts with triethyl orthoacetate or trimethyl orthovalerate to form acetylenic ketals, a new class of compounds:

$$PhC{\equiv}CH + CH_3C(OEt)_3 \xrightarrow[\text{heat}]{ZnCl_2} PhC{\equiv}C{-}C(CH_3)(OEt)_2$$
$$(34\%)$$

6.3. Synthesis of Acetylenic Orthoesters

Tetraethyl orthocarbonate gives an acetylenic orthoester:[15]

$$PhC{\equiv}CH + C(OEt)_4 \xrightarrow[\text{heat}]{ZnCl_2} PhC{\equiv}CC(OEt)_3$$
$$(14\%)$$

References

1. Copenhaver, J. W., and Bigelow, M. H., "Acetylene and Carbon Monoxide Chemistry," New York, Reinhold Publishing Corp., 1949.
2. Plauson, H., and Vielle, J. A., British Patent 156,116 (1921).
3. Dalton, P. B., et al., "Kirk-Othmer Encyclopedia of Chemical Technology," Second ed., Vol. 1, p. 598, New York, Interscience Publishers, 1963.
4. Behn, E. Z., U.S. Patent 2,871,273 (Jan. 27, 1959).
5. Chukhadzhyan, G. A., et al., Izv. Akad. Nauk Arm. SSR, Khim. Nauk, 14, 444 (1961); Chem. Abstr., 58, 437 (1963).
6. Oka, S., Bull. Chem. Soc. Japan, 35, 562 (1962); Chem. Abstr., 57, 8422 (1962).
7. Moore, G. L. (to Cumberland Chem. Corp.), U.S. Patent 3,218,362 (Nov. 16, 1965); Chem. Abstr., 64, 4941 (1966).
8. Murahashi, S., and Hagihara, N., Mem. Inst. Sci. Ind. Res. Osaka Univ., 6, 96 (1948); Chem. Abstr., 45, 10216 (1951).
9. Mahan, J. E., and Osborn, C. W. (to Phillips Petroleum Co.), U.S. Patent 2,884,316 (Apr. 28, 1959); Chem. Abstr., 53, 14406 (1959).
10. Lynch, R. A. (to Dow Chem. Co.), U.S. Patent 3,190,929 (June 22, 1965); Chem. Abstr., 63, 9811 (1965).
11. Leeds, M. F., Russell, J. P., and Vitcha, J. F. (to Air Reduction Co.), U.S. Patent 3,108,140 (Oct. 22, 1963); Chem. Abstr., 60, 2765 (1964).
12. Shapovalova, A. N., and Lyubomilov, V. I., Zh. Prikl. Khim., 39, 962 (1966); Chem. Abstr., 65, 2114 (1966).
13. Nogaideli, A. I., and Tkeshelashvili, R. Sh., Zh. Prikl. Khim., 38, 1639 (1965); Chem. Abstr., 63, 9798 (1965).

14. Frantz, R. K. (to Air Reduction Co.), U.S. Patent 3,105,098 (Sept. 24, 1963); *Chem. Abstr.*, **60**, 1589 (1964).

15. Howk, B. W., and Sauer, J. C., *J. Am. Chem. Soc.*, **80**, 4607 (1958); *Org. Syn.*, **39**, 59 (1959).

PART FIVE

Ethynylation and Alkynylation of Dicarbonyl Compounds

1. BACKGROUND

Although relatively little has been done on ethynylation and alkynylation of dicarbonyl compounds, some of the work was reported very early. Zelinsky[1] in 1902, and Acree[2] in 1904, described the alkynylation of diketones such as biacetyl and acetonylacetone by acetylenic Grignard reagents. In 1923, Wilson and Hyslop[3] reported that the reaction of biacetyl and phenylacetylene Grignard reagent in ether gave 45% yield of glycol (m.p. 117°) and 3.4% yield of its stereoisomer (m.p. 125°). Acetylacetone did not react. Milas (1948) and Papa (1954)[4] described the ethynylation of biacetyl and acetonylacetone. Cymerman-Craig reacted 1-hexynyl Grignard with 1,4-cyclohexanedione and obtained 1,4-dihexynyl-1,4-cyclohexanediol. In 1964, Disselnkötter[5] noted that Grignards of vinylacetylene and isopropenylacetylene were easy to make, and reacted with aldehydes and ketones to give 60–85% yields of carbinols. Biacetyl and acetonylacetone also reacted well to form the α- and β-diols.

Professor W. Ried at the University, Frankfort-Main, has reported much of the recent work. Ried and his many co-workers have done a large number of ethynylations and alkynylations, and have used a remarkable variety of carbonyl and (mostly) dicarbonyl compounds. They have reacted cyclohexanediones, quinones and unconventional diketones such as N-substituted phthalimides. They studied many reactions of their products, including reduction to cumulenes. Ried reviewed this work in 1964.[6]

2. DIALDEHYDES

Very few ethynylations or alkynylations of dialdehydes have been reported. Glyoxal reacts with the Grignard of 1-hexyne to form the expected α-glycol.[7] The acetone cyclic acetal of the glycol separated into two fractions on a column of alumina. The lower-melting fraction cleaved faster by lead tetraacetate and therefore was the racemic form. The other fraction was the *meso* form.

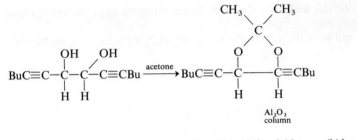

(a) b.p. 102–104° at 0.15 mm (b) b.p. 105° at 0.1 mm

hydrolysis to glycol

m.p. 68°   m.p. 78°
racemic   *meso*

The glycol from 1-heptyne and glyoxal melted at 44°. Other Grignards of alkynes have also been reacted with glyoxal.[8]

Terephthaldehyde reacts with the Grignard reagent from 1-butyn-3-ol to form the diacetylenic tetrol:[9]

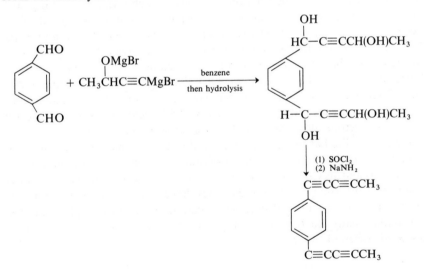

3. DIKETONES

3.1. Ethynylation of Cyclohexanediones

1,2- and 1,4-Cyclohexanedione react with sodium acetylide in ammonia (20–24 hours) to form *trans*-diethynyl glycols. 1,3-Cyclohexanedione does not react. Ried[10] obtained 1,2-diethynyl-1,2-dihydroxycyclohexane in 57% yield (m.p.

105°). This is the first report of ethynylation of cyclohexanedione. After shorter times, only one of the keto groups was ethynylated. The ethynyl group of the 1,2-glycol was sufficiently reactive that simple treatment with alkaline hypobromite gave the dibromodiethynyl glycol in 30% yield. The ethynyl groups were easily reduced to ethyl groups by Raney nickel, and the hydroxyl groups were easily esterified. The compound reacted with formic acid under Rupe rearrangement conditions to give 1,2-diacetyl-2,5-cyclohexadiene.

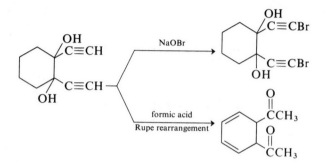

1,4-Cyclohexanedione and sodium acetylide in ammonia gave 67% yield of the 1,4-glycol (m.p. 202°). Short reaction times did not give monoethynylation as noted for the 1,2-dione. The hydroxyl groups reacted with pyridine-acetic anhydride to form the diacetate. Other reactions are:

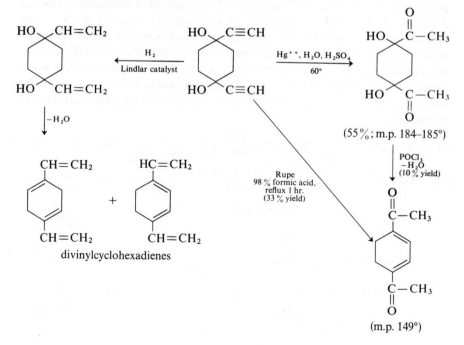

divinylcyclohexadienes

3.2. Alkynylation of Cyclohexanedione

The Grignard reagent from allylacetylene reacts with 1,4-cyclohexanedione in ether to give the following glycol:

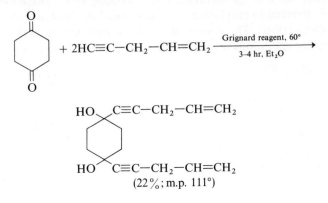

$$HC\equiv C-CH_2-CH=CH_2$$

HO, $C\equiv C-CH_2-CH=CH_2$

HO $C\equiv C-CH_2-CH=CH_2$

(22%; m.p. 111°)

4. *o*-QUINONES

4.1. Ethynylation

Ethynylation of 4,5-dimethyl-1,2-benzoquinone (1) by lithium acetylide in ammonia at $-50°$ gave 1,2-diethynyl-1,2-dihydroxy-4,5-dimethylcyclohexa-3,5-diene (2).[12] The glycol was reduced with stannous chloride in 50% acetic acid at 60–70° to form 1,2-diethynyl-4,5-dimethylbenzene (3), which, like most other diethynyl aromatic hydrocarbons, displays strong blue-violet fluorescence in chloroform and dioxane. Hydration by heating for a long time with mercuric acetate in 90% acetic acid gave 1,2-diacetyl-4,5-dimethyl-benzene (4), which reacted with hydrazine hydrate in glacial acetic acid to form 1,4,6,7-tetramethylphthalazine (5):

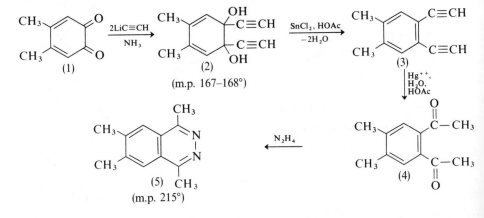

Phenanthenequinone reacts with 2 moles of sodium acetylide in ammonia to give 40% yield of

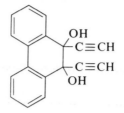

o-Quinol acetates react with sodium acetylide to form some unusual products:[13]

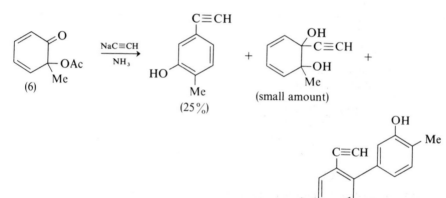

The mechanism of the reaction is:

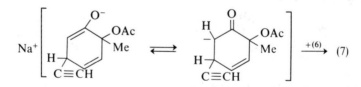

Another unusual reaction is:

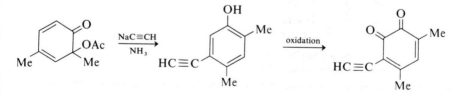

4.2. Alkynylation

Lithium phenylacetylide has been reacted with *o*-quinones. Some of the products are shown in Table 5-32.[15]

TABLE 5-32
Products from *o*-Quinones and Lithium Phenylacetylide[15]

Product	Method[a]	m.p. (°C)	% Yield
1,2-bis(phenylethynyl)-1,2-dihydrochrysenediol	A	174–175	64
3,4,5,6-tetrachloro-1,2-bis(phenylethynyl)-cyclohexadiene-3,5-diol-1,2	A B	152–154	0.5 6
4,6-Di-*t*-butyl-1,2-bis(phenylethynyl)-cyclohexadiene-3,5-diol-1,2	A B	137–139	10 27
4,6-Di-*t*-butyl-1-phenylethynylcyclohexa-dien-3,5-ol-1-one-2	A B	264 (dec.)	6 5
3-phenylethynyl-2,3-dihydroindon-2-ol-3	B	214–215	28
2,3-bis(phenylethynyl)-2,3-di-hydrothionaphthenediol-2,3	B	234–235	10

[a] In method A, ammonia was the solvent. In method B, boiling ether was used as the diluent.

Products from some other alkynylations of o-quinones are listed in Table 5-33.

TABLE 5-33
Alkynylation of o-Quinones[16] by LiC≡CR

R	Product	% Yield
—C≡C—CH=CH—OCH₃	(structure) m.p. 166–167°	20–30
—C≡C—φ	(structure) m.p. 159–160°	20–30
—C≡C—φ	(structure) m.p. 158–159°	20–30

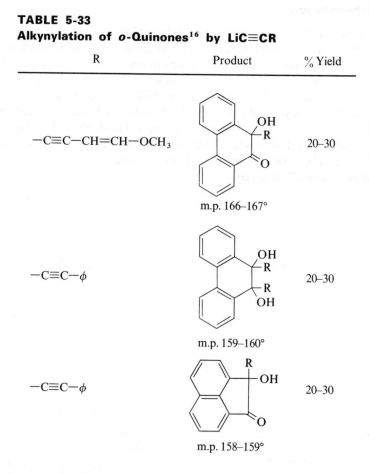

Lead tetraacetate cleavage of the product from lithium phenylacetylide and phenanthrenequinone gave a diketone:[15]

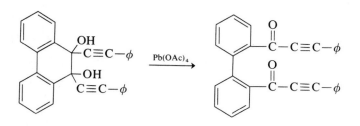

5. p-QUINONES

5.1. Ethynylation

Ried[17] reported that quinones and acetylene Grignard reagent gave poorly defined products, but sodium acetylide in ammonia gave good reactions and easily identified products. Diethynylhydroquinones were the only products formed over a wide temperature range. Best results were obtained when the quinone in toluene was added to sodium acetylide in ammonia at -30 to $-40°$ and the reaction was allowed to proceed for 8–10 hours. Under these conditions, quinone gave 30–45 % yield of glycol (m.p. 196°). The diethynylhydroquinones are very stable in neutral or weakly alkaline solution, but react in dilute halogen acid solution. They are unchanged by light and air.

Some reactions of the glycol are:

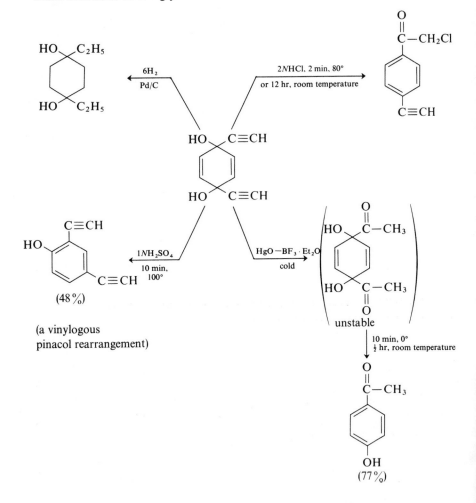

The unusual reaction with HCl to form the chloromethyl ketone can be explained in the following manner:

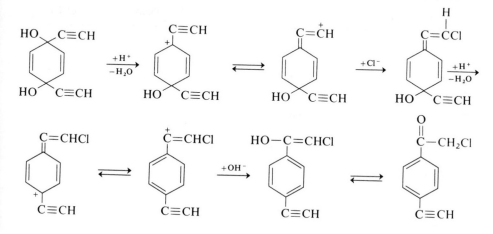

Other quinones were ethynylated by sodium acetylide (Table 5-34). Lithium acetylide in ammonia was used for chloroanil and for 2-methylnaphthoquinone (Table 5-34). 2-Methylnaphthoquinone with sodium acetylide in ammonia gave a resin. Formation of the amino product (b) (Table 5-34) from 2-methyl-naphthoquinone is rationalized:

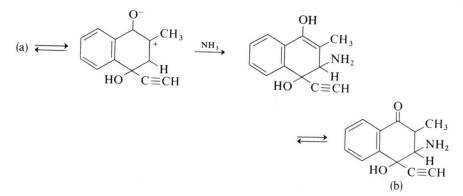

Product (b) does not react with carbonyl reagents; therefore, it exists mostly in the enol form. On heating or treatment with sodium carbonate solution, (b) loses ammonia to form (a).

Oxidative coupling of the diethynyl glycols gave quinone bis(alkynetetraols), which were reduced to quinone bis(cumulenes). The diethynyldiols can also be reduced to aromatic diethynyl hydrocarbons[18] by treatment with stannous chloride, sodium dithionate or titanium trichloride.[19] The quinone-acetylene product gave fluorescent crystals of p-diethynylbenzene. The naphthoquinone

TABLE 5-34
Ethynylation of *o*-Quinones by Sodium Acetylide[17]

Quinone	Product (*trans*)	% Yield	m.p. (°C)
Chloroanil		17	234 (dec.)
1,4-Naphthoquinone		15	122–123
9,10-Anthraquinone		60	199 (dec.)
2-Methylquinone		13.5	95–96
2-Methylnaphthoquinone (a)		17.5	143
(b)		49	143

product reduced to 9,10-diethynylanthracene, yellow needles, which polymerized to a dark-brown infusible material when heated at 87°. Chodkiewicz[14] reported similar reactions. Two moles of sodium acetylide and one mole of quinone in ammonia gave diethynylhydroquinones, called diquinols by Chodkiewicz, and in the case of quinone, 50% yield of hydroquinone by reduction (Table 5-35).

Chodkiewicz also reduced the diquinols with stannous chloride in acetic acid: p-diethynylhydroquinone gave 50% yield of p-diethynylbenzene.

TABLE 5-35
Ethynylation of p-Quinones by Sodium Acetylide[14]

Quinone	Solvent	Yield Diquinol	m.p. (°C)
Quinone	Ammonia	25–30	—
Anthraquinone	Ammonia	90	206
	N-Methylpyrrolidone-ammonia or DMF-ammonia	40 (monoquinol)	235
Phenanthrenequinone	Ammonia	40	202

TABLE 5-36
Reduction of p-Quinone Acetylenic Glycols to
p-Diethynyl Hydrocarbons[20]

Product	Method[a]	m.p. or Decomposition Point (°C)	% Yield
p-Diethynylbenzene	A and B	95–96	—[14]
2,3,5,6-Tetrachloro-p-ethynylbenzene	A	130–140	
1,4-Diethynylnaphthalene	A	60	49
2,3-Dichloro-1,4-diethynylnaphthalene	A and B	133–151	23 (A) 80 (B)
9,10-Diethynylanthracene	A and B	86–88	
9,10-Diethynylphenanthrene	A	130	27

[a] Method A: Stannous chloride.
   Method B: HI.

TABLE 5-37
Stannous Chloride Reduction of p-Quinone
Alkynyl Glycols[20]

Product	m.p. (°C)	% Yield
1,4-Bis(phenylethynyl)benzene	181–182	50–60
1,4-Bis(2-vinylethynyl)benzene	55	40
1,4-Bis(2-methoxymethylethynyl)benzene	42–43	70
9,10-Bis(phenylethynyl)phenanthrene	157	80

Ried[20] reduced *p*-quinone acetylenic diols with (A) stannous chloride or (B) HI (Table 5-36). Dialkynyl hydroquinones gave slightly better yields (Table 5-37).

Since the reduction to diethynyl aromatic hydrocarbons is a general preparative reaction, some details illustrating methods A and B of Table 5-36 are appropriate:

Method A, Stannous Chloride: To 0.04 mole $SnCl_2 \cdot H_2O$ in 25 ml of 50% acetic acid at 30° is added 0.02 mole of 1,4-diethynyl-1,4-dihydroxy-1,4-dihydronaphthalene in 25 ml of ethanol, and the mixture is stirred for 10 minutes. Then 40 ml of 2N HCl is added, and the mix is cooled in an ice bath. The precipitate is removed by filtration and washed with water. The product is recrystallized first from petroleum ether and then from methanol (49% yield).

Method B, HI: To 1.5 grams of 2,3-dichloro-1,4-dihydroxy-1,4-diethynyl-1,4-dihydronaphthalene in 20 ml of methanol is added 10 ml of 2N HI, and the solution is boiled for 5 minutes. The mix is cooled, filtered and extracted with ether; the ether solution is then washed with sodium thiosulfate until most of the yellow color is removed. The ether is evaporated, and the solid is recrystallized (80% yield).

The HI reduction can be complicated by side reactions, which depend on the concentration of the HI:

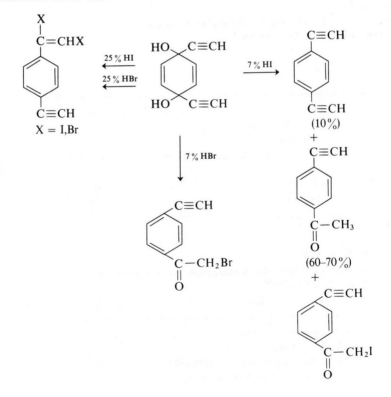

Reduction of the iodo ketone by excess HI to form the p-ethynylacetophenone is evidence that the iodo ketone is one intermediate.

Ried and Lukas[21] studied the ethynylation of substituted anthraquinones. If anthraquinone is substituted at the 1-position with an electron-releasing group, a vinylogous carbonamide forms at the 9-position:

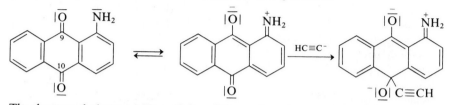

The decreased electrophilic activity of the carbonyl group in position 9 causes lithium acetylide to make a nucleophilic attack on the carbonyl group in position 10.

If the substituent, such as $-NH_2$, is on the carbon in the 2-position, the 10-carbonyl is vinylogous and negative; lithium acetylide reacts at the 9-carbonyl:

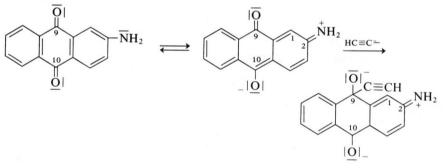

The carbonyl absorption (infrared) in 1-aminoanthraquinone is at a longer wavelength than in 2-aminoanthraquinone and is split. The relationship between carbonyl absorption wavelength and position of reaction of lithium acetylide is shown in Table 5-38.

An electron-attracting nitro group on the 2-position causes the major product to be the 10-ethynylcarbinol. When the nitro group is on the 1-position, ethynylation occurs on the 9-carbonyl group (the reverse of the effect of $-NH_2$).

5.2. Alkynylation

5.2.1. BENZOQUINONE

Ried[16] prepared lithium derivatives of monosubstituted acetylenes in ammonia, or reacted lithium amide with the acetylene in dry toluene, and added quinone. Anthraquinone reacted better with two of the lithium alkynylides (Table 5-39)

TABLE 5-38
Ethynylation of Substituted Anthraquinones

Substituted Anthraquinone	IR, C=O (cm^{-1})		Position of Ethynylation	Solvent	% Yield	m.p. (°C)
1-Amino-	1678		10	Dioxane	30	192–193
2-Amino-	1665	1611	9	Dioxane	22	277
1-Dimethylamino-	1676	1625				
2-Dimethylamino-	1667	1650				
1-Nitro-	1685		9	EtOAc	75	220–221
2-Nitro-	1687		10	THF	71	224 (dec.)
1-Chloro-	1682		10	Toluene	38	162–163
2-Chloro-	1680		9	Toluene	46	208–209
1-Fluoro-			10	EtOAc	48	193–194
2-Fluoro-			9	EtOAc	59	185 (dec.)
2-Acetamino-			9	EtOAc	43	228–230 (dec.)

TABLE 5-39
Alkynylation of p-Quinones

R	m.p. (°C)	% Yield	Reaction Time (hr)
—C≡C—ϕ	178	50–55	5
—C≡C—CH=CH—OCH$_3$	168–170	20	5
—C≡C—CH$_2$—OCH$_3$	105	27	34
—C≡C—CH=CH$_2$	167 (dec.)	60	17

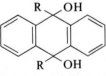

(from LiAcetylides in NH$_3$)

| —C≡C—ϕ | 196–197 | 80–90 | 7–8 |
| —C≡C—CH=CH—OCH$_3$ | 126 | 50–60 | 7–8 |

Some reactions, including cyclizations of the quinone-phenylacetylene product are:[16]

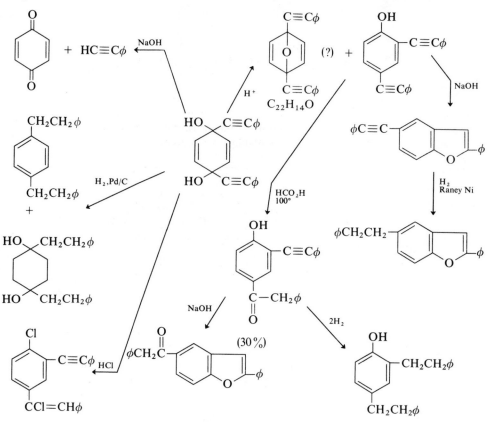

5.2.2. OTHER p-QUINONES. CONVERSION OF ALKYNYL PRODUCTS TO CUMULENES

The alkynylation products of other p-quinones are given in Table 5-40. Some products from benzoquinone are included for comparison.

The acetylenic carbinols and glycols from p-quinones are converted to cumulenes by treating dioxane solutions of the ethynyl compounds with stannous chloride and HCl. The intensive colors of the cumulenes develop quickly. The cumulenes prepared from three of the acetylenic compounds are typical (see table on page 228).

When anthraquinone reacts with lithium alkynylides in ammonia, carbinols resulting from the addition of one acetylenic compound to one carbonyl are major products. The diacetylenic diol from the reaction at both carbonyls forms

Prepared from[a]	Formula

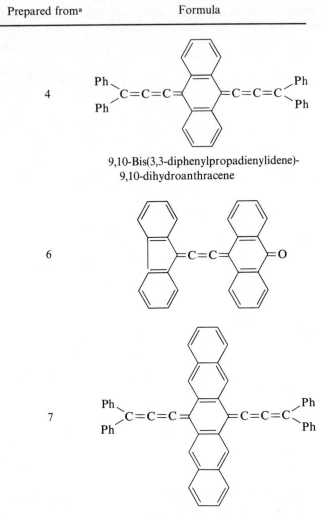

4

9,10-Bis(3,3-diphenylpropadienylidene)-
9,10-dihydroanthracene

6

7

[a] Table 5-40.

easily in dioxane at 100°. Three procedures have been used to prepare both products from several acetylenes and anthraquinones:[22]

(a) Lithium was stirred in ammonia at −40°, and ferric nitrate (2 grams per mole of lithium) was added as catalyst. Formation of lithium amide was indicated by disappearance of the blue color. The monosubstituted acetylene was added slowly, and the reaction continued for ½ hour at −40°. The anthraquinone was added in portions, and the suspension was stirred for 18–20 hours.

(b) The acetylene was refluxed for 2 hours in dioxane with lithium amide and then the anthraquinone was added. The solution was refluxed for 15 hours, and the solvent removed.

TABLE 5-40
Alkynylation of *p*-Quinones[11]

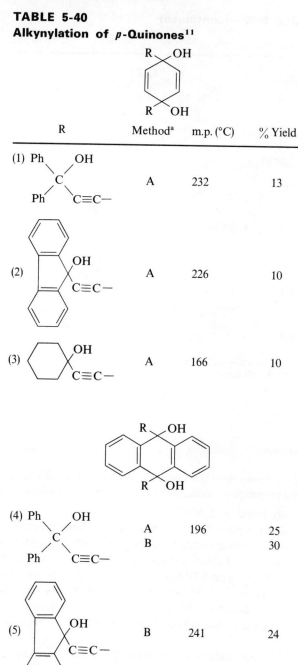

R	Method[a]	m.p. (°C)	% Yield
(1) Ph, OH / C / Ph, C≡C—	A	232	13
(2) OH / C≡C—	A	226	10
(3) OH / C≡C—	A	166	10
(4) Ph, OH / C / Ph, C≡C—	A B	196	25 30
(5) OH / C≡C—	B	241	24

TABLE 5-40—(continued)

R	Method[a]	m.p. (°C)	% Yield

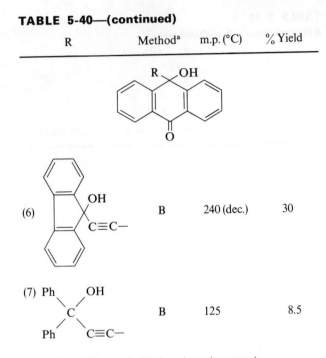

	Method[a]	m.p. (°C)	% Yield
(6)	B	240 (dec.)	30
(7)	B	125	8.5

[a] Method A: Lithium alkynylide reacted with the quinone in ammonia.
Method B: Lithium alkynylide prepared in toluene, and reacted with the quinone in toluene.

The product was isolated by treating with water, water washing until neutral, drying and recrystallizing.

(c) To prepare the monoethynylated product, lithium amide and acetylene were used in slight excess, and the reaction was like (b) except that a period of 5-6 hours was sufficient.

Some products are listed in Table 5-41.

Some of the diols were converted into diethynylanthracenes. The diol in acetone or dioxane at room temperature reacted with a solution of stannous chloride in 50% acetic acid. After a short time, the yellow crystals were filtered, dried and recrystallized. The 9,10-dialkynylanthracenes prepared in this way are summarized in Table 5-42. Many of these compounds were reduced to the corresponding ethyl derivatives by hydrogenation with Raney nickel. A few were semihydrogenated to the ethylene derivatives in the presence of Lindlar catalyst.

Chodkiewicz[23] used sodamide in tetrahydrofuran to prepare sodium alkynylides which reacted easily with anthraquinone. The monoquinol from the alkynylation reacted with acetylene-KOH to give ethynylalkynyldiquinols

TABLE 5-41
Alkynylation of Anthraquinones[22]

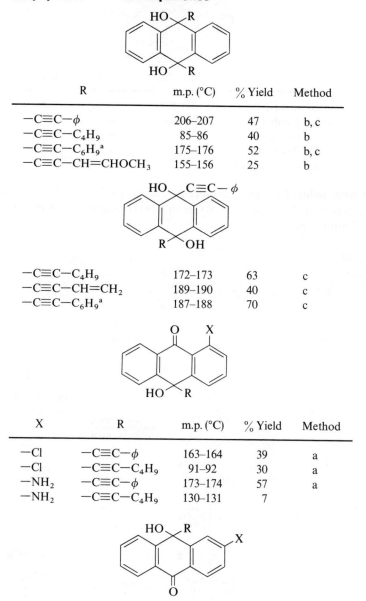

R	m.p. (°C)	% Yield	Method
—C≡C—φ	206–207	47	b, c
—C≡C—C₄H₉	85–86	40	b
—C≡C—C₆H₉[a]	175–176	52	b, c
—C≡C—CH=CHOCH₃	155–156	25	b

	m.p. (°C)	% Yield	Method
—C≡C—C₄H₉	172–173	63	c
—C≡C—CH=CH₂	189–190	40	c
—C≡C—C₆H₉[a]	187–188	70	c

X	R	m.p. (°C)	% Yield	Method
—Cl	—C≡C—φ	163–164	39	a
—Cl	—C≡C—C₄H₉	91–92	30	a
—NH₂	—C≡C—φ	173–174	57	a
—NH₂	—C≡C—C₄H₉	130–131	7	

—Cl	—C≡C—φ	186–187	62	a
—Cl	—C≡C—C₄H₉	105–106	34	a
—NH₂	—C≡C—φ	205–206	48	a

TABLE 5-41—(continued)

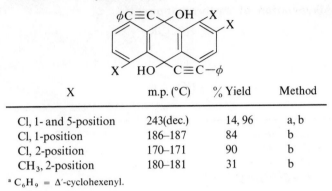

X	m.p. (°C)	% Yield	Method
Cl, 1- and 5-position	243(dec.)	14, 96	a, b
Cl, 1-position	186–187	84	b
Cl, 2-position	170–171	90	b
CH₃, 2-position	180–181	31	b

ᵃ C_6H_9 = Δ′-cyclohexenyl.

which were reduced to the anthracenes. The ethynyl group then reacted with benzophenone in the presence of KOH to form the carbinol, which was reduced to the 3-cumulene:

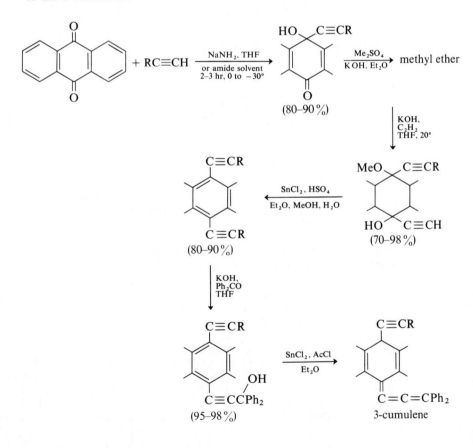

TABLE 5-42
9,10-Dialkynylanthracenes[22]

Substituted Anthracene	m.p. (°C)	% Yield
9,10-bis(phenylethynyl)	249–250	82
9,10-Dihexyn-1-yl	91–92	79
9,10-Bis(Δ'-cyclohexenylethynyl)	216–217	81
9-Hexen-1-yl-10-phenylethynyl	230–232	74
9-Vinylethynyl-10-phenylethynyl	265 (dec.)	62
9-(Δ'-Cyclohexenylethynyl)-10-phenylethynyl	226–228	75
1-Chloro-9,10-bis(phenylethynyl)	205–206	95
2-Chloro-9,10-bis(phenylethynyl)	226–227	95
1,5-Dichloro-9,10-bis(phenylethynyl)	231 (dec.)	90
2-Methyl-9,10-bis(phenylethynyl)	224	76

Chodkiewicz[24] showed the preparation of 2-, 3- and 5-cumulenes from anthraquinone:

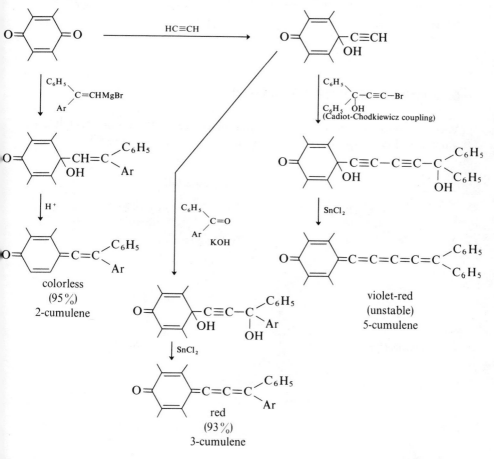

The carbonyl group in the cumulene quinones is reactive to nucleophiles, the reactivity decreasing as the number of double bonds in the cumulene increases. The 2-cumulene gave 64% yield of the phenylethynylquinol on reaction with phenylacetylene-KOH.

Some methenocumules were also prepared:

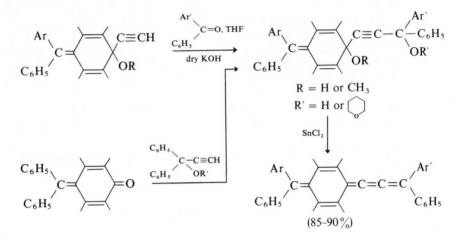

$R = H$ or CH_3

$R' = H$ or ☐

(85–90%)

6. p-QUINOLS, ETHYNYLATION

Wessely[13] ethynylated quinols and quinolacetates with sodium acetylide in ammonia. Rearrangements and reactions of the products are outlined:

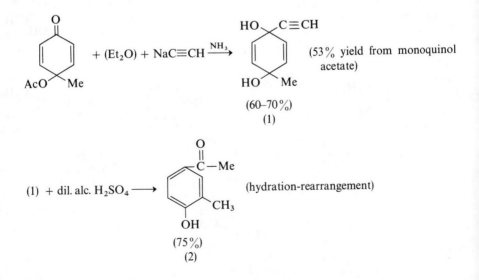

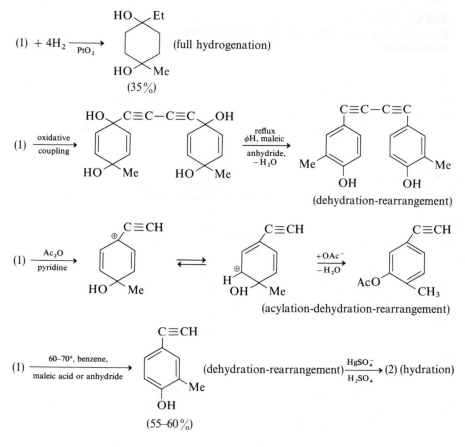

7. QUINONE MONOANILS—ETHYNYLATION AND ALKYNYLATION

Tautomeric anthranols cannot be ethynylated by alkali acetylides, because they react to form alkali salts. No tautomerism is possible in quinone monoanils. Ried[25] reacted some quinone monoanils with many acetylenes and reduced some of the acetylenic carbinols to quinocumulenes. The best reaction with the acetylenes was usually obtained in 3 : 2 ammonia-ether at -35 to 45°. Five different methods gave satisfactory yields of products: (A) lithium alkynylide in ammonia; (B) sodium alkynylide in ammonia; (C) lithium alkynylide in ammonia-ether; (D) sodium alkynylide in ammonia-ether; (E) lithium alkynylide in ether. The products and yields are listed in Table 5-43. Propargyl alcohol reacted with anthraquinonanil to form the acetylenic glycol anil in 76% yield (m.p. 194.5°). Ethynylbenzhydrol gave glycol in 59% yield (m.p. 199.5°).

TABLE 5-43
Ethynylation and Alkynylation of Quinone Monoanils[25]

R	Method	% Yield	m.p. (°C)
H—	B	23.2	192
	D	97.6	
n-C$_4$H$_9$—	C	83.5	86.5
CH$_3$OCH$_2$—	C	71.8	117
(CH$_3$)$_2$NCH$_2$—	C	80.2	191
CH$_3$OCH=CH—	C	74.3	143
ϕ—	A	29.2	149.5
ϕ—	C	91.8	
ϕ—	D	88.4	
ϕ—	E	81.7	

C	84	242.5 (dec. > 235)

Ethynylfluorenol gave 33% of a product glycol (m.p. 147°). 9-Hydroxy-10-phenylimino-9-ethynyl-9,10-dihydroanthracene gave products which could not be purified. Ried hydrogenated all of the products to the corresponding ethanes by Raney nickel, and some of the products hydrogenated further. The products from 2,6-dimethyl-p-quinone monoanil are given in Table 5-44.

8. N-SUBSTITUTED IMIDES

8.1. Ethynylation

Some N-substituted phthalimides were ethynylated when treated with lithium acetylide, while others were cleaved to phthalic acid derivatives[26] (Table 5-45).

TABLE 5-44

Ethynylation and Alkynylation of a Quinone Monoanil[25]

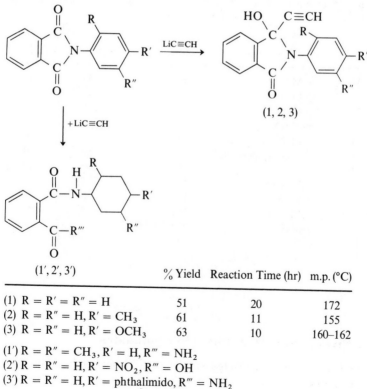

R	% Yield	m.p. (°C)
$-H$	10	108
$-CH_2OCH_3$	61.7	131.5
$-CH_2N(CH_3)_2$	68.9	132.5
$-\phi$	60.8	154

TABLE 5-45

Reaction of Lithium Acetylide with N-substituted Phthalimides[26]

	% Yield	Reaction Time (hr)	m.p. (°C)
(1) $R = R' = R'' = H$	51	20	172
(2) $R = R'' = H, R' = CH_3$	61	11	155
(3) $R = R'' = H, R' = OCH_3$	63	10	160–162
(1') $R = R'' = CH_3, R' = H, R''' = NH_2$			
(2') $R = R'' = H, R' = NO_2, R''' = OH$			
(3') $R = R'' = H, R' = $ phthalimido, $R''' = NH_2$			

Thus, certain electronegative substituents on the 3-position of the N-phenyl group completely inhibit ethynylation. Methyl groups on the 2- and 5-positions have the same effect.

8.2. Alkynylation

Later work confirmed that monoaddition of alkali acetylides to the N-substituted phthalimides depends on the substituents in the N-phenyl and phthalyl groups (Table 5-46). Phthalimides whose infrared carbonyl absorption was below 1710 cm^{-1} reacted with lithium acetylides, while those having absorptions above this wavelength did not.

TABLE 5-46
Alkynylation of N-substituted Phthalimides[27]

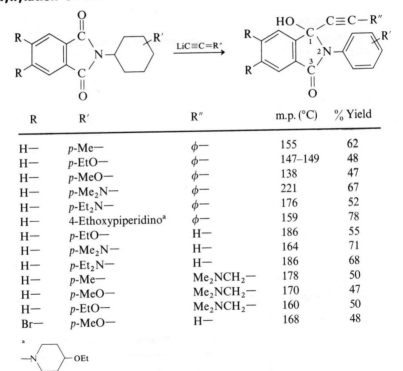

R	R′	R″	m.p. (°C)	% Yield
H—	p-Me—	φ—	155	62
H—	p-EtO—	φ—	147–149	48
H—	p-MeO—	φ—	138	47
H—	p-Me$_2$N—	φ—	221	67
H—	p-Et$_2$N—	φ—	176	52
H—	4-Ethoxypiperidino[a]	φ—	159	78
H—	p-EtO—	H—	186	55
H—	p-Me$_2$N—	H—	164	71
H—	p-Et$_2$N—	H—	186	68
H—	p-Me—	Me$_2$NCH$_2$—	178	50
H—	p-MeO—	Me$_2$NCH$_2$—	170	47
H—	p-EtO—	Me$_2$NCH$_2$—	160	50
Br—	p-MeO—	H—	168	48

8.3. Ethynylation of N-Phenylphthalimides

N-phenylnaphthalimides reacted similarly to N-phenylphthalimides, but the yields were lower:

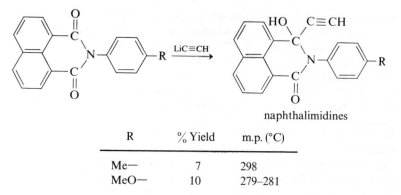

naphthalimidines

R	% Yield	m.p. (°C)
Me—	7	298
MeO—	10	279–281

8.4. Attempted Alkynylation of Quinazolones and Phthalazones

Quinazolones and phthalazones do not react with lithium alkynylides under conditions similar to those given in the preceding sections.[27]

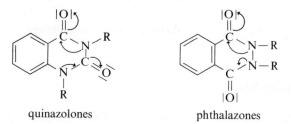

quinazolones   phthalazones

As the formulas indicate, the electrophilic character of the carbonyls is decreased by the free electron pair from N.

References

1. Zelinsky, N., *Chem. Ber.*, **35**, 2138 (1902).
2. Acree, S. F., *Chem. Ber.*, **37**, 2753 (1904).
3. Wilson, F. J., and Hyslop, W. McN., *J. Chem. Soc.*, **123**, 2612 (1923).
4. Papa, D., Villani, F. J., and Ginsberg, H. F., *J. Am. Chem. Soc.*, **76**, 4446 (1954).
5. Disselnköter, H., and Kurtz, P., *Ann. Chem.*, **679**, 26 (1964).
6. Ried, W., *Angew. Chem.*, **76**, 933, 973 (1964).
7. Holand, S., and Epsztein, R., *Compt. Rend.*, **252**, 1633 (1961).
8. Koulkes, M., and Marszak, I., *Compt. Rend.*, **246**, 785 (1958); Marszak, I., *et al.*, *Bull. Soc. Chim. France*, 1895 (1967).
9. Bohlmann, F., and Politt, J., *Chem. Ber.*, **90**, 130 (1957).
10. Ried, W., and Schmidt, H.-J., *Chem. Ber.*, **90**, 2499 (1957).
11. Ried, W., and Dankert, G., *Chem. Ber.*, **92**, 1223 (1959).
12. Ried, W., and Wesselborg, K., *Naturwissenschaften*, **46**, 142 (1959).

13. Wessely, F., Zbiral, E., and Lohrmann, E., *Chem. Ber.*, **92**, 2141 (1959).
14. Chodkiewicz, W., Cadiot, P., and Willemart, A., *Compt. Rend.*, **245**, 206 (1957).
15. Ried, W., and Suarez-Rivero, E., *Chem. Ber.*, **96**, 1475 (1963).
16. Ried, W., and Urschel, A., *Chem. Ber.*, **91**, 2459 (1958).
17. Ried, W., and Schmidt, H.-J., *Chem. Ber.*, **90**, 2553 (1957).
18. Ried, W., and Dankert, G., *Angew. Chem.*, **69**, 614 (1957).
19. Ried, W., Schmidt, H.-J., and Wesselborg, K., *Angew. Chem.*, **70**, 270 (1958).
20. Ried, W., Schmidt, H.-J., and Urschel, A., *Chem. Ber.*, **91**, 2472 (1958).
21. Ried, W., and Lukas, H., *Chem. Ber.*, **93**, 589 (1960).
22. Ried, W., Donner, W., and Schlegelmilch, W., *Chem. Ber.*, **94**, 1051 (1961).
23. Chodkiewicz, W., and Cadiot, P., *Compt. Rend.*, **247**, 2383 (1958).
24. Cognacq, J.-C., and Chodkiewicz, W., *Bull. Soc. Chim. France*, 1999 (1966).
25. Ried, W., and Neidhardt, H., *Chem. Ber.*, **94**, 373 (1961).
26. Ried, W., and Fastabend, W., *Chem. Ber.*, **95**, 1562 (1962).
27. Ried, W., Fastabend, W., and Hersek, S., *Chem. Ber.*, **98**, 245 (1965).

PART SIX

The Mannich Reaction with Acetylenes

1. BACKGROUND

The Mannich reaction of acetylenes is by definition an ethynylation. It is similar to ordinary ethynylation, except that the products are aminomethylacetylenes instead of hydroxymethylacetylenes.

Mannich and Chang[1] in 1933 found that "activated" acetylenes such as phenylacetylene react with formaldehyde and a secondary amine in dioxane at 100° to give good yields of substituted propargylamines.

$$PhC\equiv CH + HCHO + R_2NH \longrightarrow PhC\equiv CCH_2NR_2$$

Vinylacetylene behaves similarly.[2] Acetylene itself is not reactive enough, so cuprous catalysts are used. Reppe reported the first cuprous-catalyzed reactions.[3,4] Acetylene under pressure reacts as a difunctional molecule to give diaminobutynes, $R_2NCH_2C\equiv CCH_2NR_2$. If no formaldehyde is present, 2 moles of acetylene and 1 mole of amine react to form aminobutynes,

$$R_2N\overset{\overset{\displaystyle H}{|}}{\underset{\underset{\displaystyle CH_3}{|}}{C}}-C\equiv CH.$$

2. MECHANISM

Ried[5] believes this is an S_E2 reaction, as suggested before for acid-catalyzed Mannich reactions. The proton is furnished by ionization of the acetylene compound. The following mechanism is suggested for the Mannich reaction with dialkynyl compounds:

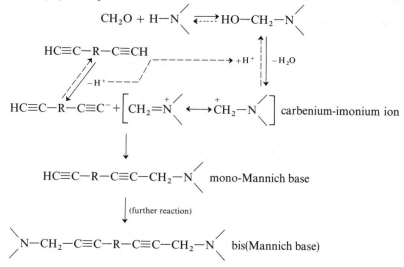

Study of the Mannich reaction with propargyl alcohol supports this mechanism.[12]

3. MANNICH REACTION OF ACETYLENE

3.1. Primary Amines

Moore and Vitcha[6] reacted primary amines with aldehydes and acetylene in the presence of cuprous catalysts at 170 psig and 60°. The general reaction is:

$$RNH_2 + R'CHO + C_2H_2 \longrightarrow RN(\overset{\displaystyle R'}{\overset{|}{C}HC\equiv CH})_2$$

Secondary amines give $RR'NCH_2C\equiv CH$, the N-propargylamines.

3.2. Secondary Amines: Low-pressure Mannich Reaction of Acetylene

Fegley[7] described a simple low-pressure system for preparing 1,4-dimethylamino-2-butyne:

Bis(dimethylaminomethane), 5 moles, was mixed with 36% formaldehyde, 5.75 moles, below 50°. Cuprous chloride, 0.2 mole, and then acetylene at 1.33 atmospheres were added. Within 50 minutes, 5.23 moles of acetylene had been absorbed. The products were

3-dimethylamino-1-propyne (9 % yield) and 1,4-dimethylamino-2-butyne (73 % yield). Isomerization of the dimethylamino-2-butyne at 70° by sodium metal gave 85% yield of 1,4-bis(dimethylamino-1,3-butadiene), which on heating with a primary amine gave N-substituted pyrroles in low yields.

4. MANNICH REACTION OF SUBSTITUTED ACETYLENES

4.1. Primary Amines

In the presence of cuprous chloride catalyst, 3-diethylamino-1-propyne reacts with ethylamine and formaldehyde in water to give 44% yield of ethylbis(4-diethylamino-2-butyn-1-yl)amine:[8]

$$Et_2NCH_2C{\equiv}CH + EtNH_2 + HCHO \xrightarrow[\text{temperature, 5 hr at 50°}]{\text{1 hr at room}} (Et_2NCH_2C{\equiv}CCH_2)_2NEt$$

4.2. Secondary Amines

Ferric chloride catalyzes the reaction between paraformaldehyde, diethylamine and isopropenylacetylene in dioxane at 100°. The yield of 1-diethylamino-4-methyl-4-hexen-2-yne is 89%; the yield without ferric chloride is only 3.5%. Thus, catalysis by cuprous salts is not unique in the Mannich reaction with acetylenes.

Benzoylpropargylamine reacts with paraformaldehyde and diethylamine in dioxane-water at 50°, in the presence of cuprous chloride catalyst, to give 1-diethylamino-4-benzamido-2-butyne.[9] Other aroylpropargylamines and other amines react similarly.

Ethoxyacetylene and other acetylenic ethers do not give the normal Mannich reaction. Ethoxyacetylene, aqueous formaldehyde and nonaromatic amines give ethyl esters of derivatives of β-aminopropionic acid.[10]

Nonconjugated diethynyl hydrocarbons undergo a normal Mannich reaction in refluxing dioxane. The reaction is slow, and the yield depends on the acidity of the diethynyl hydrocarbon.[5] Apparently the reaction takes place in two steps, the mono product forming first and then reacting with more formaldehyde and secondary amine. The yield of bis(Mannich bases) from diethynylcyclohexanes is 30–100% after 100 hours reaction time. Morpholine gives better yields than piperidine.

Tertiary diacetylenic alcohols react with paraformaldehyde and secondary amines to form Mannich bases:[11]

$$RR'C(OH)C{\equiv}CC{\equiv}CH + HCHO + R''_2NH \xrightarrow[\text{reflux 2 hr}]{\text{dioxane}}$$

$$R''_2NCH_2C{\equiv}CC{\equiv}CC(OH)RR'$$
(63–88 % yield)

Heating the Mannich base with a trace of KOH at 150° under vacuum decomposes the carbinol to $HC{\equiv}CC{\equiv}CCH_2NR''_2$. The diacetylenic amine reacts (as the sodio derivative in ammonia) with aldehydes to give 1,6-bis-(dimethylamino)-2,4-hexadiynes.

Propargyl alcohol presents special problems in the Mannich reaction. Reaction with formaldehyde and amines takes place preferentially at the hydroxyl group to form $ROCH_2NR'_2$. Salvador and Simon found that they could induce a normal Mannich reaction at the acetylenic hydrogen by using a little cupric sulfate as catalyst in a particular reaction procedure. The cupric ion is presumably reduced to cuprous by the propargyl alcohol. The reaction using dimethylamine is typical: Dimethylamine was dissolved in water, and the pH was adjusted to 9 by adding sulfuric acid. Aqueous formalin and propargyl alcohol were added, and then an aqueous solution of cupric sulfate (5 grams of $CuSO_4$ per mole of propargyl alcohol) was added, followed by adjustment of pH to 8.4 with excess dimethylamine. The mixture was then refluxed at 80°. The solution gradually turned yellow (copper propargylide) and deposited metallic copper after 55 minutes. The yield of 4-diethyl-amino-2-butyn-1-ol was 81 %. The pH had a large effect on the reaction (Table 5-47). The Mannich bases prepared in this work are listed in Table 5-48.

Acetylenic compounds with "acidic" ethynyl hydrogen undergo the Mannich reaction easily, and some do not require catalysts (e.g., phenylacetylene).

TABLE 5-47
Reaction of Propargyl Alcohol with Formaldehyde and Dimethylamine—Effect of pH[12]

Initial pH	% Yield	Time of run	Remarks
9.0	62	55 min	Metallic copper precipitates
→8.4 (optimum)	80	55 min.	Some precipitation of metallic copper
7.9	80	$5\frac{1}{2}$ hr	Some copper propargylide remains
6.0	80	$5\frac{1}{2}$ hr	Some copper propargylide remains
5.0	77	$5\frac{1}{2}$ hr	Copper propargylide forms slowly
4.5	75	$5\frac{1}{2}$ hr	Copper propargylide forms slowly
3.8	65	$5\frac{1}{2}$ hr	Copper propargylide forms slowly
3.0	0	$5\frac{1}{2}$ hr	Copper propargylide does not form
7.0	0	$5\frac{1}{2}$ hr	No copper ion present

TABLE 5-48[12]

$$HO-CH_2-C\equiv C-CH_2-N\overset{R}{\underset{R}{\diagdown}} \quad (80°, pH = 8.4)$$

R	b.p. (°C, @ mm Hg)	% Yield
Methyl	76–78, @ 1.5	81
Ethyl	92–93, @ 2	80
Pyrrolidino	106–107, @ 1.5	84
Piperidino	112–113, @ 1.5	80
Morpholino	104–106, @ 0.1	80
Isopropyl	96–98, @ 2	87.5

Acetylenic compounds with electron-releasing groups such as hydroxyl are much less acidic, so formation of acetylene anion is decreased, and activity in the Mannich reaction is decreased. The copper catalyst must react with the ethynyl hydrogen of propargyl alcohol to form copper propargylide (the yellow precipitate observed), which can furnish anions which react with amine-formaldehyde.

$$CuSO_4 + \text{propargyl alcohol (basic solution)} \longrightarrow HOCH_2C \equiv C^- Cu^+$$

The form in which formaldehyde and amine react has been the subject of much debate. Fegley[7] used bis(dimethylamino)methane as the source of amine in his Mannich reactions. Salvador and Simon[12] identified two intermediates when they used piperidine as the amine: N-methylolpiperidine[1] and bis-(piperidino)methane.[2]

Taking all their observations into account, Salvador and Simon propose this mechanism, similar in many respects to Ried's[5] for other acetylenes (see Section 2):

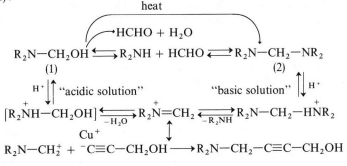

References

1. Mannich, C., and Chang, F. T., *Chem. Ber.*, **66**, 418 (1933).
2. Coffman, D. D., *J. Am. Chem. Soc.*, **57**, 1978 (1935).
3. Copenhaver, J. W., and Bigelow, M. H., "Acetylene and Carbon Monoxide Chemistry," New York, Reinhold Publishing Corp., 1949.
4. Reppe, W., *et al.*, *Ann. Chem.*, **596**, 1 (1955); **601**, 81 (1956).
5. Ried, W., and Wesselborg, K., *Ann. Chem.*, **635**, 97 (1960).
6. Moore, G. L., and Vitcha, J. F. (to Cumberland Chem. Corp.), U.S. Patent 3,268,583 (Aug. 23, 1966); *Chem. Abstr.*, **65**, 19498 (1966).
7. Fegley, M. F., Bortnick, N. M., and McKeever, C. H., *J. Am. Chem. Soc.*, **79**, 4140, 4144 (1957).
8. Krugilikova, R. I., and Pikalov, V. E., *Izv. Vysshikh Uchebn. Zavedenii, Khim. i Khim. Tekhnol.*, **8**, 349 (1965); *Chem. Abstr.*, **63**, 11333 (1965).
9. Krugilikova, R. I., and Umanskaya, T. A., *Zh. Organ. Khim.*, **1**, 230 (1965); *Chem. Abstr.*, **62**, 14561 (1965).
10. Arens, J. F., Koerts, D. H., and Plieger, P., *Rec. Trav. Chim.*, **75**, 1454 (1956).
11. Gusev, B. P., *Izv. Akad. Nauk SSSR, Ser. Khim.*, 846 (1965); *Chem. Abstr.*, **63**, 11342 (1965).
12. Salvador, R. L., and Simon, D., *Can. J. Chem.*, **44**, 2570 (1966).

Chapter Six

COUPLING OF ACETYLENIC COMPOUNDS

1. BACKGROUND

One of the most useful properties of terminal acetylenes is their ability to couple under very mild conditions to form conjugated polyacetylenes. The two most widely used systems are:

(1) Oxidative coupling, frequently called Glaser coupling.

(2) The newer Chodkiewicz-Cadiot coupling of an acetylene with a 1-haloacetylene.

A third method, Grignard reagent coupling, is analogous to the Chodkiewicz-Cadiot reaction, but is less widely used.

The Glaser and Chodkiewicz-Cadiot systems are the most important and they complement each other. Intense interest in naturally occurring polyacetylenes has spurred research on coupling reactions in recent years.[1,2] Equally interesting is the discovery that oxidative coupling can be modified so that α,ω-diynes can be coupled and cyclized to macrocyclic polyacetylenes[3] (see also Chapter 7). Coupling reactions can also be used to form linear polymers.

Eglinton and McCrae[4] wrote a comprehensive review covering the literature through 1961. Their tables include most coupling reactions known at that time.

2. OXIDATIVE OR GLASER COUPLING

2.1. Glaser Conditions

Glaser[5] reported the first acetylene coupling reaction in 1869. He added phenyl-acetylene to ammoniacal cuprous chloride and isolated the cuprous derivative. He then oxidized the cuprous phenylacetylide to form diphenyldiacetylene. This method is not used very often because the cuprous acetylides are sometimes hard to isolate and because they are frequently too insoluble to couple well. A recent example is the preparation of dicyanodiacetylene:[6]

$$KO_2CC\equiv CCO_2K \xrightarrow[100°]{water} HC\equiv CCO_2K \xrightarrow[H_2SO_4]{MeOH} HC\equiv CCO_2Me \xrightarrow{NH_4OH}$$

$$HC\equiv CCONH_2 \xrightarrow{P_2O_5} HC\equiv CCN \xrightarrow[NH_4OH]{CuCl} CuC\equiv CCN \xrightarrow[2-5°]{K_3Fe(CN)_6} NCC\equiv CC\equiv CCN$$

$$(33\% \text{ from } HC\equiv CCN)$$

In 1920, Moreau[7] first reported this coupling, and in 1955 Brockman[8] proved that the product is dicyanodiacetylene. Brockman described his dicyanodiacety-lene as an unstable white solid. Saggiomo[6] obtained pure crystalline stable product by careful distillation and sublimation under nitrogen.

2.2. Modified Glaser Coupling

A generally better method, still called the Glaser reaction, is to mix the acetylenic compound with aqueous cuprous chloride-ammonium chloride solution in an atmosphere of air or oxygen. This system was used for many years with little variation, until recently. Thousands of coupling reactions have been reported.[4]

2.3. Cross-coupling

The Glaser reaction can be used to cross-couple two different acetylenes. Baeyer reported the first cross-coupling in 1882.[9] Cross-coupling gives all three of the possible coupled products, the ratios depending on the nature of the acetylenic compounds:

$$RC\equiv CH + HC\equiv CR' \longrightarrow RC\equiv CC\equiv CR + RC\equiv CC\equiv CR' + R'C\equiv CC\equiv CR'$$

A large number of propargylic amines, $RR'\overset{\underset{\displaystyle NR''R'''}{|}}{C}-C\equiv CH$, are known. They include the simplest amine, propargylamine[10,11], through the fully alkylated homologs[12] and all the intermediate substitution states.[11-14] The amines can have primary, secondary or tertiary nitrogen on primary, secondary or tertiary carbon.[15] The corresponding propargylic alcohols are easily available as start-ing materials for making the amines. Hennion[16] prepared a series of diacetylenic 1,6-amino alcohols and derivatives for physiological screening. He found in some cases that Zal'kinds[16a] Glaser coupling procedure gave high selectivity to the amino alcohol (A-B):

$$\overset{\underset{\displaystyle |}{NR''R'''}}{RR'C}-C{\equiv}CH + HC{\equiv}CC\overset{\underset{\displaystyle |}{OH}}{R^1R^2} \longrightarrow A\text{-}B + A\text{-}A + B\text{-}B$$
$$\phantom{RR'C-C{\equiv}CH \;}A \phantom{+ HC{\equiv}CC}B$$

With 1 mole of A and 5 moles of B, the product was largely the amino alcohol A-B and contained only a little glycol B-B. If the amino alcohol and the glycol melted above 100°, extraction by dilute HCl and recrystallization gave pure amino alcohol. Amines and carbinols with tertiary carbons gave the best yields and the most stable products.

The products with primary carbon are often sensitive to light and air. Three moles of hydrogen add rapidly to the products in the presence of Raney nickel, and the fourth mole adds slowly. For secondary, and particularly tertiary, amines, hydrogenolysis to remove the amine group is a serious side reaction during hydrogenation.

2.4. Side Reactions: Straus Coupling

Glaser coupling is frequently complicated by an important side reaction, first observed by Straus[17] in 1905, and called "Straus" coupling. This reaction is actually a vinylation, analogous to the vinylacetylene synthesis discovered later by Nieuwland. The product is an enyne instead of a diyne. Straus coupling is minimized by avoiding strong acid conditions and large concentrations of cuprous acetylides in the reaction mixture. The Straus reaction has been used to prepare a number of enyne hydrocarbons and acids and apparently has very wide scope. Thus,[18]

$$PhCH{=}CHC{\equiv}CCu \xrightarrow[\text{(2) hydrolysis}]{\text{(1) HOAc, O}_2} \textit{trans-}PhCH{=}CH{-}C{\equiv}CCH{=}CHCH{=}CHPh$$

Kauer[18a] found that alkynes can be coupled to form enynes in a special system. A homogeneous solution of cuprous chloride-HCl in benzonitrile at 140° catalyzes the dimerization only in the presence of oxygen. Propyne gives 25% yield of cis-2-hexen-4-yne and 11% yield of trans-2-hexen-4-yne. The oxidative coupling product, 2,4-hexadiyne, is the major by-product (10% yield).

2.5. The Cupric Salt-Pyridine System

Coupling by cupric salts in pyridine is an important variation developed by Eglinton and Galbraith.[3] The acetylenic compound is simply mixed with a pyridine solution of cupric acetate. Cuprous salt is probably present in large enough concentration to start the reaction:

$$2RC{\equiv}CH + 2CuX_2 \longrightarrow RC{\equiv}CC{\equiv}CR + Cu_2X_2 + 2HX$$

Pyridine neutralizes the HX formed. In addition, pyridine complexes with the copper salts and is a powerful solvent for most of the reactants and products. Co-solvents such as methanol can be added. With catalytic amounts of cupric salts, the reactions are very slow, but with excess cupric salt, they are fast. This is one of the best laboratory procedures, and probably is the most satisfactory method for making macrocyclic acetylenes. Alkynes generally couple slowly, but they couple rapidly under slightly acidic Glaser conditions, so the two methods complement each other.

2.6. Mechanism of Oxidative (Glaser) Coupling

2.6.1. CATALYST

Copper compounds are the only known catalysts for oxidative coupling. The specific effect of copper has puzzled chemists for years. Copper is probably an electron acceptor in the reaction, and other variable valence ions might be expected to be active. However, ferric, cobaltic, ferrous or cobaltous,[4] and stannic or mercuric[19] salts are not catalysts. Cuprous ion and acetylene bonds apparently can form σ bonds from the d orbitals of the carbon and the free π orbitals of the metal, but the other metals cannot. In addition, the redox potential of cuprous to cupric ion is apparently just right for coupling conditions.[4] Palladium chloride complexes with benzene: Pd^{++} accepts protons to form metallic palladium and biphenyl.[20] Palladium salts also complex with acetylenes, but they have not been reported as catalysts for coupling acetylenes.

2.6.2. EFFECT OF pH

Klebanskii[21] used cuprous chloride in aqueous pyridine with oxygen, or cupric chloride without oxygen, to couple phenylacetylene, phenylpropynol, methylbutynol and other acetylenes. He reported that the coupling of 3-methyl-1-butyn-3-ol in the presence of cuprous chloride–ammonium chloride is very sensitive to pH, the rate declining rapidly with increased acidity. This contradicts Armitage's results.[22] Klebanskii found that electrolytic oxidation is also a good coupling procedure if a copper anode is used.

Armitage and co-workers[22] used methylethynylcarbinol as a model acetylene to study the effect of the pH of the cuprous chloride-ammonium coupling solution on the yield of coupled product. Their results show a definite optimum at pH 3, where the best yield (94%) was obtained in the shortest time (4 hours; Table 6-1).

Several other carbinols and enynols coupled under the best conditions to give 82–98% yields of coupled products. Maximum yield and minimum Straus coupling are obtained above pH 2.

TABLE 6-1

Effect of pH on the Oxidative Coupling of Methylethynyl carbinol (0.2 Mole of Carbinol, 0.5 Mole of Cuprous Chloride, 1.5 moles of Ammonium Chloride)[22]

pH	Time (hr)	% Yield of Coupled Product
13	4	28
7	12	56
4	4	78
3	4	94
2	4	90
2	14	70[a]
2	40	90[b]

[a] 0.4 mole of ammonium chloride.
[b] 0.4 mole of carbinol. 0.2 mole of cuprous chloride.

2.63. KINETICS AND MECHANISM

From his extensive studies, Klebanskii[21] concluded that cupric ion is the actual oxidizing agent. He pictured coupling in aqueous solution as a three-step process:

$$RC\equiv CH \underset{}{\overset{slow}{\rightleftharpoons}} RC\equiv C^- + H^+$$
$$RC\equiv C^- \overset{Cu^{++}}{\longrightarrow} RC\equiv C\cdot + Cu^+$$
$$2RC\equiv C\cdot \longrightarrow RC\equiv CC\equiv CR$$

$RC\equiv CCu$ was not detected by polarography. Thus, in alkaline solutions the rate-determining step is ionization of the acetylenic hydrogen, accelerated by the base and the copper ions.

For kinetic studies, homogeneous solutions are necessary, but in practice, mixes are frequently two or more phases. Bohlmann[23] used a solution of cuprous chloride-ethanolamine hydrochloride in 80% aqueous methanol for his extensive and significant kinetic work. He performed the Glaser couplings at pH 3, and followed the progress of the reactions by measuring UV extinction. Kinetics showed that the Glaser coupling is second order. The times necessary for 50% reaction show that the rate decreases with increasing conjugation of the acetylenic bonds (Table 6-2).

Using Eglinton's cupric salt–pyridine system, Bohlmann determined times for 50% reaction (Table 6-3). This system is alkaline. Increasing conjugation of the triple bonds increases the rate, the reverse of the situation in acidic Glaser coupling.

It is difficult to find a simple explanation for the data. Klebanskii's postulate that dissociation of the acetylenic compound is rate determining cannot explain

TABLE 6-2
Times for 50% Reactions in Oxidative Coupling[23]

(Concentration of acetylenic = 37.5 mmole/liter, Cu^+ = 150 mmole/liter)

	$t_{1/2}$ (min)		$t_{1/2}$ (min)
p-O_2N—C_6H_4—$C{\equiv}CH$	85	H_3C—$(CH_2)_4$—$C{\equiv}CH$	1,000
C_6H_5—$C{\equiv}CH$	260	H_3C—$CH{=}CH$—$C{\equiv}C$—$C{\equiv}CH$	1,500
p-H_3CO—C_6H_4—$C{\equiv}CH$	460	H_3C—$(CH_2)_3$—$C{\equiv}C$—$C{\equiv}CH$	3,700
$HOCH_2$—$CH{=}CH$—$C{\equiv}CH$	510	H_3C—$C{\equiv}C$—$C{\equiv}CH$	6,900
(cyclohexane with OH and C≡CH)	580	C_6H_5—$C{\equiv}C$—$C{\equiv}CH$	11,000
		C_6H_5—$C{\equiv}C$—$C{\equiv}C$—$C{\equiv}CH$	30,000

TABLE 6-3
Times for 50% Reaction in Cupric
Salt-Pyridine Coupling[23]

(Concentration of acetylenic = 8 mmole/liter,
Cu^{++} = 100 mmole/liter)

	$t_{1/2}$ (min)	Temperature (°C)
C_6H_5—$C{\equiv}C$—$C{\equiv}CH$	65	0
(cyclohexene)—$C{\equiv}C$—$C{\equiv}CH$	160	0
	2	20
C_7H_{15}—$C{\equiv}C$—$C{\equiv}CH$	80	20
H_3C—$C{\equiv}C$—$C{\equiv}CH$	200	20
p-O_2N—C_6H_4—$C{\equiv}CH$	660	20
p-H_3CO—C_0H_4—$C{\equiv}CH$	230	60
C_6H_5—$C{\equiv}CH$	35,000	20
	320	60
(cyclohexene)—$C{\equiv}CH$	1,800	60
$AcOCH_2$—$CH{=}CH$—$C{\equiv}CH$	27,000	20
C_4H_9—$C{\equiv}CH$	4,400	60
$(CH_2)_8$ with CO_2CH_2—$CH{=}CH$—$C{\equiv}CH$ and CO_2CH_2—$CH{=}CH$—$C{\equiv}CH$	25[a]	20[a]
	20[b]	20[b]

[a] Acetylenic = 1, 2 or 3 mmoles/liter. Cu^{++} 15 mmoles/liter.
[b] Same as a, except 15 mmoles cuprous ion added.

the kinetics. Rate-determining dissociation would cause first-order kinetics, and Bohlmann observed second-order kinetics.

In the acidic Glaser coupling, rate increases as concentration of cuprous ion increases. A plausible explanation is rate-determining formation of a π complex. The easier the formation of the complex, the faster is the rate. Conjugated acetylenes are slower, consistent with their known sluggishness in electrophilic additions. The π complex accelerates the dissociation:

$$RC\!\equiv\!\underset{\overset{|}{Cu^+}}{C}\!H \rightleftharpoons RC\!\equiv\!\underset{\overset{|}{Cu^+}}{C^-} + H^+$$

The complex is the molecule which ionizes. Experimental results confirm this. For *p*-nitrophenylacetylene, the triple bond character is weak because the acceptor action of the nitro group is weak, and the complex formation is very fast. The phenyl group can be a donor or an acceptor, but a diyne group next to phenyl is an acceptor, so diyne coupling is slower. Triple bond character can be measured by NMR. Figure 6-1 is a plot which shows the relationship between triple bond character and the rate of coupling.

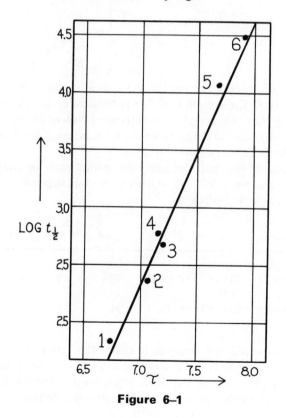

Figure 6–1

In the alkaline pyridine-cupric ion system, the anion can form without π complexing. Here the mobility of the acetylenic hydrogen is rate determining: the greater the acidity of the acetylenic hydrogen, the faster is the rate. Cupric ion must complex in order to be the oxidation catalyst. The reaction is second order, so the complex must contain two acetylene molecules:[23]

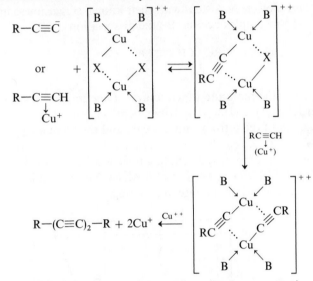

Increased acidity of the copper complex and increased concentration of cupric ion increase the rate. The coupling of diynes to form cyclic acetylenes is first order, confirming that two acetylene groups are involved in the cupric complexes. The rate in pyridine in the presence of a large excess of cupric and cuprous ions is independent of concentration of diyne.

Mixed coupling of two pairs of acetylene compounds in pyridine-cupric acetate illustrates that the selectivity to a given product depends on the relative acidities of the acetylenic hydrogens:[23]

Acetylenes	% AA	% AB	% BB
A $C_6H_5-(C\equiv C)_2H$			
B $HOCH_2-CH=CH-C\equiv CH$	99.6	0.3	0.1
A $C_6H_5-C\equiv CH$			
B $HOCH_2-CH=CH-C\equiv CH$	51	38.5	10.5

The mechanism is still not completely clear. The rate in alkaline medium varies with amine concentration. The rate in solutions of substituted pyridines depends on the basicity of the pyridine. Thus, the relative rates in pyridine, α-picoline and 2,6-lutidine are $40:7:1$.[23] Sometimes a definite complex gives faster rates. For example, tetramethylethylenediamine accelerates the coupling reaction significantly.[25]

2.7. Catalytic Glaser Coupling

In 1960, Hay[24] reported another significant improvement in Glaser coupling reactions. Certain cuprous salt-amine complexes can be used in catalytic amounts to effect rapid Glaser coupling. Pyridine is able to serve as both ligand and solvent. Cupric carboxylates are the only cupric salts which are catalysts, but cuprous salts are much better. In one example, phenylacetylene at 35° gave 96% yield of diphenyldiacetylene in only 40 minutes under best conditions.

Hay[25] found later that his cuprous chloride-tertiary amine catalysts couple aliphatic acetylenic compounds slowly. He was able to prepare much more active catalysts by using bidentate ligands, such as N,N,N′N′-tetramethylethylenediamine. The complexes are more soluble in organic solvents and thus are doubly advantageous. To illustrate the effectiveness of the various systems, Hay compared the rate of coupling of phenylacetylene, 1-ethynyl-cyclohexanol and 1-hexyne in three systems:

(A) Eglinton's cupric acetate-pyridine,
(B) Cuprous chloride-pyridine-oxygen,
(C) Cuprous chloride-tetramethylethylenediamine-oxygen.

Times for half reaction at 30°, with $0.4M$ acetylenic compound are:

| Moles of Cu × 10^{-3} | Acetylenic Compound | Coupling System | | |
| | | A | B | C |
		(half-reaction, min)		
5	Phenylacetylene	270	96	10
15	1-Ethynylcyclohexanol	420	360	13
60	1-Hexyne	550	950	55

The yields of other coupled products by method C are summarized in Table 6-4.

Hay's procedure is important. It is not only convenient for laboratory work, but it is potentially an economical commercial method. Catalytic amounts of cuprous chloride give fast, high-yield reactions. Reppe[26] in 1955 reported catalytic coupling of propargyl alcohol. Fifty moles of alcohol coupled per mole of cuprous chloride, but it was necessary to use oxygen under pressure.

2.8. High-dilution Coupling-Cyclization Reactions

Simple α,ω-diynes have been known for years. In 1959, Eglinton and Galbraith[3] reported the first cyclic conjugated diyne

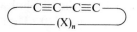

TABLE 6-4

Catalytic Coupling by Cuprous Chloride-Tetramethylethylenediamine[25]

(5 mole % cuprous catalyst, 28°)

Acetylenic Compound	% Yield	m.p. of Coupled Product (°C)
Ethynylcyclohexanol	93	177
Phenylacetylene	97	87–88
3-Methyl-1-butyn-3-ol	85	138
3-Methyl-1-pentyn-3-ol	82	93–95
1-Ethynylcyclopentanol	89	138–140

and introduced a new method for cyclic coupling of diacetylenic compounds. This method is now known as the "high-dilution" oxidative coupling procedure. They reasoned that the oxidative coupling mechanism could be represented by the equations:

$$4RC\equiv CH + 2Cu^{++} \xrightarrow{\text{fast}} (RC\equiv C)_2 + 2RC\equiv CCu + 4H^+$$

$$2RC\equiv CCu + 2Cu^{++} \xrightarrow{\text{slow}} (RC\equiv C)_2 + 2H^+ + 2Cu^+$$

These equations are correct for the reaction at pH 6, buffered to avoid developing acidity which slows the reaction. Coupled product forms rapidly, in 50% yield, and about half of the acetylenic compound forms the insoluble cuprous salt. If excess cupric ion is available, additional coupled product slowly forms according to the second equation. Thus, good coupling-cyclization reactions would require a homogeneous solution, under high-dilution conditions, to prevent the formation of linear polymeric products and insoluble cuprous salts.

Anhydrous cupric acetate in ether-pyridine is one homogeneous reaction system:

In a typical high-dilution experiment, 1 gram of di(but-3-yn-1-yl) sebacate in 140 ml of 1:6 ether-pyridine was added to a refluxing solution of cupric acetate (3.4 grams) in 700 ml of the same solvent. The drops of ester solution were added so that they were continuously entrained in the refluxing solvent in a specially modified continuous extraction apparatus. Addition required 2.5 hours. After an additional hour, the green solution was worked up. The yield of cycloocta-3,5-diynylene sebacate was 63% (m.p. 55°).

High-dilution coupling of tetradeca-1,3-diyne gave 17–40% yield of 1,3-cyclotetradecadiyne. Linear dimer also formed. The cyclic monomeric diyne darkened at room temperature in air, with the formation of carbonyl groups. Thus, it is more strained and less stable than the cyclic dimer. The dihexynyl ester of terephthalic acid, prepared from the alcohol and terephthaloyl chloride, coupled to form 30% yield of dimer, m.p. 210°. The infrared spectra showed that the $C \equiv C$ stretching frequencies are relatively insensitive to the substituent groups and are of such low intensity that they can be masked by overtone and combination bands, especially in aromatic and oxygenated compounds.

Bohlmann's[23] observation that the more acidic ethynyl compounds couple more rapidly in the pyridine-cupric acetate system was confirmed by the reaction rates noted in this study.[3]

Low concentrations as in the high-dilution reaction system give the lowest cyclic oligomer which is sterically favorable. In some cases, yields of single products are as high as 88%. Sondheimer, however, used ordinary concentrations to couple-cyclize numerous α,ω-diynes, and usually obtained complex mixtures and low yields of individual products.[28,29] Others[30] have used only slightly lower concentrations and have obtained high yields of single products in certain cases. This confusion led to a study of the effect of concentration on the cyclization of 1,7-octadiyne.[27] Reaction products were analyzed by total hydrogenation of the mixture and GLC separation of the saturated cycloparaffins. The method could not detect the cyclic tetramers and higher.

A molar concentration of cupric acetate four times the initial diyne concentration was used. With decreased cupric acetate concentration, the amount of insoluble long-chain polymer decreased, the ratio of acyclic to cyclic dimer and trimer increased, and the ratio of cyclic dimer to cyclic trimer increased (Table 6-5).

TABLE 6-5
Coupling of 1,7-Octadiyne in 1:1 Pyridine-Methanol at 55°[27]

Initial diyne (mmoles/liters)	Initial Cu(OAc)$_2$ (mmoles/liters)	Polymer (% of diyne)	Cyclic Dimer / Cyclic Trimer	Acyclic / Cyclic
100	400	55	1.1	No acyclic
50	200	43	1.6	0.15
25	100	26	2.4	6.7
12.5	50	0	3.9	20

Sondheimer[31] prepared cyclic trimers, dimers, tetramers, pentamers and hexamers simultaneously by simply heating diacetylenes in homogeneous coupling media. Usually, very little linear coupling product formed. One part of nona-1,8-diyne in 100 parts of pyridine stirred with 15 parts of neutral cupric acetate is a typical reaction charge. The products were separated by chromatography on alumina. The cyclic polyacetylenes were crystalline. They had no infrared band at 3300 cm^{-1} for acetylenic hydrogen and formed no precipitate with silver nitrate. The carbon-hydrogen determinations gave low carbon values because most of the polyacetylenes exploded when combusted. Coupled products and yields are listed in Table 6-6.

TABLE 6-6

Simultaneous Formation of Cyclic Dimers, Trimers, etc., by Oxidative Coupling[31]

$$HC{\equiv}C(CH_2)_n C{\equiv}CH \longrightarrow \begin{array}{c} \text{---}(CH_2)_n\text{---} \\ \text{---}C{\equiv}C\text{---}C{\equiv}C]_x\text{---} \end{array} \left(\begin{array}{l} x = 2, \text{dimer} \\ x = 3, \text{trimer} \\ x = 4, \text{tetramer} \\ \text{etc.} \end{array} \right)$$

n	x	% Yield
5	2	10
	3	13
	4	11
	5	9
	6	4
4	2	9
	3	14
	4	8
	5	8
3	2	0
	3	3
	4	4
2	3	6
	4	6

Some recent examples of other Glaser coupling reactions are given in Table 6-7.

3. CHODKIEWICZ-CADIOT COUPLING

In 1957, Chodkiewicz and Cadiot[43,44] reported a different method for coupling acetylenic compounds: A terminal acetylene reacts with a 1-bromoacetylene in the presence of a cuprous salt catalyst and an amine.

$$RC{\equiv}CH + BrC{\equiv}CR' \xrightarrow[\text{H}_2\text{NOH}\cdot\text{HCl}]{\text{Cu}_2\text{Cl}_2\text{-EtNH}_2} RC{\equiv}C{-}C{\equiv}CR' + HBr$$

This system solved many problems, particularly in the field of naturally occurring polyacetylene because unsymmetrical diacetylenes are the major products, without the complications resulting from the other products formed in Glaser cross-coupling. The method is particularly valuable when small quantities of hard-to-get acetylenes must be coupled.

The procedure is simple. Catalyst cuprous chloride is dissolved in aqueous ethylamine, or in ethylamine-methanol, and a little reducing agent, usually hydroxylamine hydrochloride, is added to keep copper in the cuprous state. The

TABLE 6-7

Recent Examples of Glaser Coupling of Acetylenic Compounds

$$2RC{\equiv}CH \longrightarrow RC{\equiv}CC{\equiv}CR$$

R	Coupling Medium	% Yield Dimer	m.p. (°C)	References
(cis) —CH=CHCH₃Cl				32
—(CH₂)₄C≡CCH₂OMe	CuCl—NH₄Cl—O₂	80		33
[aryl: —N=N—C₆H₄—C≡CH with NH₂]	Pyridine-Dimethylformamide	Dimer, Linear hexamer		34, 34
—C—Me₂ (NH₂)	CuCl·NH₄OH-O₂	91	50–62	35
—CH₂NH₂	CuCl·NH₄OH—O₂	10		35
—C≡C(CH₂)₂CO₂Me	CuCl·NH₄Cl-HCl-MeOH-O₂	92	86	36
[tetrahydropyranyl]	CuCl·NH₄Cl-HCl-O₂	70	b.p. 167, @ 2 mm	37
[tetrahydropyranyl]	CuCl·NH₄Cl-HCl-O₂	70	b.p. 153, @ 4 mm	37
—Ph (Me, CCOH, H)	Cu(OAc)₂-(pyridine-methanol) (1:1)	70–80		38
[p-tolyl—C≡C—C(Me)(COOH)H]	CuCl-pyridine-O₂	92	205	39
Biphenyl	Cu(OAc)₂-pyridine	Dimer		40
t-Butyl	CuCl-pyridine-O₂	55	131	41
t-Amyl	CuCl-pyridine-O₂	25		41
Other t-alkyl	CuCl-pyridine-O₂	2–50		41
—SEt	CuCl·NH₄OH-MeOH-O₂		b.p., @ 0.55 mm	42
—S—t-Bu	CuCl·NH₄OH-MeOH-O₂		50	42

acetylenic compound is added and dissolved, and the solution is stirred vigorously. The 1-bromoacetylene in a solvent is added, usually with external cooling. The reaction is fast. It is terminated by adding acid to neutralize the base. The product is extracted into ether. The reactions can be represented as:

$$RC{\equiv}CH + Cu^+ \xrightarrow{\text{fast}} RC{\equiv}CCu + H^+$$
$$RC{\equiv}CCu + BrC{\equiv}CR' \longrightarrow RC{\equiv}C{-}C{\equiv}CR' + CuBr$$

Free cuprous ion concentration is kept low to avoid coupling of the bromoacetylene to form a symmetrical diacetylene:

$$2R'C{\equiv}CBr + Cu^+ \longrightarrow R'C{\equiv}C{-}C{\equiv}CR' + CuBr_2$$

Acetylenic bromide concentration is kept low by adding the 1-bromoacetylene slowly to the catalyst solution of acetylenic compound.

Chodkiewicz-Cadiot coupling has not been used successfully to make macrocyclic acetylenes.

3.1. Mechanism of Chodkiewicz-Cadiot Coupling

Very little is known about the mechanism of this reaction. Cuprous ion is the only catalyst reported. The rate may depend on the acidity of the acetylenic hydrogens (but see references 45 and 46), so ionization of a solvated cuprous complex is likely. The great reactivity of the 1-bromoacetylenes probably also results from cuprous complexing at the triple bond. Mercuric and silver salts form similar complexes, but these have not been reported as catalysts. The reaction tolerates a wide variety of acetylenes and bromoacetylenes, solvents, and conditions. It is usually carried out at 15–50° in water, alcohols, tetrahydrofuran, ether, dimethylformamide or N-methylpyrrolidone, depending on the solubility of reagents.

The coupling gives at least two nitrogen-containing by-products: an amidoxime and an amidine.[47] The reaction of phenylacetylene with 1-bromo-2-phenylacetylene in n-butylamine-ethanol gave the two by-products:

$$
\begin{array}{ccc}
\overset{\displaystyle NBu}{\underset{\displaystyle \|}{}} & & \overset{\displaystyle NBu}{\underset{\displaystyle \|}{}} \\
PhCH_2CNHBu & \text{and} & PhCH_2CNHOH \\
\text{amidine} & & \text{amidoxime}
\end{array}
$$

1-Bromoacetylenes are apparently not as inert to nucleophilic substitution as usually believed.[48]

3.2. Examples

The Chodkiewicz-Cadiot reaction with acetylene tends to go an additional step:

$$RC{\equiv}CBr + HC{\equiv}CH \longrightarrow RC{\equiv}CC{\equiv}CH \longrightarrow R(C{\equiv}C)_3R$$

The second step is much less likely in the case of diacetylene.[49] Thus, diacetylene and 5-bromo-4-pentyn-1-ol give a high yield of the expected terminal triynol. Phenylbromoacetylene reacts with diacetylene at 0° to give 70% yield of phenyltriacetylene and only 30% yield of diphenyltetraacetylene.

The synthesis of biformin, a diol found in some microorganisms, involves Chodkiewicz-Cadiot coupling:[40]

$$\text{HC} \equiv \text{CC} \equiv \text{CH} + \text{BrC} \equiv \text{CCH}_2\text{CH} - \text{CH} \xrightarrow[\text{(2) hydrolysis}]{\text{(1) C-C coupling}} \text{H(C} \equiv \text{C)}_3\text{CH}_2\text{CHOHCH}_2\text{OH}$$

with the CH—CH bearing O   O bridged by CMe$_2$

The coupling is the key step in the synthesis of angelica acid esters.[50] An ultraviolet light isomerization converts the coupled product to an ester identical to the one found in *Aster Novi Belgii L.* (see Section 6).

$$\underset{\text{EtCHC} \equiv \text{CH}}{\overset{\text{OH}}{|}} + \text{BrC} \equiv \text{CCH} = \text{CHCO}_2\text{Me} \longrightarrow \underset{\text{EtCHC} \equiv \text{CC} \equiv \text{CCH} = \text{CHCO}_2\text{Me}}{\overset{\text{OH}}{|}}$$

$$\text{trans}$$
$$(65\%)$$

$$\xrightarrow{\text{UV, 2 hr}} \text{Et}\overset{\overset{\text{O}}{\|}}{\text{C}}\text{CH} = \text{CHC} \equiv \text{CCH} = \text{CHCO}_2\text{Me (m.p. 72°)}$$

$$\quad\quad\quad trans \quad\quad\quad\quad trans$$

angelica acid, methyl ester

Chodkiewicz-Cadiot coupling was used to prepare a series of conjugated enediynoic acids:[51]

$$\text{RC} \equiv \text{CH} + \text{BrC} \equiv \text{CCH} = \text{CHCO}_2\text{H} \longrightarrow \text{RC} \equiv \text{C} - \text{C} \equiv \text{CCH} = \text{CHCO}_2\text{H}$$

R	% Yield	m.p. (°C)
1-Hydroxycyclohexyl	72	174
1-Hydroxycyclopentyl	75	149
Diphenylcarbinyl	82	166
p-Nitrophenyl	30	256

Two acids prepared by this reaction were active against *Bacillus subtilis* and *Staphylococcus aureus*: $\text{Ph(C} \equiv \text{C)}_3\text{CH} = \text{CHCO}_2\text{H}$ (20% yield) and

$$\underset{\text{Ph}_2\text{C(C} \equiv \text{C)}_3\text{CH} = \text{CHCO}_2\text{H}}{\overset{\text{OH}}{|}} \text{ (95\% yield).}[51]$$

Capillin is a powerful antifungal agent *in vitro*, but it is too irritating for topical application. The synthesis of capillin involved Chodkiewicz-Cadiot coupling:[52]

$$\underset{\substack{| \\ \text{OH}}}{\text{PhCHC}}\equiv\text{CH} + \text{BrC}\equiv\text{CMe} \xrightarrow{\text{Cu}_2\text{Cl}_2\text{-EtNH}_2} \underset{\substack{| \\ \text{OH}}}{\text{PhCHC}}\equiv\text{CC}\equiv\text{CMe} \xrightarrow{\text{MnO}_2}$$

$$\underset{\substack{|| \\ \text{O}}}{\text{PhCC}}\equiv\text{CC}\equiv\text{CMe}$$

(90%)

capillin

Pattison[53] compared alkylation and Chodkiewicz-Cadiot coupling reactions as methods for forming long-chain diynes from 1-iodo-ω-fluoroalkanes and 1-alkynes:

$$\text{F(CH}_2)_n\text{C}\equiv\text{CLi} + \text{I(CH}_2)_m\text{F} \longrightarrow \text{F(CH}_2)_n\text{C}\equiv\text{C(CH}_2)_m\text{F} + \text{LiI}$$
(65–89%)

$$2\text{F(CH}_2)_n\text{I} + \text{LiC}\equiv\text{CC}\equiv\text{CLi} \longrightarrow \text{F(CH}_2)_n\text{C}\equiv\text{CC}\equiv\text{C(CH}_2)_m\text{F} + 2\text{LiI}$$
(40–50%)

$$\text{F(CH}_2)_n\text{C}\equiv\text{CH} + \text{BrC}\equiv\text{C(CH}_2)_m\text{F} \longrightarrow \text{F(CH}_2)_n\text{C}\equiv\text{CC}\equiv\text{C(CH}_2)_m\text{F} + \text{HBr}$$
(55–71%)

TABLE 6-8

Recent Examples of Chodkiewicz-Cadiot Coupling of Acetylenes

$$\text{R}-\text{C}\equiv\text{CH} + \text{BrC}\equiv\text{C}-\text{R}' \longrightarrow \text{RC}\equiv\text{C}-\text{C}\equiv\text{CR}'$$

R	R'	% Yield of Dimer	References
(Alkyl)$_2$NCH$_2$—	Various	40–90	54
Ar	—Ar	Ph: 87	45, 46
		p-BrPh: 86	
		p-MeOPh: 97	
		p-NO$_2$Ph: 89	
$\underset{\substack{| \\ \text{OH}}}{\text{PhCH}}$—	—Me	87	52
MeO$_2$C(CH$_2$)$_2$C≡C—	—(CH$_2$)$_2$CO$_2$H	74	36
Ph—	—CH$_2$OH	80	56
(thiophene structure)	—CH=CHCH$_2$OH	80	56
HOCH$_2$CH$_2$—	—Ph	40	56
MeCH=CH—	—CH$_2$CH$_2$OH	48	56
Ph—	—(CH$_2$)$_3$OH	80	56
HO$_2$CCH$_2$—	—CH=CHCH$_2$OH		57
Me(CH$_2$)$_3$C≡C—	—C≡CMe	46	58

In the earlier preparations, anodic coupling was used to prepare even-numbered carbon products. The acetylenic method is equally good for the production of odd- or even-numbered carbon α,ω-difluoroalkanes (by the hydrogenation of alkynes).

Dumont[54] prepared a series of tertiary diacetylenic β-amines $R(C\equiv C)_2CH_2NR'_2$ by the Mannich reaction or by condensation of a 1-bromo-alkyne with a propargylic amine in the presence of cupric salt and ethylamine. The Mannich reaction gave 17–70% yields; Chodkiewicz-Cadiot coupling was better—the yields were 40–90%. β-Aminoalkynes also couple with 1-bromo-acetylenic acids to form the acetylenic β-amino acids.

Other examples of Chodkiewicz-Cadiot coupling are listed in Table 6-8.

3.3. Cross-coupling of 1-Bromoacetylenes

The side reaction known to occur when the concentration of a 1-bromoacetylenic compound is too high in the Chodkiewicz-Cadiot coupling has been used as a synthetic cross-coupling method:[55]

$$HC\equiv CCH_2Cl + NaCH(CO_2Et)_2 \xrightarrow{EtOH} HC\equiv CCH_2CH(CO_2Et)_2 \xrightarrow[\substack{(2)\ H^+ \\ (3)\ heat}]{(1)\ NaOH}$$
$$(56\%)$$

$$HC\equiv CCH_2CH_2CO_2H \xrightarrow[H_2O]{Br_2\text{-}NaOH\text{-}} BrC\equiv CCH_2CH_2CO_2H \xrightarrow[\substack{HONH_2\cdot HCl\ + \\ HOC(R)_2C\equiv CBr}]{Cu_2Cl_2\text{-}EtNH_2\text{-}}$$
$$(80\%)$$

$$HOC(R)_2C\equiv CC\equiv CCH_2CH_2CO_2R'$$
$$(40\text{--}55\%)$$

4. GRIGNARD COUPLING

The reaction of acetylenic Grignard reagents with 1-haloacetylenes is similar to Chodkiewicz-Cadiot coupling, but is not nearly as useful. In addition to the disadvantages of using Grignard reagents, all three possible products result because of interchange reactions.[59]

Viehe[60] used dichloroacetylene in some Grignard coupling reactions. With phenylacetylenemagnesium chloride, 1-phenyl-4-chlorodiacetylene formed in 33% yield. 1-Chloroacetylenes gave smaller amounts of mixed coupling products than 1-bromo- and 1-iodoacetylenes.

Grignard reagents also oxidatively couple. This method has not been used very much. The coupling of the zinc "Grignard" reagent of trifluoropropyne in the presence of cupric chloride in dimethylformamide is an interesting recent example.[61]

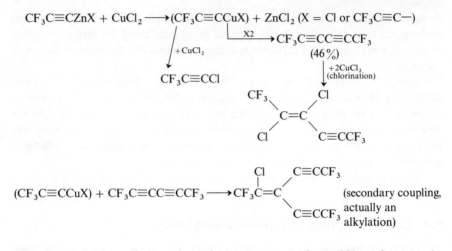

Hexafluoro-2,4-hexadiyne polymerizes spontaneously at 25° to form an infusible, insoluble polymer, and reacts with aromatic azides to form triazoles in high yield.

5. THERMAL CO-COUPLING REACTIONS

Cyanogen and acetylene at 840° passed through a quartz tube react to form propiolonitrile. With a 7:1 ratio of cyanogen to acetylene and 5 volumes of argon as diluent, a residence time of 1 second allowed 46 % conversion of acetylene and 95 % yield of propiolonitrile. Phenylacetylene, propyne and vinylacetylene also reacted to form the acetylenic nitriles.[62]

Acetylene and HCN can also react thermally to give propiolonitrile. Krebaum[63] passed a 15:1 mixture of HCN and acetylene diluted with argon through a tube at 900°. At 0.31 second residence time, conversion of acetylene was 73 % and the conversion of HCN was 4 %. The yield of propiolonitrile was 31 % based on acetylene and 41 % based on HCN. The reaction is either: $HC≡C· + HCN \longrightarrow$ products, or $HC≡CH + ·CN \longrightarrow$ products. There is no evidence which allows a choice. Acrylonitrile and ethylene were major by-products. Acrylonitrile is probably not intermediate to propiolonitrile, because acrylonitrile gave only a little propiolonitrile under these reaction conditions. Cyanogen was a major by-product from the HCN (25 % yield). The cyanogen could be recycled in order to improve the overall yield, using Comp's[62] conditions.

These reactions are very interesting as potential commercial methods for converting acetylene into functional derivatives. Acetylenic acids, amines, nitriles and amides are among the most valuable acetylenic compounds.

6. POLYACETYLENES—SYNTHETIC AND NATURALLY OCCURRING

Coupling reactions have been the keys to recent developments in the field of naturally occurring polyacetylenes. The subject of Sir E. R. H. Jones' Pedler Lecture in 1959 was polyacetylenes, which he reviewed in an interesting way.[64] The first Pedler Lecture was given by W. H. Perkin in 1926. The subject was the early history of closed carbon chain compounds. Perkin's ideas on making small ring compounds were brought to fruition during the years 1882–1886 while he was at Munich, at that time the organic chemistry center of the world. During those years, Baeyer, who had just finished his studies on indigo, was looking for a change of work. He was thinking about the properties of polyacetylenes, and whether these compounds would be "explosive diamonds." Perkin said, "It was the author's good fortune to be allowed to take part in and watch these experiments on polyacetylenes and the experience of the experimental skill with which Baeyer carried out these very ticklish operations with no other apparatus than test tubes and glass rods, is to this day a very lively recollection." Baeyer[65] was the first to make diacetylene (by a coupling reaction), still regarded as a dangerous, unstable material. Baeyer attempted to prepare and handle tetraacetylenedicarboxylic acid. This acid has not yet been prepared satisfactorily. The explosive properties of polyacetylenes led Baeyer to the strain theory, still one of the fundamental concepts of organic chemistry.

Dehydrohalogenation is another very useful route to polyacetylenes. Mixed ethylenic-acetylenic systems on dehydrohalogenation give unsymmetrical products, and not the expected symmetrical ones, by an unknown mechanism:[66]

$$CH_3CHClCH=CH(C\equiv C)_2CH=CHCHClCH_3 \xrightarrow{NaNH_2} CH_3(CH=CH)_2(C\equiv C)_3CH_3$$

By both the coupling and the dehydrohalogenation reactions, F. Bohlmann at Brunswick and M. C. Whiting at Manchester and Oxford prepared these polyacetylenes:

$$CH_3(C\equiv C)_nCH_3 \quad n = 1\text{–}6$$

$$Ph(C\equiv C)_nPh \quad n = 1\text{–}6, 8$$

$$t\text{-}Bu(C\equiv C)_n t\text{-}Bu \quad n = 1\text{–}8, 10$$

The preparation and study of the polyacetylenes required new techniques because these acetylenes are stable in light at room temperature for only a few seconds. Jones'[67] development of the method for preparing acetylene mono-Grignard was the key to preparation of cis-pentenynol, essential for synthesis of the acetylenic esters from Compositae.

Triacetylene is more unstable than diacetylene, and tetraacetylene has not yet been isolated. Disubstituted polyacetylenes are more stable than the ethylnyl-terminated polyacetylenes. Most polyacetylenes are very light sensitive, but sometimes are relatively stable in dilute solution. Crystals of diacetylenic compounds often become coated with a scarlet polymer after only an hour or so in light. Yellow dimethylhexaacetylene crystals become black and insoluble after only a few minutes at 20°. This is probably caused by close packing of the polyacetylene chains in crystal lattices. The closest approach of linear chains is 3.8–4.0 Å in dimethyltriacetylene and diacetylenedicarboxylic acid. Bohlmann[68] believed that bulkier terminal groups should prevent this closeness, and thus would cause greater stability. He prepared a series of di-t-butylpolyynes with up to seven acetylenic groups and found them to be much more stable than the dimethylpolyacetylenes. Di-t-butylheptaacetylene is remarkably stable, decomposing only slowly above 150°. Even di-t-butyldecaacetylene is reasonably stable. Higher polyacetylenes terminated by t-butyl groups can probably be made.

When Jones started his work, solution spectra of polyacetylenes had not been reported. Jones observed that tetraacetylene had a remarkable spectrum.[69] The low-intensity bands shifted to longer wavelengths (2800–3500 Å) and bands of very high intensity appeared at 200–2400 Å. This corresponds to the high-intensity bands at 1600 Å noted in gas phase spectra of diacetylene and dimethyldiacetylene. Di-t-butyldecaacetylene has an extremely intense absorption near 2000 Å, and Jones was disappointed that the extinction coefficient did not reach the million level!

By 1960, Bohlmann[70] had surveyed the polyacetylenes produced by more than 50 plants of the genus *Centaurae*. He found that the 13-carbon hydrocarbon $CH_3CH=CH(C\equiv C)_4CH=CH_2$ is the most frequently occurring acetylenic compound. This hydrocarbon may be formed from a chlorohydrin or its acetate or diacetate, since these are found in the roots of the plants. By mid-1964, Bohlmann had studied the polyacetylenes from 750 of the 14,000 known species of *Compositae*,[2] and he is still working in this area.[1] Ten plant families are now known to make fungitoxic polyacetylenes.[71]

The first known naturally occurring material with an allenic group is mycomycin, isolated by Celmer in 1952.[72] Mycomycin is $HC\equiv CC\equiv CCH$ $=C=CHCH=CHCH=CHCH_2CO_2H$. Alkaline isomerizations of mycomycin, nemotin and other compounds were most helpful in structure studies. Jacobs[73] in 1951 reported the first quantitative studies of the equilibria attained in such isomerizations. He found that the 2-isomer is most favored in the equilibrium. Hyperconjugation contributions are highly important to stabilization of the acetylenic systems. The predominant isomer is usually the one in which the unsaturated system is flanked by the greatest number of methyl or methylene groups:

$$HC\equiv CCH_2Et \underset{EtOH}{\overset{4NKOH,}{\rightleftarrows}} H_2C=C=CHEt \overset{175°}{\rightleftarrows} MeC\equiv CEt$$
$$(3.5\%) \qquad\qquad (95\%)$$

More than 20 allenic compounds have now been identified in naturally occurring products.[2]

Jones has screened about 1000 species of the 20,000 known *Basidiomycete* fungi for the production of acetylenes. Absorption spectra can differentiate between such closely related systems as A and B or C and D:

$$A\equiv-\equiv-\equiv-CO_2H \qquad C\equiv-\equiv-\equiv-\equiv$$
$$B\equiv-\equiv-=-CO_2H \qquad D\equiv-\equiv-=-=$$

Some indication of the kinds of functional groups is obtained from adsorption and distribution properties. The chain lengths of monofunctional materials are easily determined by hydrogenation and reduction by lithium aluminum hydride, and by GLC of the saturated alcohols so obtained. All of this valuable information can be obtained from as little as 3 mg of an acetylenic compound.[64]

All of the polyacetylenes from plants or microorganisms are straight chain. One of the functional groups is almost always acidic or readily derived from carboxylic acid. This suggests biogenesis from acetate units comparable to the biogenesis of fatty acids. All of the compounds with an even number of carbons have a methyl group or its oxidation product at the other end of the chain. The products with an odd number of carbons always have a free ethynyl group at the other end of the chain. This suggests that decarboxylation of α,β-acetylenic acids can be done by the enzyme systems present in many fungi. Thus, cell-free extracts of the mycelium of *Coprinus quadrifidus* can decarboxylate a dicarboxylic acid:

$$HO_2C(C\equiv C)_3CH_2CH_2CO_2H \longrightarrow H(C\equiv C)_3CH_2CH_2CO_2H$$

One hypothesis holds that the acetylenic bond is formed by a dehydrogenation reaction. Bu'Lock and Smith[75] found that *Tricholoma grammopodium* converts 10-^{14}C-oleic acid into 10-^{14}C-octadec-9-en-12-ynoic acid and 2-^{14}C-dec-2-en-4,6,8-triyn-1-ol. Further, two postulated intermediates are found in polyacetylene-producing fungi: *cis*-octadec-9-en-12-ynoic acid (crepenynic acid), and *cis,cis*-octadec-9,14-dien-12-ynoic acid (dehydrocrepenynic acid). This confirms the theory that certain organisms produce acetylenic bonds by dehydrogenation and that several known polyacetylenes arise from a common precursor fatty acid.

Many naturally occurring polyacetylenes which have an olefin group have the *cis* configuration about the double bond. Synthesis of naturally occurring products then requires a method of isomerizing *trans* to *cis* double bonds, since *trans* products are easier to make. Chemical methods such as dehydration, anionotropic rearrangement and stereospecific reduction of acetylenic bonds are not too general, because the reagents frequently cause isomerization, cyclization and other side reactions.

Jones[74] studied the photoequilibration reaction as a preparative method for converting acetylenic-olefinic compounds to their *cis* isomers. As an example, *Lachnophyllum* ester occurs naturally as both the *cis* and the *trans* isomers. When Jones irradiated the *trans* form in petroleum ether at 20° for 1 hour, using light of greater than 3100-Å wavelength, 80 % of the *trans* isomer was converted to the *cis*. The free *trans* acid isomerized to the *cis* form, and the *cis* acid isomerized to the γ-lactone:

$$MeCH_2CH_2(C{\equiv}C)_2CH{=}CHCO_2R \xrightarrow{h\nu} MeCH_2CH_2C{\equiv}CCH$$
cis

Jones[64] concluded his Pedlar Lecture by observing that the polyacetylenes, which were almost unknown a decade ago, seem to occur rather widely in nature and, although they are often remarkably unstable, "this distressing property is amply compensated for by the comparative ease with which they can be identified and estimated." Before 1950, only seven naturally occurring acetylenic compounds were known. By 1966, more than 300 had been identified. It appears that many more will be isolated, identified and synthesized in the years ahead.

References

1. Bu'Lock, J. D., "Polyacetylenes and Related Compounds in Nature," in "Progress in Organic Chemistry," Vol. 6, p. 86, London, Butterworth's, 1964.
2. Jones, E. R. H., *Chem. Brit.*, **2**, 6 (1966).
3. Eglinton, G., and Galbraith, A. R., *J. Chem. Soc.*, 889 (1959); *Chem. Ind.* (*London*), 737 (1956).
4. Eglinton, G., and McCrae, W., in "Advances in Organic Chemistry. Methods and Results," Vol. 4, p. 225, New York, Interscience Publishers, 1963.
5. Glaser, G., *Chem. Ber.*, **2**, 422 (1869); *Ann. Chem.*, **154**, 159 (1870).
6. Saggiomo, A. J., *J. Org. Chem.*, **22**, 1171 (1957).
7. Moreau, C., and Bongrand, J. C., *Ann. Chim.* (*Paris*), **14**, 47 (1920).
8. Brockman, F. J., *Can. J. Chem.*, **33**, 507 (1955).
9. Baeyer, A., and Landsberg, L., *Chem. Ber.*, **15**, 50, 57, 87 (1882).
10. Paal, C., and Hermann, C., *Chem. Ber.*, **22**, 3076 (1889).
11. Marszak-Fleury, A., *Ann. Chim.* (*Paris*), **3**, 656 (1958).
12. Hennion, G. F., and Hanzel, R. S., *J. Am. Chem. Soc.*, **82**, 4908 (1960).
13. Rose, J. D., and Weedon, B. C. L., *J. Chem. Soc.*, 782 (1949).
14. Hennion, G. F., and Teach, E. G., *J. Am. Chem. Soc.*, **75**, 1653 (1953).
15. Hennion, G. F., and Price, L., *J. Org. Chem.*, **27**, 1587 (1962).
16. Hennion, G. F., and Perrino, A. C., *J. Org. Chem.*, **26**, 1073 (1961).
16a. Zalkind, Y. S., and Fundwiler, F. B., *Chem. Ber.*, **69B**, 128 (1936).
 Zalkind, Y. S., and Aizikovich, M. A., *J. Gen. Chem. USSR*, **7**, 227 (1937); *Chem. Abstr.*, **31**, 4283 (1937).
17. Straus, F., *Ann. Chem.*, **342**, 190 (1905).
18. Akhtar, M., Richards, T. A., and Weedon, B. C. L., *J. Chem. Soc.*, 933 (1959).
18a. Kauer, J. C. (to E. I. du Pont de Nemours & Co.), U.S. Patent 2,952,718 (Sept. 13, 1960).

19. Klebanskii, A. L., Grachev, I. V., and Kuznetsova, O. M., *Zh. Prikl. Khim.*, **31**, 1869 (1958); *Chem. Abstr.*, **53**, 10026 (1959).
20. vanHelden, R., and Verberg, G., *Rec. Trav. Chim.*, **84**, 1263 (1965).
21. Klebanskii, A. L., Grachev, I. V., and Kuznetsova, O. M., *Zh. Obshch. Khim.*, **27**, 2977 (1957); *Chem. Abstr.*, **52**, 8034 (1958).
22. Armitage, J. B., *et al.*, *J. Chem. Soc.*, 1998 (1952).
23. Bohlmann, F., *et al.*, *Chem. Ber.*, **97**, 794 (1964).
24. Hay, A. S., *J. Org. Chem.*, **25**, 1275 (1960); (to General Electric Co.), U.S. Patent 3,300,456 (Jan. 24, 1967).
25. Hay, A. S., *J. Org. Chem.*, **27**, 3320 (1962).
26. Reppe, W., *et al.*, *Ann. Chem.*, **596**, 1 (1955); **601**, 81 (1956).
27. Campbell, I. D., and Eglinton, G., *J. Chem. Soc.*, 1158 (1964).
28. Sondheimer, F., Amiel, Y., and Wolovsky, R., *J. Am. Chem. Soc.*, **81**, 4600 (1959).
29. Sondheimer, F., *Pure Appl. Chem.*, **7**, 363 (1963).
30. Akiyama, S., Misumi, S., and Nakagawa, M., *Bull. Chem. Soc. Japan*, **35**, 1826, 1829 (1962).
31. Sondheimer, F., Amiel, Y., and Wolovsky, R., *J. Am. Chem. Soc.*, **79**, 4247 (1957).
32. Mavrov, M. V., Derzhinskii, A. R., and Kucherov, V. F., *Izv. Akad. Nauk SSSR, Ser. Khim.*, 1460 (1965); *Chem. Abstr.*, **63**, 16223 (1965).
33. Epsztein, R., and Marszak, I., *Compt. Rend.*, **243**, 283 (1956).
34. Tani, H., Tanaki, S., and Toda, F., *Bull. Chem. Soc. Japan*, **36**, 1267 (1963); *Chem. Abstr.*, **60**, 437 (1964).
35. Londergan, T. E. (to E. I. du Pont de Nemours & Co.), U.S. Patent 2,867,662 (Jan. 6, 1959); *Chem. Abstr.*, **53**, 10036 (1959).
36. Derzhinskii, A. R., Mavrov, M. V., and Kucherov, V. F., *Izv. Akad. Nauk SSSR, Ser. Khim.*, 544 (1965); *Chem. Abstr.*, **63**, 485 (1965).
37. Gouin, L., *Ann. Chem. (Paris)*, **5**, 529 (1960); *Chem. Abstr.*, **55**, 8399 (1961).
38. Campbell, I. D., and Eglinton, G., *Org. Syn.*, **45**, 39 (1965).
39. Fisher, L. B., and Kotlyarevskii, I. L., *Izv. Akad. Nauk SSSR, Ser. Khim.*, 692 (1965); *Chem. Abstr.*, **63**, 6895 (1965).
40. Tani, H., Toda, F., and Matsumiya, J., *Bull. Chem. Soc. Japan*, **36**, 391 (1963); *Chem. Abstr.*, **59**, 5092 (1963).
41. Mesheryakov, A. P., and Petrova, L. V., *Izv. Akad. Nauk SSSR, Ser. Khim.*, 1488 (1964); *Chem. Abstr.*, **64**, 19386 (1966).
42. Arens, J. F., in "Advances in Organic Chemistry. Methods and Results," Vol. 2, p. 117, New York, Interscience Publishers, 1960.
43. Chodkiewicz, W., *Ann. Chim. (Paris)*, **2**, 819 (1957).
44. Chodkiewicz, W., *et al.*, *Compt. Rend.*, **245**, 322 (1957).
45. Yen, V.-Q., *Ann. Chim. (Paris)*, **7**, 785 (1962).
46. *Ibid.*, **7**, 799 (1962).
47. Behr, O. M., *et al.*, *J. Chem. Soc.*, 1147 (1964).
48. Wolf, V., and Block, W., *Ann. Chem.*, **637**, 119 (1960).
49. Bohlmann, F., Herbst, P., and Gleinig, H., *Chem. Ber.*, **94**, 948 (1961).
50. Bohlmann, F., and Grau, G., *Chem. Ber.*, **98**, 2608 (1965).
51. Meier, J., *et al.*, *Compt. Rend.*, **245**, 1634 (1957).
52. Nash, B. W., *et al.*, *J. Chem. Soc.*, 2983 (1965).
53. Pattison, F. L. M., and Dear, R. E. A., *Can. J. Chem.*, **41**, 2600 (1963).

54. Dumont, J. L., *et al.*, *Compt. Rend.*, **260**, 215 (1965).
55. Derzhinskii, A. R., Mavrov, M. V., and Kucherov, V. F., *Izv. Akad. Nauk SSSR, Ser. Khim.*, 1237 (1965); *Chem. Abstr.*, **63**, 14691 (1965).
56. Bohlmann, F., Enkelmann, R., and Plettner, W., *Chem. Ber.*, **97**, 2118 (1964).
57. Bew, R. E., *et al.*, *J. Chem. Soc.* (*C*), 135 (1966).
58. Jones, E. R. H., Lowe, G., and Shannon, P. V. R., *J. Chem. Soc.* (*C*), 139 (1966).
59. Black, H. K., Horn, D. H. S., and Weedon, B. C. L., *J. Chem. Soc.*, 1704 (1954).
60. Viehe, H. G., *Chem. Ber.*, **92**, 3064 (1959).
61. Norris, W. P., and Finnegan, W. G., *J. Org. Chem.*, **31**, 3282 (1966).
62. Comp, J. L. (to Monsanto Chem. Co.), U.S. Patent 3,079,423 (Feb. 26, 1963); *Chem. Abstr.*, **59**, 2656 (1963).
63. Krebaum, L. J., *J. Org. Chem.*, **31**, 4103 (1966).
64. Jones, E. R. H., *Proc. Chem. Soc.*, 199 (1960).
65. Baeyer, A., *Chem. Ber.*, **18**, 674, 2269 (1885).
66. Bohlmann, F., and Herbst, P., *Chem. Ber.*, **91**, 1631 (1958).
67. Jones, E. R. H., Skattebøl, L., and Whiting, M. C., *J. Chem. Soc.*, 4765 (1956); *Org. Syn.*, **39**, 56 (1959).
68. Bohlmann, F., *Chem. Ber.*, **86**, 63, 657 (1953).
69. Armitage, J. B., Jones, E. R. H., and Whiting, M. C., *J. Chem. Soc.*, 2014 (1952).
70. Bohlmann, F., and Postulka, S., and Ruhnke, J., *Chem. Ber.*, **91**, 1642 (1958).
71. Fawcett, C. H., *et al.*, *Chem. Commun.*, 422 (1965).
72. Celmer, W. D., and Solomans, I. A., *J. Am. Chem. Soc.*, **74**, 1870, 2245, 3838 (1952); **75**, 1372, 3430 (1953).
73. Jacobs, T. L., Akawie, R., and Cooper, R. G., *J. Am. Chem. Soc.*, **73**, 1273 (1951).
74. Jones, J. B., *J. Chem. Soc.*, 5759 (1963).
75. Bu'Lock, J. D., and Smith, G. N., *J. Chem. Soc.* (*C*), 332 (1967).

Chapter Seven

CYCLIC AND MACROCYCLIC ACETYLENES

PART ONE

Small Ring Cyclic Acetylenes and Allenes

Introduction

Cyclooctyne is the smallest cycloalkyne[1] which can be isolated. Cyclononadiene is the smallest known cyclic allene.[2,3] Cyclic alkynes with less than eight carbons in the ring probably exist fleetingly in some reactions; trapping reactions give results best interpreted as involving cycloalkynes.

Several recent reviews describe the cycloalkynes thoroughly; Wittig (1963);[4] Heaney (1962);[5] and den Hertog and van der Plas (1965).[6]

A brief discussion of cyclic allenes is included here because these compounds are so intimately related to cyclic acetylenes.

1. SMALL RING ACETYLENES

Wittig,[4] who has worked with small ring acetylenes for more than 20 years, refers to their chemistry as *"als ob,"* or "as if:" Cycloynes with less than eight

269

carbons are believed to exist only because trapping reactions indicate they do. Cycloynes can be made by treating cyclic 1,2-dihaloolefins with magnesium metal or by oxidizing bis(hydrazones) of α-diketones with mercuric oxide.[1,7] Diphenylisobenzofuran is an excellent trapping agent:

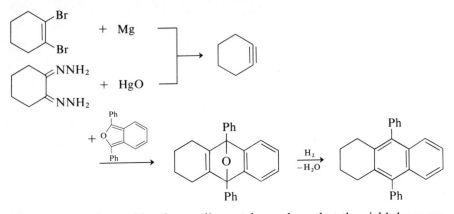

The same reactions with other cyclic acetylenes show that the yield decreases with decreasing ring size, and consequently increasing ring strain (Table 7-1).

Cycloalkynes have also been identified by their dimerization, trimerization and tetramerization products. The products from cyclohexyne are examples:[4]

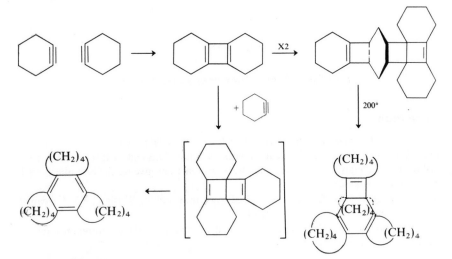

2. BENZYNE AND OTHER ARYNES

Benzyne (cyclohexadienyne) is only formally a small ring acetylene. Benzyne and other arynes are interesting examples of the "*als ob*" compounds. Many

TABLE 7-1

Small Ring Cyclic Acetylenes[4]

Cycloalkyne	% Yield of Cycloalkyne-Diphenylisobenzofuran Adduct	
	From Dibromide + Magnesium	From Bis(hydrazone)
Cycloheptyne	64	26
Cyclohexyne	50.5	7
Cyclopentyne	2.1	0.5
Cyclobutyne	8	—
(Benzyne	85)	—

substitution reactions of halobenzenes are presumed to involve the benzyne intermediate, especially reactions in ammonia catalyzed by sodium amide or potassium amide. Thus, halotoluenes react with sodium amide in ammonia to give different aminotoluenes, by addition of amide anion to benzyne at carbons other than the original halogen-bearing carbon. Other nucleophilic reactions give similar results. Potassium amide in ammonia can induce nucleophilic displacement of nonactivated aryl halides. When Scardiglia and Roberts[8] reacted sodium phenylacetylide and bromobenzene in liquid ammonia in the presence of KNH_2, they obtained diphenylacetylene in 26% yield. When they used p-bromotoluene, the product contained small amounts of 3- and 4-tolylphenylacetylenes, and large amounts of diaryl- and triarylamines. Benzyne intermediates were involved. The ratio of isomers of phenyltolylacetylenes is close to the ratio of aminotoluenes obtained in the sodium amide-bromotoluene reaction. Other nucleophiles react with benzyne in ammonia in the presence of potassium amide. Benzyne does not show much selectivity in its additions, as expected, since the high exothermicity of the addition reactions shows benzyne is under considerable ring strain. The order of reactivity of nucleophiles with benzyne is different from the order of their reactivity with aliphatic halides. This shows that the transition state in the aliphatic S_N2 reactions is different from the transition state in benzyne.

Benzyne not only adds to the B ring of anthracene, to form triptycene, but also reacts with the less active A ring to form 6,11-disubstituted-5,12-dihydro-5,12-ethenonaphthacenes. These are typical Diels-Alder reactions.[9]

In 1960, Arnett[10] reported the first example of alkylation of a benzyne intermediate by an olefin. In an attempted Diels-Alder reaction between benzyne and 2,5-dimethyl-2,4-hexadiene, the product was 2,5-dimethyl-3-phenyl-1,4-hexadiene:

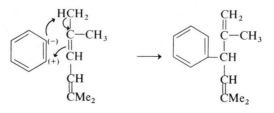

Pyrolysis or photolysis of arendiazonium-2-carboxylates gives arynes, which can add to dienes, acids and other compounds. Stiles[11] generated benzyne by this reaction and found that it reacted in a novel manner with phenylacetylene. The major product was 5,6-diphenyldibenzo[a,e]cyclooctatetraene, and by-product was a phenanthrene:

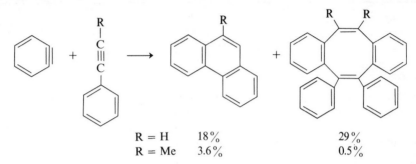

R = H   18%   29%
R = Me   3.6%   0.5%

1-Phenylpropyne was less reactive than phenylacetylene, and diphenylacetylene did not react at all. The cyclooctatetraene probably formed by dimerization of an intermediate benzocyclobutene. Ethoxyacetylene also gave a surprising result:

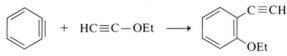

3. HETEROARYNES

Heterocyclic small ring acetylenes are also known, again by indirect evidence.[4,6] Some of these are: benzofuryne, pyridyne, quinolynes, naphthyridiynes and pyrimidynes. Very little work has been done in this area.

4. SMALL RING ALLENES

4.1. Preparation from 1-Halocycloalkenes

Allenes are not formed by the reaction of six-, seven- and eight-membered 1-chlorocycloalkenes with sodium amide in ammonia.[2] 1-Chlorocycloheptene gives 32% yield of a dimer, presumably from two molecules of 1,2-cyclo-heptadiene. Nine- and ten-carbon 1-halocycloolefins give cyclic allenes: 1-Chlorocyclononene gives 43% yield of 1,2-cyclononadiene (b.p. 160°), and 1-chlorocyclodecene gives 39% yield of 1,2-cyclodecadiene (b.p. 70° at 12 mm of Hg). Sodium on alumina instead of sodium amide in ammonia gives 44 and 64% yields, respectively.

Molecular models of these two cyclic allenes can be made without bending the σ bonds or twisting the π bonds. As the ring size decreases, more bending and twisting is required. In the six-carbon ring, it is impossible to make a 1,2-diene model.

Mixtures of cyclodecyne and cyclo-1,2-cyclodecadiene were prepared by dehydrohalogenation of the isomeric 1-chlorocyclodecenes by slowly distilling from a melt of KOH-ethanol. The yield of product was 60%, and the allene : acetylene ratio was 3:2.[15] 1,2-Cyclononadiene was prepared by the same technique. The cyclic allenes could be semihydrogenated or completely hydrogenated, and both the acetylenes and allenes reacted with 2,4-dinitrobenzene-sulfenyl chloride to form crystalline 1:1 adducts. The cyclic acetylenes and allenes isomerized when heated with strong base. Prolonged heating gave cyclic dienes other than allenes (up to 100% yields). Thus, conjugated dienes are probably the by-products frequently observed in preparations of cyclic allenes by dehydrohalogenation.

4.2. Preparation from Dihalocyclopropanes

Doering and La Flamme[12] found that the dehydrohalogenation of 1,1-dihalo-cyclopropanes by sodium on alumina gave allenes. Gardner and Narayana[13] used this method to prepare 1,2-cyclononadiene (58% yield, b.p. 94° at 44 mm of Hg).

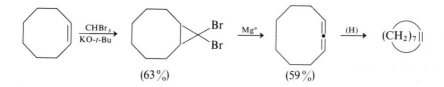

Moore and Ward[3] preferred to use an alkyllithium as reagent for dehydro-bromination-cleavage of the dibromocyclopropanes. In ether at 0 to −80°, alkyllithiums gave 1,2-cyclononadiene and 1,2-cyclodecadiene in 70–90% yield. With cyclohexene, there was no evidence of intermediate carbene formation. Later, Moore and Landor[14] elaborated on this procedure. Of all the reagents tried, the best was storage-stable methyllithium in ether. The cyclic allenes are easily purified because there are no side reactions.

5. EQUILIBRATION OF CYCLIC ALLENES AND ACETYLENES

From published enthalphy data, a schematic showing enthalpies of various changes in an equilibrium system of acyclic acetylenes and allenes was constructed:[16]

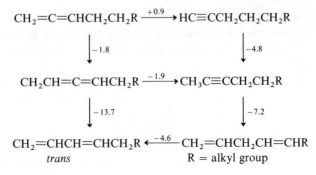

If the acetylene and allene groups are in cyclic structures large enough that strain is not a factor, this stability order should apply. As ring size decreases, some changes or even reversals may occur, because the rigid acetylene bond requires four carbons in a straight line, while allene requires only three.

The isomerization of some cyclic acetylenes and allenes has been studied in several systems.[16] Sodamide in ammonia gave the fastest equilibration. Equilibrium was nearly complete in one-half hour. As times increased, isomerization to other dienes became more important. The 11-carbon system was normal. For the study of equilibration at different temperatures, potassium t-butoxide in t-butanol was best. The values obtained are apparent equilibrium constants, not thermodynamic constants. Since the activity coefficients must be very close to unity, the two equilibrium constants must be nearly identical (Table 7-2). The same results were obtained from either cyclic allene or cyclic acetylene.

TABLE 7-2
Equilibrium Allene: Acetylene Ratios[16]

Cyclic Hydrocarbon	Average Allene: Acetylene Ratio			
	KO-t-Bu in t-BuOH 79.4°	120.0°	KOH-EtOH 131–134°	NaNH$_2$-NH$_3$ −33.4°
1,2-Cyclonoadiene, cyclonoyne	16.38	11.22	12.3	19.1
1,2-Cyclodecadiene, cyclodecyne	1.89	1.77	1.70	1.11
1,2-Cycloundecadiene, cycloundecyne	0.312	0.380	0.439	0.061

The evidence all indicates that smaller ring allenes could be made and that they should be more stable than the corresponding cycloalkynes (see reference 2).

Table 7-3 lists some thermodynamic data for the isomerization of cyclic allenes to cyclic alkynes.

TABLE 7-3

Standard Free Energies, Enthalpies and Entropies of Isomerization of Cycloalkynes to Cyclic Allenes (t-Butanol, 373.2°K)[16]

Ring Size	ΔF^0 (kcal/mole)	ΔH^0 (kcal/mole)	ΔS^0 (cal/mole °K)
9	−1.91	−2.56	−1.7
10	−0.45	−0.45	0.0
11	0.79	1.35	1.5

6. THERMALLY INDUCED REACTIONS OF CYCLIC ALLENES

In 1965, Skattebøl[17] reviewed the literature on thermal reactions of allenes. At high temperatures (150° for several days, or passed through a tube at 500°), allenes form cyclobutanes. Allene itself gives bis(methylene)cyclobutanes. The synthesis of allenes by adding dihalocarbenes to olefins makes available molecules with an allenic group and another allenic or olefinic group.[3,12]

When 1,2-cyclononadiene was heated at 130° for 18 hours, the crystalline products were identified as stereoisomers of tricyclo[9.7.0.0^{2,10}]octadeca-2,18-diene:

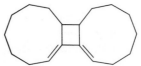

1,2,6-Cyclononatriene gave a more complex reaction. The products were 2,3-divinylcyclopentene and two other dimers:

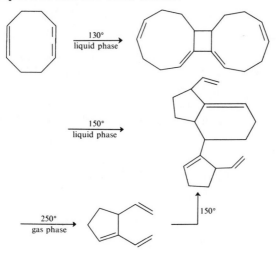

Open-chain allenes gave similar reactions. Conjugated allenic systems can lead to unusual products:

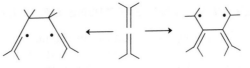

$$Me_2C=C=CH-CH=C=CMe_2 \xrightarrow{250°}$$

(not isolated)

A diradical mechanism best explains the products. The diradical can be vinylic or allylic. The allylic radical is more stable, and thus more likely. Reactions to form the diradicals occur at the central part of the allene system:

(Vinylic diradical)   (Allylic diradical)

1,5-Hexadiyne was reported by Huntsman[18] to isomerize to 3,4-dimethylenecyclobutene at 350°. The diyne may have isomerized to the corresponding diallene before cyclizing. Neither 1,6-heptadiyne nor 1,7-octadiyne isomerized up to 450°.[17]

Harris[19] rearranged 1,2,6,7-cyclodecatetraene at 300°. The product was 2,3-divinyl-1,3-cyclohexadiene, which polymerized easily. At higher temperatures, the product was tetrahydronaphthalene. The driving force is the allene-diene energy loss:

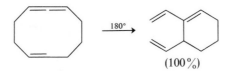

(100%)

Skattebøl[20] also obtained 100% yield in this reaction and found that divinyl-cyclohexadiene irradiated by UV light at −78° in pentane gave 6–7% yield of tetravinylethylene.

Harris[19] obtained a similar reaction with an olefinic cyclic allene:

(100%)

The mechanism is similar to the Cope rearrangement.

References

1. Blomquist, A. T., et al., J. Am. Chem. Soc., **73**, 5510 (1951); **74**, 3636, 3643 (1952); **75**, 2153 (1953).
2. Ball, W. J., and Landor, S. R., J. Chem. Soc., 2298 (1962).
3. Moore, W. R., and Ward, H. R., J. Org. Chem., **25**, 2073 (1960).
4. Wittig, G., Pure Appl. Chem., **7**, 173 (1963).
5. Heaney, H., Chem. Rev., **62**, 81 (1962).
6. den Hertog, H. J., and van der Plas, H. C., in "Advances in Heterocyclic Chemistry," Vol. 4, p. 121, New York, Academic Press, 1965.
7. Prelog, V., et al., Helv. Chim. Acta, **34**, 1598 (1952); **36**, 471 (1953).
8. Scardiglia, F., and Roberts, J. D., Tetrahedron, **3**, 197 (1958).
9. Klanderman, B. H., J. Am. Chem. Soc., **87**, 4649 (1965).
10. Arnett, E. M., J. Org. Chem., **25**, 324 (1960).
11. Stiles, M., Burckhardt, A., and Haag, A., J. Org. Chem., **27**, 4715 (1962).
12. Doering, W., von E., and La Flamme, P. M., Tetrahedron, **2**, 75 (1959).
13. Gardner, P. D., and Narayana, M., J. Org. Chem., **26**, 3518 (1961).
14. Moore, W. R., and Ward, H. R., J. Org. Chem., **27**, 4179 (1962).
15. Moore, W. R., and Bertelson, R. C., J. Org. Chem., **27**, 4182 (1962).
16. Moore, W. R., and Ward, H. R., J. Am. Chem. Soc., **85**, 86 (1963).
17. Skattebøl, L., and Solomon, S., ibid., **87**, 4506 (1965).
18. Huntsman, W. D., and Wristers, H. J., ibid, **89**, 342 (1967).
19. Harris, J. F., Jr., Tetrahedron Letters, 1359 (1965).
20. Skattebøl, L., ibid., 2257 (1966).

PART TWO

Macrocyclic Acetylenic Compounds

Introduction

Acetylenic chemistry has played an important role in recent developments in macrocycle research. Oxidative coupling reactions and sodium alkynylide-alkyl halide substitution reactions have been the keys to new syntheses of a variety of macrocycles.

One interesting feature of macrocyclic polyacetylenes is the possibility of transannular reactions. If triple bonds are located in favorable positions, cyclizations can occur.[1] Triple bonds in macrocyclic compounds can be easily semihydrogenated. Hydration of a cyclic diyne has given a cyclic diketone. Other addition reactions have not been studied very much. The conjugated diyne systems rearrange prototropically to form conjugated dienyne systems, which can be semihydrogenated to form conjugated triene units.

Some macrocyclic structures are strained. An acetylenic bond flanked by two methylene groups produces a linear four-carbon rod. A conjugated diacetylenic group in the same situation forms a linear six-carbon rod. If it is necessary to bend or bow the rods to form a ring, the molecule will be more or less strained.

Several recent reviews are available: Sondheimer (1963),[2] Ziegler (1955);[3] Belen'skii (1964);[4] and Baker (1965).[5]

The chemistry of macrocyclic acetylenes is divided into three sections in this chapter:

(1) Macrocyclic unsubstituted acetylenic hydrocarbons. Sondheimer pioneered this area and applied several crucial reactions to transform polyacetylenes into fully conjugated macrocyclic polyolefins (annulenes).

(2) Macrocyclic acetylenic hydrocarbons with aromatic rings in the chains. Eglinton and Galbraith in 1957 (see reference 6) reported the first example of these macrocycles, made by coupling o-diethynylbenzene to form the cyclic dimer.

(3) Macrocycles with hetero atoms in the rings. Cyclic esters, ethers, lactones, sulfur compounds and tin compounds have been made from acetylenic starting materials.

1. MACROCYCLIC UNSUBSTITUTED CONJUGATED ACETY-LENIC HYDROCARBONS—SYNTHESIS OF ANNULENES

Sondheimer, Wolovsky and their co-workers, and Dale, Hubert and co-workers have generated much of the knowledge of macrocyclic conjugated polyunsaturated hydrocarbons.

In 1963, Sondheimer reviewed the work his group has done on the aromaticity of large ring conjugated polyunsaturated hydrocarbons.[2] The question of whether aromaticity is unique to the benzene ring has intrigued theoretical chemists for years. In 1911, Willstätter made cyclooctatetraene to see if it is aromatic. It is not. By one criterion, an aromatic compound must: (1) be reasonably planar, and (2) have a closed shell of $(4n + 2)$ π electrons where $n = 0$ or an integer (that is, it must have an odd number of double bonds). This is Hückel's rule, derived from quantum mechanical calculations. (For an extensive discussion of aromaticity, see reference 2a). According to the "classical" definition, aromatic compounds are those which tend to enter substitution reactions rather than additions.

By examining scale drawings, Sondheimer concluded that the first fully conjugated macrocycle which should be aromatic has 18 carbons. These conjugated cyclics are now called "annulenes," and the 18-carbon compound is designated (18)-annulene.[7] (10)-Annulene has an odd number of double bonds and thus obeys Hückel's rule, but the inner hydrogens are so close together that the molecule cannot be planar. (12)-Annulene does not obey Hückel's rule and cannot be planar. (14)-Annulene obeys Hückel's rule but may not be completely planar because of some crowding of the inner hydrogens. (16)-Annulene does not obey Hückel's rule. (18)-Annulene obeys Hückel's rule, and the molecule is large enough to be completely planar.

1.1. Oxidative Coupling-Cyclization

Before 1956, it was impossible to prepare macrocyclic polyacetylenes. Eglinton's discovery of the high-dilution coupling-cyclization reaction, and Sondheimer's discovery of coupling-cyclization of terminal diynes in aqueous ethanol in the presence of cuprous chloride, ammonium chloride and oxygen were the key reactions needed (see Chapter 6). Single products have been obtained in several cases from reactions at ordinary concentrations (i.e., not high dilution).[26] Thus, 36 grams of cuprous chloride and 57.6 grams of ammonium chloride in water at pH3 were stirred, and 15 grams of 1,7-octadiyne was added. The solution was stirred while air bubbled through for 6 hours at room temperature. The cyclic dimer was formed in 61.2% yield. The cupric acetate system has been modified for reactions at more usual concentrations. Eight grams of cupric acetate in 20 ml of dimethylformamide was heated with 0.01–0.015 mole of polyyne for 1–3 hours at 120°. The products formed are listed in Table 7-3a.

TABLE 7-3a

**Coupling-Cyclodimerization of
Polyynes in Dimethylformamide[24]**

$$
\begin{array}{c}
\;\;\; \boxed{\quad X \quad} \\
(CH_2)_n \qquad\qquad (CH_2)_n \\
\;\;\; \boxed{\; C\equiv C-C\equiv C \;} \\
\text{cyclic dimer}
\end{array}
$$

X	n	% yield
CH_2	5	58.5
$C\equiv CC\equiv C$	4	45
$C\equiv C$	4	62
$C\equiv C$	5	78
$C\equiv C$	6	86

   Several problems remained to be solved. Once the cyclic acetylenes formed, the conjugated diyne groups had to be isomerized to dienynes. Potassium *t*-butoxide in *t*-butanol was excellent for this prototropic rearrangement. Next, the dienyne unit had to be semihydrogenated to a conjugated triene unit. Hydrogenation over palladium or platinum catalysts at atmospheric pressure worked well. Another serious experimental problem was also encountered. The coupling-cyclization reactions frequently gave a large number of products, which had to be separated. Sondheimer found that chromatography over activated alumina was an excellent separative method. The excruciating care necessary for good separation was rewarded by many successful experiments. Finally, the aromaticity of the fully conjugated cyclic olefins had to be established. NMR is ideal for this: If the π bonds are delocalized, they will sustain a ring current induced by an external magnetic field.

   The annulenes which have prepared from acetylenes are listed in Table 7-4.

TABLE 7-4

Annulenes Prepared from Acetylenes[a]

Annulene	Obeys Hückel's Rule	Planar	Aromatic by NMR[b]
(24)-Annulene	No	Probably	No
Tridehydro-(18)-annulene	Yes	Yes	Yes
(18)-Annulene	Yes	Yes	Yes
Bisdehydro-(16)-annulene (isomer A)	No	No	No
(16)-Annulene	No	?	No
Bisdehydro-(14)-annulene	Yes	Yes	Yes
(14)-Annulene	Yes	No	Yes[8]
Tridehydro-(12)-annulene	No	No	No[9,10]
Bisdehydro-(12)-annulene (two isomers)	No	No	No
(12)-Annulene	(Not yet prepared pure[11])		

[a] Described in reference 2, unless otherwise indicated.
[b] For NMR studies of annulenes, see reference 12.

1.1.1. THE (18)-ANNULENES

Catalytic coupling-cyclization of 1,5-hexadiyne gave numerous conjugated cyclic polyacetylenes, separated by alumina chromatography[7] (for another coupling method, see reference 13). The products included: trimer, 6% yield; tetramer, 6% yield; pentamer, 6% yield; hexamer, 3% yield. The cyclic trimer, with six acetylenic bonds, rearranged to symmetrical tridehydro-(18)-annulene when treated with potassium t-butoxide in t-butanol at 90° for a half hour. The rearrangement yield was 50%. This was the first dehydroannulene prepared by Sondheimer's group. The ring consisted of 1-($trans$)-en-3-(cis)-en-5-yne units. Tridehydro-(18)-annulene was aromatic by NMR. Semihydrogenation in benzene using palladium catalyst gave (18)-annulene, also aromatic by NMR. Semihydrogenation changed the major ultraviolet absorption band from 334–369 mμ and almost doubled the intensity. The dehydroannulenes described by Sondheimer in 1962[7] are the first fully conjugated olefinic and acetylenic monocyclic systems ever made.

In 1965, Wolovsky[14] reexamined the coupling-cyclization of 1,5-hexadiyne to form the cyclic trimer. The product trimer was rearranged as usual by potassium t-butoxide in t-butanol, and the rearranged mixture was analyzed by thin-layer chromatography on silver nitrate-coated substrate. The product separated into two new bond sequence isomers of tridehydro-(18)-annulene [(1) and (2)]. A third product was also isolated (3). The total yield of (1), (2) and

(3) was 2% from 1,5-hexadiyne, and the compositions were: (1) 70–75%, (2) 20–25%, and (3) 5–8%. Semihydrogenation of (3) over palladium on carbon gave (18)-annulene (4).

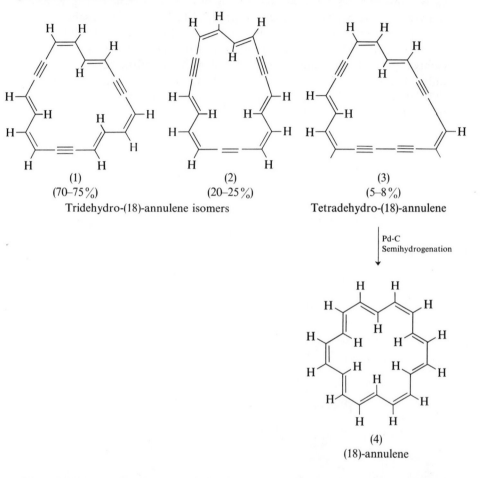

(1)
(70–75%)

(2)
(20–25%)

(3)
(5–8%)

Tridehydro-(18)-annulene isomers

Tetradehydro-(18)-annulene

Pd-C
Semihydrogenation

(4)
(18)-annulene

Although (18)-annulene is aromatic by the modern criteria (planarity and NMR), it does not react like a classical aromatic compound. It adds bromine readily and gives Diels-Alder addition products with maleic anhydride. In several attempted aromatic substitution reactions (sulfonation, Friedel-Crafts acylations), (18)-annulene decomposed.

Sondheimer's group worked next on the higher cyclic conjugated polyenes, but these materials were not crystalline. This study of aromaticity was so difficult experimentally that they decided to concentrate on the lower cyclics between cyclooctatetraene and (18)-annulene. The experience with (20)-annulenes, described next, illustrates some of the difficulties.

1.1.2. THE (20)-ANNULENES

Sondheimer and Gaoni[15] prepared two unstable completely conjugated twenty-carbon macrocycles. Cyclization-coupling of 1,5,9-decatriyne by cupric acetate in pyridine gave 6% yield of cyclic dimer 1,3,7,11,13,17-cycloeicosahexayne (1). Heated in *t*-butanol-benzene with potassium *t*-butoxide at 90° for 1 hour, (1) rearranged to (2), with a 30% yield. Semihydrogenation of (2) over Lindlar's catalyst gave (3), (20)-annulene. Bisdehydro-(20)-annulene (2) was stable for only 24 hours as a solid and for only 12 days in dilute solution in benzene. (20)-Annulene itself was also unstable in solution. Dehydro-(20)-annulene was made and was equally unstable.

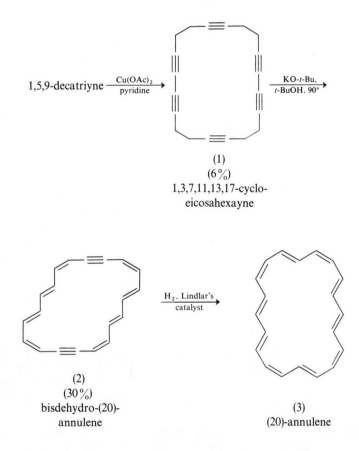

1,5,9-decatriyne $\xrightarrow[\text{pyridine}]{\text{Cu(OAc)}_2}$

(1)
(6%)
1,3,7,11,13,17-cyclo-
eicosahexayne

$\xrightarrow[\text{$t$-BuOH. 90°}]{\text{KO-$t$-Bu,}}$

(2)
(30%)
bisdehydro-(20)-
annulene

$\xrightarrow[\text{catalyst}]{\text{H}_2\text{, Lindlar's}}$

(3)
(20)-annulene

Wolovsky and Sondheimer[16] studied the cyclization-coupling of 1,5,9-decatriyne further. The cyclic monomer, cyclodecatriyne (4) was so unstable that it immediately added the elements of acetic acid (from the coupling agents) to form acetates (5) and (6). The two acetates are the smallest highly unsaturated unbridged ring compounds known.

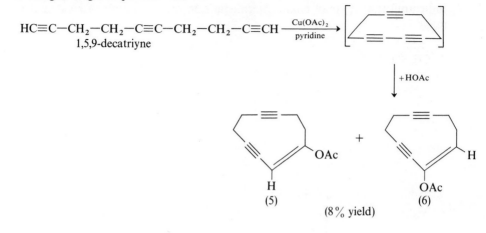

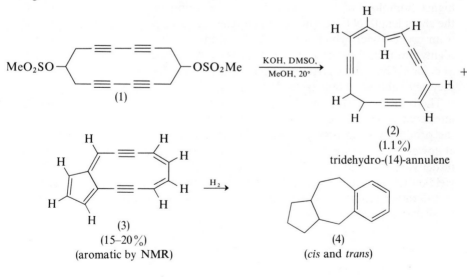

1.1.3. TRIDEHYDRO-(14)-ANNULENE

Mayer and Sondheimer[1] used base-induced elimination from 5,6,10,12-cyclotetradecatetrayne-1,8-diol dimenthanesulfonate (1) as a new method for making the dehydro-(14)-annulenes. A solution of the dimethanesulfonate in dimethyl sulfoxide was treated with 2% KOH in 97% aqueous methanol for 1 hour and was then chromatographed on alumina-silver nitrate. The major product (3) and its hydrogenation product (4) illustrate some of the transannular reactions which can occur if unsaturated linkages are suitably located in the macrocyclic rings:

Under more vigorous elimination conditions (refluxing 7% KOH-MeOH) the products were different.[17] The same products formed from either (1) or (3), indicating that (3) may be an intermediate in the formation of products (5), (6) and (7):

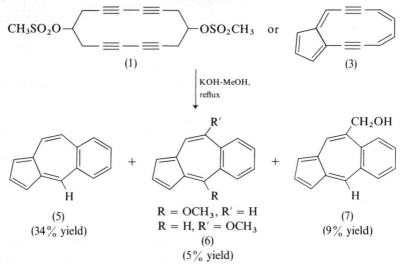

(1)   or   (3)

KOH-MeOH, reflux

(5)
(34% yield)

+

R = OCH$_3$, R' = H
R = H, R' = OCH$_3$
(6)
(5% yield)

+

CH$_2$OH

(7)
(9% yield)

1.1.4. THE (12)-ANNULENES

In 1965, Wolovsky and Sondheimer[11] continued earlier attempts[18] to prepare dehydro-(12)-annulene by the oxidative coupling of 1,5-hexadiyne. Coupling by cupric acetate in pyridine gave cyclic trimers and higher, but no dimer.[7] Glaser coupling gave an unusually large amount of brown insoluble polymer,[19] while higher homologs of 1,5-hexadiyne gave cyclic dimers, the yield increasing as the chain length of the diyne increased. The insoluble polymer might be formed from cyclic dimer, which was unstable. Models of the cyclic dimer show it is highly strained, with "bowed" 1,3-diyne rods. When they tried the same reaction as before,[19] but with a large amount of benzene to keep the products in solution, they were able to obtain cyclic dimer in solution, 9.5% yield.[11]

The bisdehydro-(12)-annulene could not be purified because linear products interfered, so the entire coupling mixture was isomerized in the usual way, and the product was chromatographed. The isomerization went much faster and at lower temperature than usual, probably because of the strained ring of bisdehydro-(12)-annulene. The first product eluted was biphenylene (1) in 7.4% yield on 1,5-hexadiyne. The biphenylene probably formed by base isomerization of the dimer (another example of the transannular reactions which occur in smaller ring polyacetylenes):

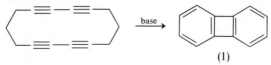

base

(1)

(*Note:* Nonaromatic four-carbon rings have not been found in polyynes.[19] The possibility of such rings was suggested by Cram and Allinger.[20]) This transannular reaction is apparently the first synthesis of biphenylene from non-benzenoid precursors.

The second compound eluted was bisdehydro-(12)-annulene (isomer A), 1.5% yield. The third compound eluted was isomer B, 0.65% yield:

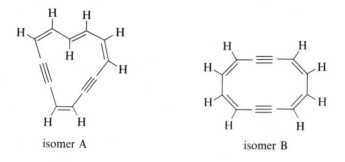

isomer A   isomer B

Potassium *t*-butoxide under rearrangement conditions did not convert either isomer to the other. The isomers apparently are formed by independent paths, and they are not intermediates in the formation of biphenylene (1). Semi-hydrogenation of isomer A over Lindlar's catalyst[21] gave impure (12)-annulene which could not be purified.

Tridehydro-(12)-annulene was not made until 1966: Untch and Wysocki dehydrobrominated a twelve-carbon hexabromo hydrocarbon to form tride-hydro-(12)-annulene in 65% yield.[9] The product is in the form of brick-red needles, melts at 95° and is not aromatic. Either as solid crystals or in solution, it reacts very rapidly with oxygen. It is stable in solution in the absence of oxygen. Sondheimer[22] compared Untch's product with a compound prepared by base isomerization of 1,3,7,9-cyclododecatetrayne. He found that he too had made tridehydro-(12)-annulene, presumably by a dehydrogenation reaction.

2. MACROCYCLIC SUBSTITUTED ACETYLENIC HYDRO-CARBONS

2.1. The Hexamethyl-(18)-annulenes

Hexamethyl-(18)-annulenes were reported in 1963.[23] The six methyl groups probably lie outside the ring. 3-Butyn-2-ol was the starting material for the synthesis (see structure on page 286).

Oxidative coupling of (1) (p. 286) with cupric acetate in pyridine gave a product which was mostly cyclic. A pure cyclic compound could not be isolated, presumably because each cyclic coupling product would be a mixture

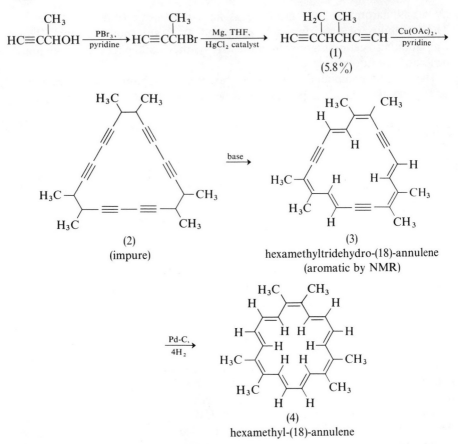

of stereoisomers resulting from the several asymmetric centers. Rearrangement of the total coupling product from (1) gave no clear cut results. After treatment with potassium *t*-butoxide in refluxing *t*-butanol for three-quarters of an hour, the only product isolated pure was hexamethyltridehydro-(18)-annulene (3) in about 1% yield based on (1). The UV spectrum was similar to the spectrum of tridehydro-(18)-annulene, except that the six methyl groups caused a bathochromic shift of about 7 mμ in the maxima. Hexamethyltridehydro-(18)-annulene was as stable as tridehydro-(18)-annulene, and was less soluble in most solvents. It could be stored practically unchanged for a long time in solution at room temperature or at $-15°$ in the solid state.

Semihydrogenation of (3) over palladium on charcoal gave (4), hexamethyl-(18)-annulene. In the UV spectrum, the six methyl groups again caused a bathochromic shift in the positions of the maxima. Hexamethyl-(18)-annulene was less stable than (18)-annulene. Dilute solutions in pentane-ether decomposed fairly rapidly at room temperature in diffuse daylight.

3. ELECTROPHILIC SUBSTITUTION REACTIONS OF (14)-ANNULENES

1,8-Bisdehydro-(14)-annulene (1a) is aromatic by NMR, and several electrophilic substitution products have been made.[24] Treatment of (1a) with cupric nitrate in acetic anhydride at room temperature gave 25% yield of the mononitro compound (1b) as black needles. Sulfonation of (1a) by oleum in dioxane at room temperature gave a water-soluble sulfonic acid, the silver salt of which reacted with methyl iodide to form the methyl ester in 30% yield. NMR indicated that the sulfonic acid ester was (1c). (1a) also reacted with acetic anhydride and BF_3·etherate in methylene chloride at room temperature to form the acetyl derivative (1d) in very low yield:

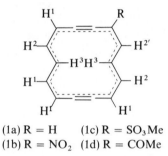

(1a) R = H   (1c) R = SO_3Me
(1b) R = NO_2 (1d) R = COMe

(1a) forms a 1:1 π complex with 1,3,5-trinitrobenzene. (14)-Annulene does not form these complexes. (1a) does not react with maleic anhydride.

Monodehydro-(14)-annulene [(2) or (3)] was nitrated to form 20% yield of the mononitro product. NMR indicated that the nitro group had replaced one of the outer protons. Sulfonation gave a 4:1 mixture of two isomeric monomethyl sulfonates (after esterification) as dark red plates, m.p. 185° (dec.). Acetylation gave a very low yield of the acetyl derivative.

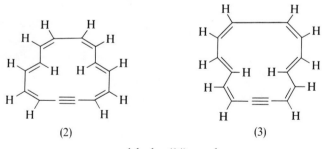

(2)   (3)

monodehydro-(14)-annulene

(14)-Annulene did not undergo these electrophilic substitution reactions.

4. LARGER MACROCYCLES CONTAINING CONJUGATED DIACETYLENIC UNITS

Sondheimer and co-workers[25] couple-cyclized 1,7-octadiyne to form the cyclic dimer, trimer, tetramer, pentamer and hexamer. They also worked with 1,6-heptadiyne, 1,9-decadiyne and 1,8-nonadiyne. In 1959, at the time of this work,[25] the 34-membered monocyclic hydrocarbon was the largest known. By the coupling-cyclization reactions, rings containing 20, 21, 27, 36, 40, 45 and 54 carbon atoms were made.

In the coupling reactions, concentrations were higher than in Eglinton's high-dilution procedure:[6] 5 grams of 1,7-octadiyne in 500 ml of pyridine with 75 grams of cupric acetate monohydrate was stirred for 3 hours at 55°. The total yield of isolated cyclic products was 54%. The various cyclic products were separated by column chromatography on activated alumina. The reactions and products are outlined schematically (see structure on page 289).

The acetylenic products were hydrogenated over pre-reduced platinum in dioxane at room temperature and atmospheric pressure to form the cyclic paraffins. The two α-diacetylenic groups in the macrocyclic acetylenes caused anomalous absorption. No proximity effects were noted in the cyclic trimers and tetramers.

All of the cyclic polyacetylenes were crystalline, colorless solids which gradually polymerized to yellow or brown polymers on exposure to air and light. Benzene solutions were stable in the dark almost indefinitely. Although color formation is quite common in linear dimers and tetramers, only a few of the cyclics formed bright colors in light.

The products shown in the schematic diagram are outlined in Table 7-5.

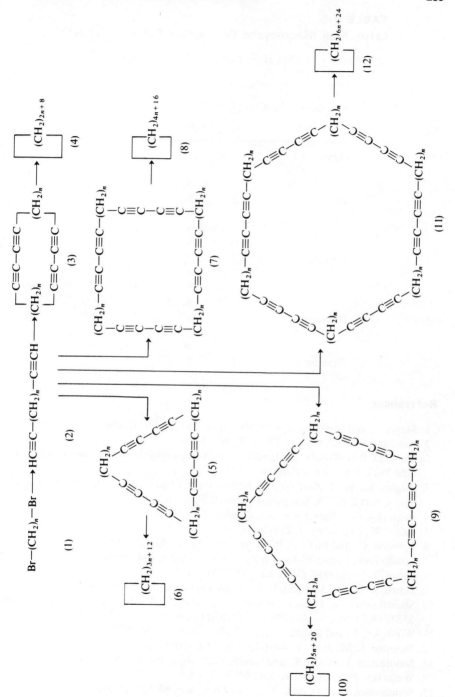

TABLE 7-5
Large Ring Macrocyclic Conjugated Polyacetylenes[25]

$$Br(CH_2)_nBr + NaC{\equiv}CH \xrightarrow{NH_3} HC{\equiv}C(CH_2)_nC{\equiv}CH \xrightarrow[\text{pyridine}]{Cu(OAc)_2,}$$

$$\left[C{\equiv}C{-}C{\equiv}C(CH_2)_n\right]_x$$

Product	x	n	% Yield
Dimer	2	4	8
		5	10
		6	3
Trimer	3	3	3
		4	14
		5	13
		6	3
Tetramer	4	3	4
		4	14
		5	11
		6	2
Pentamer	5	4	14
		5	4
		6	3
Hexamer	6	5	4

References

1. Mayer, J., and Sondheimer, F., *J. Am. Chem. Soc.*, **88**, 602 (1966).
2. Sondheimer, F., *Pure Appl. Chem.*, **7**, 363, (1963).
2a. Craig, D. P., in (Ginsburg, D., editor) "Non-Benzenoid Aromatic Compounds," p. 1, New York, Interscience Publishers, 1959.
3. Ziegler, K., in Houben-Weyl "Methoden der Organischem Chemie," Fourth ed., Vol. 4, Part 2, p. 729, Stuttgart, Thieme, 1955.
4. Belen'skii, L. I., *Russ. Chem. Rev. (English Transl.)*, **33**, 551 (1964).
5. Baker, W., *Chem. Brit.*, **1**, 250 (1965).
6. Eglinton, G., and McCrae, W., *Advan. Org. Chem.*, **4**, 225 (1963).
7. Sondheimer, F., and Wolovsky, R., *J. Am. Chem. Soc.*, **84**, 260 (1962).
8. Gaoni, Y., *et al.*, *Proc. Chem. Soc.*, 397 (1964).
9. Untch, K. G., and Wysocki, D. C., *J. Am. Chem. Soc.*, **88**, 2608 (1966).
10. Shostakovskii, M. F., Sidel'kovskaya, F. P., and Zelenskaya, M. G., *Izv. Akad. Nauk SSSR, Otd. Khim. Nauk*, 1406, 1457 (1957); *Chem. Abstr.*, **52**, 7270 (1958).
11. Wolovsky, R., and Sondheimer, F., *J. Am. Chem. Soc.*, **87**, 5720 (1965).
12. Jackman, L. M., *et al.*, *J. Am. Chem. Soc.*, **84**, 4307 (1962).
13. Sondheimer, F., Amiel, Y., and Gaoni, Y., *J. Am. Chem. Soc.*, **84**, 270 (1962).
14. Wolovsky, R., *J. Am. Chem. Soc.*, **87**, 3638 (1965).
15. Sondheimer, F., and Gaoni, Y., *J. Am. Chem. Soc.*, **83**, 1259 (1961).
16. Wolovsky, R., and Sondheimer, F., *J. Am. Chem. Soc.*, **88**, 1525 (1966).

17. Mayer, J., and Sondheimer, F., *J. Am. Chem. Soc.*, **88**, 603 (1966).

18. Wolovsky, R., and Sondheimer, F., *J. Am. Chem. Soc.*, **84**, 2844 (1962).

19. Sondheimer, F., Amiel, Y., and Wolovsky, R., *J. Am. Chem. Soc.*, **79**, 6263 (1957).

20. Cram, D. J., and Allinger, N. L., *J. Am. Chem. Soc.*, **78**, 2518 (1956).

21. Lindlar, H., and Dubuis, R., *Org. Syn.*, **46**, 89 (1966).

22. Sondheimer, F., *et al.*, *J. Am. Chem. Soc.*, **88**, 2610 (1966).

23. Sondheimer, F., and Ben-Efraim, D. A., *J. Am. Chem. Soc.*, **85**, 52 (1963).

24. Gaoni, Y., and Sondheimer, F., *J. Am. Chem. Soc.*, **86**, 521 (1964).

25. Sondheimer, F., Amiel, Y., and Wolovsky, R., *J. Am. Chem. Soc.*, **81**, 4600 (1959).

26. Zinkevich, E. P., Sarycheva, I. K., and Preobrazhenskii, N. A., *Zh. Organ. Khim.*, **2**, 2021 (1966); *Chem. Abstr.*, **66**, 75731 (1967).

PART THREE

Macrocyclic Nonconjugated Polyacetylenes

1. BACKGROUND

Most of the information about macrocycles which contain nonconjugated acetylenic bonds comes from the work of Wotiz and co-workers[1] and of Dale, Hubert and co-workers.[2] These compounds were unknown before 1956. Cram and Allinger[3] prepared the first nonconjugated carbocyclic diyne, 1,7-cyclododecadiyne, starting with disodium acetylide and 4-chloro-1-

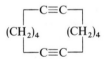

bromobutane, and requiring six steps. One step was an acyloin cyclization of an ester containing an acetylenic bond, the first example of such a reaction. The diyne was semihydrogenated to the diene. The main interest was whether the favorably located triple bonds in 1,7-cyclododecadiyne would show any indication of transannular interaction to form the elusive cyclobutadiene ring. No such tendency was detected.

2. PREPARATION AND PROPERTIES

In 1961, Wotiz[1] and Dale[2] reported independently developed syntheses for nonconjugated cyclic polyynes, much better than the previous method.[3] Wotiz's preparation and property work will be discussed first, and Dale's will follow.

Wotiz used two different methods. In method A, α,ω-dihalides reacted with a mixture of sodium acetylide and disodium acetylide. The sodium acetylide was a chain stopper, preventing the formation of large amounts of linear conjugated polyynes. In method B, the dihalide was reacted with mono- or disodioalkadiyne to form the same products.

Method A:

$$Br(CH_2)_nBr + NaC\equiv CH + NaC\equiv CNa \xrightarrow{NH_3}$$

$$HC\equiv C+(CH_2)_nC\equiv C+_xH + \underset{(2)}{\underset{\big|}{\overset{\overset{\displaystyle C\equiv C}{\big|}}{(CH_2)_n}}\;\;\underset{C\equiv C+_x}{}\;\;(CH_2)_n}$$

(1)

Method B:

$$Br(CH_2)_nBr + NaC\equiv C(CH_2)_mC\equiv CNa(\text{or } H)\xrightarrow{NH_3}$$

$$HC\equiv C+(CH_2)_mC\equiv C(CH_2)_nC\equiv C+_y(CH_2)_mC\equiv CH +$$

(3)

$$\underset{(4)}{\overset{\overset{\displaystyle C\equiv C}{}}{(CH_2)_n \qquad\qquad (CH_2)_m}\;\;C\equiv C+_y}$$

The products prepared by these reactions are listed in Table 7-6.

TABLE 7-6
Macrocyclic Nonconjugated Polyacetylenes[1]

Method	Type	n	m	x	y	b.p. °C	b.p. mm	m.p. (°C)
A	1	4	–	2	–	111	1.0	–3
A (B)	1 (3)	4	(4)	3	(1)	167	0.3	19
A	1	4	–	7	–	–	–	36
A	1	4	–	8	–	–	–	55
A	1	5	–	2	–	113	0.8	8
B	3	5	5	–	1	170	0.1	33
A	1	6	–	2	–	131	0.2	24
B	3	6	4	–	1	168	0.6	–
B	4	4	4	–	1	87	0.2	39
B	4	4	5	–	1	83	0.08	7
A (B)	2 (4)	4	(5)	1	(1)	–	–	100
B	4	6	4	–	1	98	0.7	–
B	4	6	5	–	1	103	0.1	40
B	4	4	4	3	2	215	0.2	71
A	$HC\equiv C(CH_2)_4O(CH_2)_4C\equiv CH$					128	30	–
A	$O\big\langle\overset{(CH_2)_4C\equiv C(CH_2)_4}{\underset{(CH_2)_4C\equiv C(CH_2)_4}{}}\big\rangle O$					178	0.08	75

The metal used for acetylide formation influenced the direction of the reaction in method A. This is illustrated by the data in Table 7-7.

TABLE 7-7
Reaction of 1,5-Dibromopentane with Metal Acetylides[1]

$$(MC \equiv CM : MC \equiv CH = 1)$$

| | % of Total Yield ($n = 5, x = 1$) | |
| | Linear Product | Cyclic Product |
M	(1)	(2)
Li	51	6
Na	18	25
K	30	–
Ba	9	10

The products (Table 7-6) are colorless liquids which are stable at least to 300°. The triple bonds cause the liquids to be more dense than the corresponding paraffins. Heat of combustion is lower than paraffins on a molar basis, but higher on a volume basis because of the higher density.

The linear products (1) and (3) have the strong and characteristic hydrogen absorption band of $HC \equiv$ at 3300 cm^{-1}, the terminal triple bond band at 2130 cm^{-1}, and the internal triple bond absorption, usually very weak, at 2240 cm^{-1}. The cyclic polyacetylenes (2) and (4) have only the internal triple bond absorption doublet at 2220 and 2270 cm^{-1}. These bands are weak, but are stronger than the internal triple bond absorption in linear polyacetylenes. The strong absorption band near 1330 cm^{-1} is due to methylene adjacent to the triple bond and is a valuable experimental aid. If no triple bond absorption could be observed, the band at 1330 cm^{-1} confirmed the acetylenic structure.

Dale[2] prepared cyclic nonconjugated diynes and tetraynes containing 11–26 carbon atoms. They also prepared cyclic conjugated tetraynes with 16–26 carbons from compounds containing conjugated diacetylene and conjugated triacetylene groups. In addition, they made a 22-carbon hexayne in low yield. The two-step reaction used in this work[2] is essentially the same as Wotiz's method B (see structure on page 294).

The open-chain polyynes exploded on attempted distillation, so they were not isolated. Disodium diacetylide and disodium triacetylide were made *in situ* by dehydrohalogenation of 1,4-dichloro-2-butyne and 1,6-dichloro-2,4-hexadiyne, respectively, by excess sodium amide. The reactions were done in 0.1 M solutions, not at high dilutions. The cyclic nonconjugated diynes [(5), $x = 1$] were formed in highest yield when $m = n = 5$. These products are symmetrical. Other products which were nearly symmetrical also formed in high yield. Dale's

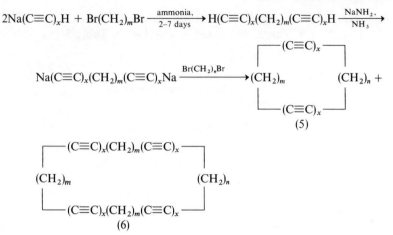

$$2Na(C{\equiv}C)_xH + Br(CH_2)_mBr \xrightarrow[\text{2–7 days}]{\text{ammonia,}} H(C{\equiv}C)_x(CH_2)_m(C{\equiv}C)_xH \xrightarrow[\text{NH}_3]{\text{NaNH}_2,}$$

method is not as general as oxidative coupling for conjugated acetylenic macrocycles, but it is simple and easy to use where applicable.

Tables 7-8, 7-9 and 7-10 show the yields and melting and boiling points of Dale's products.[2]

TABLE 7-8
Diynes, 11–22 Carbon Atoms[2]

m	n	Reaction time (days)	% Yield	m.p. (°C)	b.p. (°C, @ mm Hg)
2	5	7	1	3–5	45, @ 0.1
4	4	2	7	37–38	65–70 @ 10^{-4}
4	5	2	14⎫	7–8	70–80 @ 10^{-3}
5	4	2	40⎭		
4	6	3	16⎫	30	100–110 @ 10^{-3}
6	4	3	19⎭		
5	5	3	57	97–98	100–110 @ 10^{-3}
5	6	3	45⎫	38	105–115 @ 10^{-3}
6	5	3	24⎭		
5	7	7	10	27.5	110–125 @ 10^{-3}
6	6	3	23	– 3.5	110–120 @ 10^{-3}
5	8	7	19	41–43	120–130 @ 10^{-3}
8	5	7	0	–	–

TABLE 7-8—(continued)

m	n	Reaction time (days)	% Yield	m.p. (°C)	b.p. (°C, @ mm Hg)
7	7	7	32	97	160–180 @ 3
5	10	7	12	−8	118–134 @ 10^{-3}
8	7	7	22	56	124–150 @ 10^{-3}
8	8	4	20	38–39	145–147 @ 10^{-2}
9	9	7	10	106.5	198–202 @ 10^{-3}
5	a	5	38	128	120–125 @ 10^{-2}
b	5	5	0	–	–

[a] Starting dihalide was $(BrCH_2CH_2)_2O$.
[b] Starting diyne was $(HC{\equiv}CCH_2CH_2)_2O$.

TABLE 7-9
Tetraynes, 22–26 Carbons

$$\text{C}{\equiv}\text{C(CH}_2)_m\text{C}{\equiv}\text{C}$$
$$(CH_2)_n \qquad\qquad (CH_2)_n$$
$$\text{C}{\equiv}\text{C(CH}_2)_m\text{C}{\equiv}\text{C}$$

m	n	% Yield	m.p.(°C)
2	5	11	146
3	5	13	74–75
4	5	3	69
4	5	>6	86.5
5	4	>1	–

One 22-carbon macrocyclic conjugated hexayne was prepared : 1,3,5,12,14,16-cyclodocosahexayne [(5), $x = 3$, $m = n = 5$]. The yield was only 0.3%. Note that the maximum yield of (5) drops from 57 to 7 to 0.3% as x increases from 1 to 2 to 3, so it seems that $x = 3$ is the limit (this requires a linear eight-carbon rod in the ring for each conjugated triyne unit). The cyclohexayne explodes at 200° without melting.

Stability, ease of formation and melting point vary with constitution. In the conjugated cyclic tetraynes, the higher-melting products are stable at the melting point, but the lower-melting ones decompose at their melting points (around 160°). Most of the cyclic tetraynes are storage stable. They do not discolor as the corresponding open-chain products do.

TABLE 7-10
Conjugated Tetraynes [(1), $x = 2$]

$$\text{C} \equiv \text{C} - \text{C} \equiv \text{C}$$

$$(\text{CH}_2)_m \qquad\qquad (\text{CH}_2)_n$$

$$\text{C} \equiv \text{C} - \text{C} \equiv \text{C}$$

m	n	Reaction time (days)	% Yield 0.2 M^a	% Yield 0.07 M^a	m.p.(°C)
4	4	7	0	0.1	163
5	4	4 + 4	7	–	165
5	5	7	7	–	210
5	6	4 + 4	5	–	160
6	6	7	0	4	81
7	7	5	2	–	171
8	8	7	0	0.3	85
9	9	7	2	1.0	142
10	10	–	–	–	–

[a] Concentration of each reactant in liquid NH_3.

The infrared spectra of the cyclic polyynes are normal. Curves are frequently superimposable on curves from corresponding open-chain polyynes.[2] Infrared spectra of the silver nitrate complexes indicate a slight decrease of the multiple bond character, and a *cis*-like deformation of the linear $C-C \equiv C-C$ system. Ultraviolet spectra of the cyclic conjugated polyynes are nearly identical to the spectra of the acyclic analogs. There seems to be no spectroscopic evidence for transannular interaction between the acetylenic systems, such as Wotiz[1] suggested to explain the stability of some of his cyclic diynes. A plot of $m = n$ against melting point for diynes and tetraynes shows a very strong alternation phenomenon. The odd carbon members ($m = n =$ odd number) melt much higher than the even-numbered cyclics above and below. This is one of the most pronounced alternations known.

Hubert and Dale[8] used similar reactions to prepare some macrocycles with acetylenic bonds separated from other unsaturated systems by just two methylene groups. From steric considerations and valency angles, the 18-carbon ring should be the ideal size. Cyclooctadeca-1,5,7,11-tetrayne [(7), $m = 2$, $n = 6$] was prepared by a series of steps, the first one using excess diyne in ammonia:

$$Br(CH_2)_nBr + 2NaC\equiv C(CH_2)_mC\equiv CH \longrightarrow$$

$$HC\equiv C(CH_2)_mC\equiv C(CH_2)_nC\equiv C(CH_2)_mC\equiv CH +$$
(7a)

$$\begin{array}{c} \lceil \quad C\equiv C(CH_2)_nC\equiv C \quad \rceil \\ \mid \qquad\qquad\qquad\qquad\quad \mid \\ (CH_2)_m-C\equiv C-C\equiv C-(CH_2)_m \quad (\text{m.p. } 59°) \end{array}$$
(7)
(30%)

The triple bonds in (7) are separated by two methylene groups ($m = 2$), but attempts to alkali-isomerize (7) to conjugated cyclooctadecaoctaene gave only uncontrollable reactions and no well-defined isomerization products.

Starting with 1,8-nonadiyne (60% excess), the intermediate (7a) was prepared in 44% yield ($m = 5$, $n = 7$). Oxidative coupling-cyclization gave cyclopentacosatetrayne (8%, m.p. 25°). Complete hydrogenation of this tetrayne gave cyclopentacosane (m.p. 53°).

The base-catalyzed isomerization of products such as (7) gave poorly defined results. The presence of one olefinic bond between two acetylenic bonds might be expected to direct isomerization more definitely to polyene. A 15-carbon ring was prepared by the following sequence of reactions:[8]

$$BrCH_2CH{=}CHCH_2Br + 2HC\equiv CCH_2MgBr \longrightarrow$$

$$HC\equiv CCH_2CH_2CH{=}CHCH_2CH_2C\equiv CH \xrightarrow[\text{NaNH}_2]{+\,Br(CH_2)_5Br,}$$
(8) cis and trans

$$\begin{array}{c} \lceil \overline{\quad CH_2CH_2CH{=}CHCH_2CH_2 \quad} \rceil \\ \mid \qquad\qquad\qquad\qquad\qquad\quad \mid \\ \lfloor \underline{\quad C\equiv C(CH_2)_5C\equiv C \quad} \rfloor \end{array}$$
(9) cis only

Although the intermediate (8) was a mixture of cis and trans isomers, the cyclic product (9) was all cis. Apparently the trans-enediyne (8) cannot cyclize. The base-induced isomerization of (9) gave no identifiable products.

3. REACTIONS

3.1. Stability

Generally the macrocyclic polyynes are unusually stable and react more sluggishly than open-chain analogs. For example, Dale[2] at first did not recognize the acetylenic nature of cyclotetradeca-1,8-diyne because it reacts very slowly with permanganate and with bromine. Most of the diynes are very stable. Cyclotetradeca-1,8-diyne can be distilled at 290° under nitrogen.

3.2. Transannular Reactions

At 500° *in vacuo*, cyclotetradeca-1,8-diyne gives 40 % yield of a liquid product, tentatively identified as a mixture of decahydroanthracenes, from a transannular reaction. The nonconjugated diynes and tetraynes undergo no transannular reaction below 100° in the presence of potassium *t*-butoxide. Under these conditions, only the acetylenic bonds separated by two methylene groups isomerize to some extent. The cyclic diynes cyclize to 1,2-polymethylenebenzenes at 160–200° in the presence of potassium *t*-butoxide:

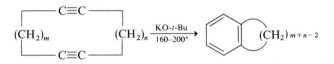

This transannular reaction was used to prepare several new 1,2-polymethylenebenzenes.[2]

3.3. Hydration

Cyclic diynes hydrate normally. Cyclotetradeca-1,8-diyne hydrates in the presence of methanol and BF_3-HgO to form 15 % yield of cyclotetradecane-1,8-dione.

3.4. Complexes

All of the symmetrical cyclic diynes give crystalline 1:1 complexes with silver nitrate. Under the same conditions, the acyclic nonterminal diacetylenes do not form insoluble complexes. Dale used this reaction as a method of purifying the cyclic diynes; treatment with sodium chloride precipitates silver chloride and releases the diyne.

3.5. Hydrogenation

Nonconjugated cyclic polyynes semihydrogenate easily on Lindlar catalyst to form *cis*-polyenes. The reaction ends once polyene formation is complete. The conjugated cyclopolyynes, on the other hand, do not stop under these conditions; even if hydrogen is discontinued after the calculated absorption, some unreacted acetylenic bonds and some saturated C—C bonds are always present.[2] Cyclic diynes are not reduced by sodium in ammonia, even though the *trans*-dienes expected are more stable than the *cis* (some *cis*-dienes are converted to *trans*-dienes by treatment with selenium at 150°).

Hubert and Dale[6] reduced cycloalkatetraynes which have two diametrically located conjugated diacetylenic bonds to the corresponding hydrocarbons containing two sets of conjugated diene bonds. Trialkylboranes were used as reducing agents.

Complete hydrogenation over platinum gives very pure cycloalkanes.[2] By this method, the previously unknown 19-carbon cycloalkane was obtained from three different polyynes. This completed the series of cycloalkanes up to 24 carbons. The 19-carbon cycloalkane is the highest melting of all cycloalkanes below 50 carbons.

3.6. Cycloaddition Reaction with Butadiene

Heimbach and Brenner[7] reacted cycloalkynes with butadiene in the presence of nickel(0)tri(2-biphenylyl)phosphite (1:1) at 40° to form bicyclic and tricyclic hydrocarbons. Cycloaddition reactions also occur with acyclic acetylenes. Cycloundecyne and 2 moles of butadiene gave 4,5-octamethylene-*cis*-1,*cis* 4,*trans*-7-cyclodecatriene in 95% yield, with 95% of the butadiene dimerizing to cyclooctadiene.

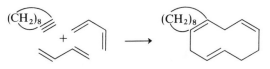

Cyclotetradecadiyne reacted with either 2 or 4 moles of butadiene. The conversion of cyclotetradecadiyne was 45%, of which 40% reacted to form tricyclic product and 55% formed bicyclic product:

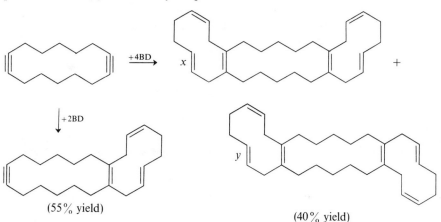

(55% yield)

(40% yield)

4. CONFORMATION

Dale[2,5] studied the conformation of the α,ω-diynes before cyclization, and the conformation of the resulting cyclodiynes. In the ideal conformations of the

α,ω-diynes, the rings must be almost pre-formed before the final cyclization. When cyclodiynes

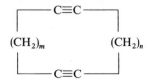

are formed, the yield depends on the values of m and n. When $m = 5$, the yield varies with the value of n:

$$n = 4, 40\%$$
$$n = 5, 57\%$$
$$n = 6, 47\%$$

The more favorable the positions of the $-C\equiv CNa$ and the $BrCH_2-$ ends of the chain for reaction, the higher is the yield of cyclodiyne.

References

1. Wotiz, J. H., Adams, R. F., and Parsons, C. G., *J. Am. Chem. Soc.*, **83**, 373 (1961).
2. Dale, J., Hubert, A. J., and King, G. S. D., *J. Chem. Soc.*, 73 (1963).
3. Cram, D. J., and Allinger, N. L., *J. Am. Chem. Soc.* **78**, 2518 (1956).
4. Eglinton, G., and McCrae, W., *Advan. Org. Chem.*, **4**, 225 (1963).
5. Dale, J., *J. Chem. Soc.*, 93 (1963).
6. Hubert, A. J., and Dale, J., *J. Chem. Soc.*, 6674 (1965).
7. Heimbach, P., and Brenner, W., *Angew. Chem. Intern. Ed. Engl.*, **5**, 961 (1966).
8. Hubert, A. J., and Dale, J., *J. Chem. Soc.*, 86 (1963).

PART FOUR

Conjugated Macrocyclic Polyacetylenes Containing Aromatic Rings

1. COUPLING-CYCLIZATION OF *o*-DIETHYNYLBENZENE

Relatively little is known about cyclic acetylenes which contain aromatic nuclei as part of the macrocyclic ring. In 1957 Eglinton and Galbraith reported that the high-dilution coupling of *o*-diethynylbenzene gave cyclic trimer. In 1959, Behr, Eglinton and Raphael[1,2] corrected this conclusion. The product is actually

dimer (1), 1,2,7,8-dibenzocyclododeca-1,7-diene-3,5,9,11-tetrayne. The hydrogenation reactions outlined gave proof of the structure and furnished additional
examples of transannular cyclization reactions to form five- and six-membered
rings:

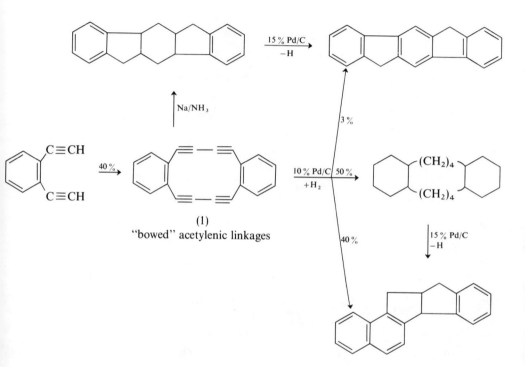

(1)
"bowed" acetylenic linkages

The structure of the coupled product was established by IR, UV and NMR
spectra, and by the hydrogenation reactions. X-ray analysis showed the pair of
"bowed" acetylenic linkages. The instability of the dimer is consistent with the
strain in the ring. The extensive transannular reactions during catalytic hydrogenation under very mild conditions were unexpected.[2]

o-Diethynylbenzene was prepared by dehydrobromination of the tetrabromide from o-divinylbenzene in an overall yield of 13%.[2] The preparation of
o-diethynylbenzene and coupling-cyclization were investigated further.[3] In the
earlier work, dehydrobromination of the tetrabromide (2) with 2 moles of
potassium t-butoxide gave o-diethynylbenzene directly. The reaction went in
steps when dehydrobromination of (2) was done with 1 mole of KO-t-Bu in each
step:

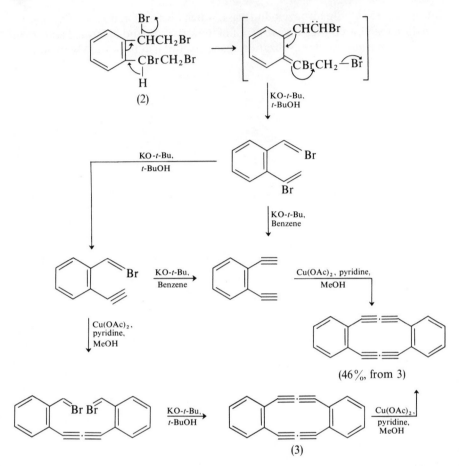

2. COUPLING-CYCLIZATION OF OTHER DISUBSTITUTED BENZENES

Conjugated and nonconjugated cyclopolyynes containing benzene rings were prepared by two methods: (1) alkylation of sodiodiynes with α,ω-dibromides, and (2) oxidative coupling.[4] Depending on the system, the macrocycles contained one or two o-, m- or p-disubstituted benzene rings as part of the macrocycle (see structure on page 303).

Disodio derivatives of the terminal diynes (1) reacted with 1,5-dibromopentane to give three cyclic products [(4), n = 5]. Since the ring size is smaller than 18 carbons, the alkali isomerization is controllable and very much slower, and the polyenes obtained are liquids. The three analogous diynes which contain

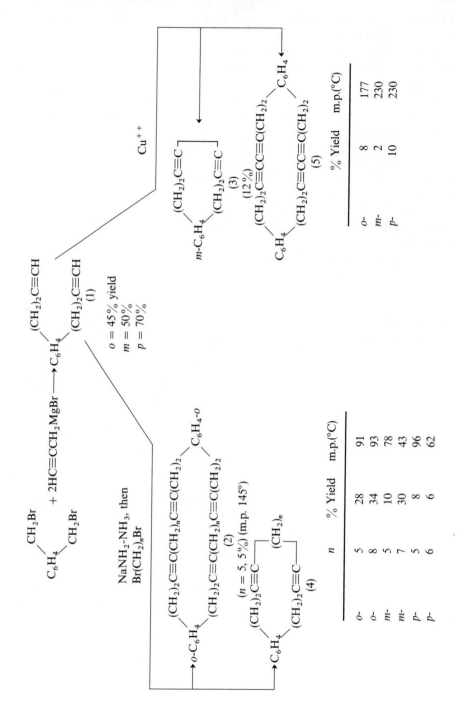

18 carbons in the macro ring $[(4):o, n = 8; m, n = 7; p, n = 6]$ isomerize more rapidly and give better defined products.

The terminal diynes (1) oxidatively coupled to form the cyclic dimers (5), whose ultraviolet spectra are superpositions of normal dialkylbenzene and dialkyldiacetylene spectra.

With the *meta* isomer, the cyclic dimer formed only in concentrated solution at 70–100° and in only 2% yield. Cyclic monomer (4) formed in 12% yield in dilute solutions at 70° and was a by-product from reactions in concentrated solutions at 70-100°. Cyclic monomer (4) is very unstable and polymerized in a few seconds to an insoluble red polymer as soon as the solvent was removed. It could be isolated by crystallization at −80°. The tension caused by the 11-carbon ring prevents the diacetylene unit from a linear arrangement, and this is reflected in the ultraviolet and infrared spectra, which are different from the dimer. In other cases, spectra of monomer and dimer were practically indistinguishable.

Full hydrogenation to polymethylenebenzenes and dibenzo analogs gave several new compounds.

3. APPLICATION OF THE CUPROUS ALKYNYLIDE-ARYL IODIDE REACTION TO FORM CYCLIC ACETYLENES

Campbell and co-workers[5] adapted Stephens'[6] cuprous alkynylide-aryl iodide metathesis reaction to the synthesis of cyclic triynes and tetraynes. Infrared, NMR and mass spectra confirmed the structures of the products:

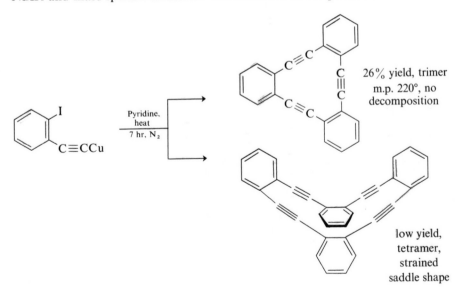

26% yield, trimer
m.p. 220°, no
decomposition

low yield,
tetramer,
strained
saddle shape

4. COUPLING-CYCLIZATION OF 1,8-DIETHYNYL-ANTHRACENE

Akiyama and Nakagawa[7] prepared 1,8-diethynylanthracene from the diacyl chloride via the ketomalonate. They prepared the cyclic dimer of 1,8-diethynyl-anthracene by coupling with cupric acetate in pyridine.

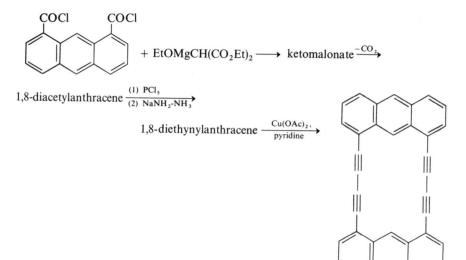

$$\text{1,8-diacetylanthracene} \xrightarrow[\text{(2) NaNH}_2\text{-NH}_3]{\text{(1) PCl}_5}$$

$$\text{1,8-diethynylanthracene} \xrightarrow[\text{pyridine}]{\text{Cu(OAc)}_2,}$$

The cyclic dimer was stable enough to be stored at room temperature, in air and light for a long time. When heated in vacuo at 370°, it turned black but did not change crystal shape. The product was not very soluble in common organic solvents, but gave greenish-yellow solutions with intense green fluorescence.

References

1. Behr, O. M., Eglinton, G., and Raphael, R. A., *Chem. Ind. (London)*, 699 (1959).
2. Behr, O. M., *et al.*, *J. Chem. Soc.*, 3614 (1960).
3. *Ibid.*, 1151 (1964).
4. Hubert, A. J., and Dale, J., *J. Chem. Soc.*, 86 (1963).
5. Campbell, I. D., *et al.*, *Chem. Commun.*, 87 (1966).
6. Stephens, R. D. and Castro, C. E., *J. Org. Chem.*, **28**, 3313 (1963).
7. Akiyama, S., and Nakagawa, M., *Chem. Ind. (London)*, 346 (1960).

PART FIVE

Macrocyclic Polyacetylenes Containing Oxygen or Sulfur Atoms

1. ESTERS

Some esters of o-ethynylphenol were prepared and cyclo-coupled:[1,2]

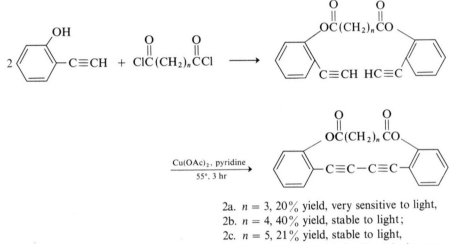

2a. $n = 3$, 20% yield, very sensitive to light,
2b. $n = 4$, 40% yield, stable to light;
2c. $n = 5$, 21% yield, stable to light,
$n = 6$ or 7, open-chain diacetylenic esters.

Scale models show that (2b) is a rigid, planar molecule. In (2c) the phenyl groups are not coplanar, because the bridging chain is too long. A model of (2a) shows that the diacetylenic linkage is forced to bend because the methylene chain is short and holds the phenyl groups in a coplanar position. The abnormal sensitivity of (2a) to light reflects the strained structure. The ultraviolet spectra of the cyclic esters are closely related, but the decrease of ε values of λ_{max} of the long-wavelength region (290–340 mμ) are in the sequence (2b) > (2a) > (2c), indicating the importance of the coplanar phenyl groups in determining the intensity of absorption.

When $n = 2$, a by-product of the reaction is 3,2:2′-dibenzofuranyl

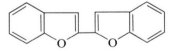

2. ETHERS

Cyclic diacetylenes containing ether oxygen, phenyl rings and olefinic bonds have been prepared.[3] The products showed anomalous infrared absorptions, caused by the interaction of the π electrons of the benzene ring (or olefinic bond) with the acetylenic bonds:

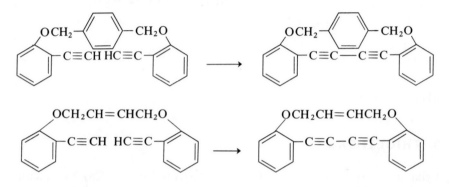

The coupling-cyclization reaction has been used to prepare cyclic oligomers of 1,5-bis(propargyloxymethyl)naphthalene:[4]

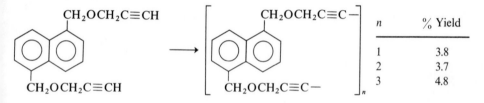

n	% Yield
1	3.8
2	3.7
3	4.8

The dimer exhibited hypochromism due to interaction between the transition moment dipoles. The molecule has a definite geometry which keeps the chromophores in a fixed spatial position.

3. LACTONES

Several macrocyclic acetylenic lactones have been prepared.[5] For example:

$$ClCH_2C{\equiv}CCH_2Cl + NaNH_2\text{-}NH_3 \longrightarrow NaC{\equiv}CC{\equiv}CNa \xrightarrow[\text{NaNH}_2\text{-NH}_3]{+HC{\equiv}C(CH_2)_3O\overset{\text{O}}{\overset{\|}{C}}(CH_2)_8I}$$

$$\left[\begin{array}{c} (C{\equiv}C)_3 \\[4pt] \overset{\text{O}}{\overset{\|}{(CH_2)_8C O(CH_2)_3}} \end{array}\right]$$
$$(11\%)$$

4. KETONES

The macrocyclic acetylenic ketones are related to lactones and have been made by high-dilution coupling reactions:[6]

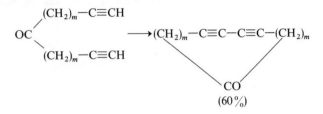

where m = 6 or 8.

5. THIOETHERS

Eglinton[7] in 1964 prepared 1,6-dithiacyclodeca-3,8-diyne (2a) by reacting 1,4-dichloro-2-butyne with aqueous sodium sulfide, or better still, ammonium sulfide.

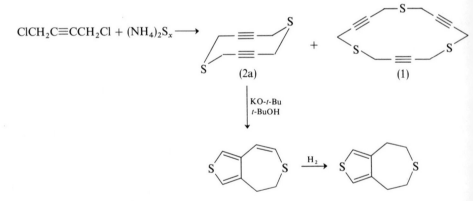

(2a) is probably the chair form, not planar or boat. Some ten-membered trimer (1) was also formed. Sondheimer[8] confirmed that Lespieau[9] actually had made the oxygen analog of (2a) by reacting acetylenedimagnesium bromide with bis(chloromethyl) ether. The oxygen analog of (1) also formed (0.5 % yield).

   (2a) easily hydrogenates to the corresponding *cis,cis*-diene; however, more drastic conditions do not form the saturated heterocycle, but rather cause desulfurization to form *n*-butane. Base-catalyzed proptotropic rearrangement of (2a) gives the substituted thiophene, which yields partially reduced thiophene derivative on catalytic hydrogenation.

6. MACROCYCLES CONTAINING TIN: SYNTHESIS FROM ACETYLENES

Leusink[10] refluxed diphenyltin dihydride with *o*-divinylbenzene in benzene and obtained 16% yield of the seven-membered ring compound (1) and 14% yield of the 14-membered ring product (2):

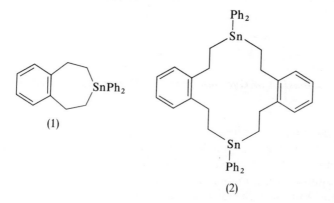

(1)

(2)

The reaction with *o*-diethynylbenzene gave both of the corresponding unsatured products (3) and (4):

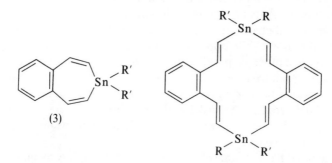

(3)

The highest yield of (3) was 17%, when R and R' were ethyl; the highest yield of (4) was 25%, when R was ethyl and R' phenyl.

References

1. Nakagawa, M., and Toda, F., *Chem. Ind. (London)*, 458 (1959).
2. Toda, F., and Nakagawa, M., *Bull. Chem. Soc. Japan*, **33**, 223 (1960); *Chem. Abstr.*, **55**, 14374 (1961).
3. Nakagawa, M., and Toda, F., *Tetrahedron Letters*, 51 (1961).
4. Ando, T., and Nakagawa, M., *Tetrahedron Letters*, 4437 (1966).

5. Bergel'son, L. D., and Molotkovskii, Yu. G., *Izv. Akad. Nauk SSSR, Otd. Khim. Nauk,* 105 (1963); *Chem. Abstr.,* **58**, 11210 (1963).

6. Bergel'son, L. D., *et al., Izv. Akad. Nauk SSSR, Otd. Khim. Nauk,* 2099 (1961).

7. Eglinton, G., *et al., J. Chem. Soc.,* 1154, (1964).

8. Sondheimer, F., Gaoni, Y., and Bregnan, J., *Tetrahedron Letters,* **26**, 25 (1960).

9. Lespieau, R., *Compt. Rend.,* **188**, 502 (1929).

10. Leusink, A. J., *et al., Rec. Trav. Chim.,* **83**, 1036 (1964).

PART SIX

Conformation of Cycloalkynes and Other Flexible Macrocycles

Dale[1] used modified space-filling molecular models to construct models of molecules with staggered single bonds. He used the models to help select conformations which are completely strainless and therefore presumably preferred. Strainless conformations are possible only for even-membered saturated rings with 14 or more carbons. Replacement of a methylene group by O, NH, $C=O$, etc., does not change the ring conformation, but multiple bonds in the ring drastically change the geometry.

One olefinic bond in a macrocyclic ring immobilizes four successive carbons, and the continuing chains are bent so that no completely strainless conformation of the saturated chain can be found. A second double bond relieves strain only when it is diametrically opposite in some even-numbered rings. This gives two equal, odd-numbered, parallel polymethylene chains connected by two bridges of either both *trans* or both *cis* double bonds. The di-*trans* configuration is preferred, because the two rows of hydrogen atoms are quite close in the di-*cis* double bond arrangement. A third double bond prevents a strainless conformation, but four double bonds may be acceptable in some even-membered rings if they are properly spaced.

One triple bond has the same effect as one double bond. A second triple bond can reestablish order if it is diametrically opposite the first, and the two saturated chains must be equal and contain an odd number of methylene groups. Three triple bonds cause strain, but four triple bonds can give strainless conformations just as four double bonds can. The triple bond is not considered sterically as three bent bonds (as proposed by Pauling). If the triple bond is three bent bonds, the two corner methylene groups at each side of the triple bond should be eclipsed with respect to each other. The observed center of symmetry requires them to be staggered as if the $C-C\equiv C-C$ unit acted sterically as an elongated single bond.

High yields of cyclization products are usually obtained when the products are high melting. The yield in cyclizations should depend on the same factors which determine the stability, since the probability of ring formation in the final cyclization step has to be high if the resulting ring is to be strainless.

Macrocyclic hydrocarbons containing two multiple bonds can have ideal conformations without angular or torsional strain, and a minimum of *gauche* bonds, only if the multiple bonds are the same kind and are located diametrically in 14-, 18-, 22-, etc., carbon rings.[3] The triple bond is more satisfactory than the double bond for study of positional isomers because no stereoisomerism is possible, and because the conjugated cycloalkadiyne, with the co-linear arrangement of six carbons, is unlikely in most rings (at least up to C_{16}). Nonconjugated cyclic diynes

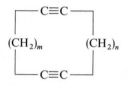

with potassium *t*-butoxide in *t*-butanol do not isomerize at low temperatures and aromatize above 160°. When the acetylenic bond is separated by only two methylene groups from an unsaturated system, *t*-butoxide-catalyzed isomerization to the conjugated 1,3-diene occurs at 125° in large rings and at 65–70° in open chains. The triple bond in simple acyclic monoacetylenic hydrocarbons migrates from the terminal to the 2-position on treatment with alcoholic potassium hydroxide at 125–175°, or on treatment with sodamide. Equilibrium is established through intermediate allenes. Potassium *t*-butoxide in *t*-butanol at 196° causes migration all through an open-chain C_7 hydrocarbon to give an equilibrium mixture containing only nonterminal acetylenes and allenes, but no conjugated diene.

Dimethyl sulfoxide and similar aprotic proton-accepting solvents cause very large increases in rates of many carbanion reactions, such as olefin isomerization. The larger macrocyclic alkadiynes isomerize at only 40° in the presence of potassium *t*-butoxide in dimethyl sulfoxide.[3] Small amounts of allenes are formed along with the isomerized acetylenes, but no conjugated dienes or trienes form. In 12-carbon rings, the allene content is higher, and these products undergo secondary transannular reactions so fast that diyne equilibrium is never obtained. Transannular side reactions are much slower in the higher members. The cyclic diynes isomerize to form the symmetrical alkadiynes as the major products, especially in the 14-carbon rings. This is somewhat less pronounced in the more flexible 18-carbon ring. As expected, there is no preference for the symmetrical isomer in the 16- and 20-carbon rings. For these cycloalkadiynes, the expected preference is for the unsymmetrical isomers with odd $n = m + 2$, since these can have conformations which are strain free. The next isomer having even $n = m + 4$ is the main component at equilibrium, even though its best conformation has a slightly strained skeleton. Apparently this disadvantage is compensated by the compact structure with favorable internal van der Waals contact points, and the presence of only one *gauche* bond within the saturated chain. The conformation of one thermodynamically favored cycloalkadiyne is pictured as:

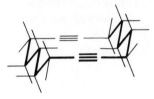 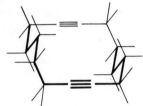

cyclotetradeca-1,8-diyne proposed
conformation

conformation actually observed in
crystals

The 14- and 16-carbon cyclics isomerize much faster at 80°, only 1 hour being required for equilibrium in dimethyl sulfoxide with KO-*t*-Bu catalyst. The presence of allenes as intermediates was shown by infrared absorption at 5.10 and 11.45 mμ of fractions separated by GLC. The less diametrically the triple bonds are located in the rings, the more rapidly do the final products form.

The benzocycloalkenes, the only products from isomerizations in *t*-butanol at 160°, do not form in dimethyl sulfoxide. This may be connected with the absence of conjugated di- and tetraenes which precede aromatization. As the triple bonds are close when the final product forms, aromatization should occur after the first transannular bridge forms, if one ring is six-membered.

Macrocyclic diynes which have a benzene ring

$$C_6H_4 \Bigg\langle \begin{array}{c} CH_2CH_2C{\equiv}C \\ \\ CH_2CH_2C{\equiv}C \end{array} \Bigg] (CH_2)_n$$

also behave differently in these solvents (*t*-butanol and dimethyl sulfoxide). In dimethy sulfoxide the triple bonds migrate faster than they isomerize to conjugated dienes. Conjugated dienes form only when an intermediate allene is separated from the aromatic nucleus by one doubly activated methylene group.

Incorporation of polyene chromophores into rings causes a bending which has a strong effect on the electronic spectra.[4] Macrocyclic hydrocarbons having the *o*-, *m*- and *p*-dibutadienylbenzene chromophores form when the corresponding dibut-3'-ynylbenzene compounds are alkali isomerized. In the analogous open-chain compounds, the tetraenes form easily. Treatment with alkali at 110° for 40 hours completes the reaction. The same isomerization in macrocyclic compounds is difficult and forms various isomers having 1,3-diene systems not conjugated with the aromatic ring. The 1,3-diene systems move around as discrete units, usually have the *cis-trans* configuration, and avoid the *s-cis*-conformation. If two diene systems meet, the resulting 1,3,5,7-tetraene immediately aromatizes except when a *p*-phenylene group and a small ring prevent the folding of the chain.

The structures established for some of the isomerized products are:

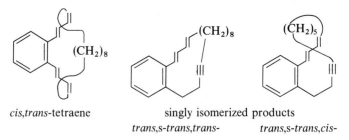

cis,trans-tetraene   singly isomerized products
                              trans,s-trans,trans-   *trans,s-trans,cis-*

In 1966, Dale[5] wrote a review on the conformation of macrocycles of various types.

References

1. Dale, J., *J. Chem. Soc.*, 93 (1963).
2. Dale, J., Hubert, A. J., and King, G. S. D., *J. Chem. Soc.*, 73 (1963).
3. Hubert, A. J., and Dale, J., *J. Chem. Soc.*, 3118 (1965).
4. Dale, J., and Hubert, A. J., *J. Chem. Soc.*, 5475 (1963).
5. Dale, J., *Angew. Chem., Intern. Ed.*, **5**, 1000 (1966).

Chapter Eight

ACETYLENIC COMPOUNDS AS DRUGS

1. BACKGROUND

Substitution reactions are usually involved in the synthesis of acetylenes to be used as drugs. The drug use is potentially important so it is included in this book on acetylene chemistry.

Acetylenic drugs are frequently more active, less toxic and more easily absorbed into the body than their olefinic or saturated analogs. In 1931 Bock[1] noted the hypnotic activity of alkynols, but this did not attract much attention. In 1951, Margolin[2] reawakened interest by his report on acetylenic carbinols as hypnotics and sedatives. 3-Methyl-1-pentyn-3-ol is a hypnotic of low toxicity, few side effects and fairly long duration. Like some other acetylenic hypnotics, it is easily counteracted by caffeine. Methylpentynol is now sold as a non-prescription drug.

The effect of the acetylenic bond on drug molecules may be due to the π-electrons.[3] Many π-electron compounds are carcinogens, but polyacetylenes are not. The increased solubility of acetylenic compounds has also been cited as a reason for increased activity. Increased surface active properties may also contribute to the increased ease of absorption in the body. Oxyethylated acetylenic carbinols and glycols are much more effective surfactants than their olefinic or saturated analogs.[4] The triple bond increases the surfactant character appreciably. Ethynylcyclohexanol carbamate ("Valmid," "Valmidate," "Valmin") is a very effective hypnotic and sedative of low toxicity at 0.5 gram doses in man.[5,6] Further, a saturated aqueous solution at 22° has 21 % lower surface tension than water.[5] Thus it is reasonable to suspect that the surfactant character of the triple bond contributes to the beneficial effects observed in some acetylenic drugs.

Alkynyl barbiturates have very low toxicity[7] but apparently are not sufficiently better than standard barbiturates to warrant commercialization. Ethynyl steroids are especially useful in progestative drugs. Acetylenic amines, such as 1,4-bis(pyrrolidino)-2-butyne (tremorine) induce Parkinson's syndrome. Tremorine is used in testing drugs for Parkinson activity. Interestingly, the closely related 1,4-bis(piperidino)-2-butyne is a tremorine antagonist.[8] The amines are also cholinesterase arrestors[9] and anesthetics. The diamide of acetylenedicarboxylic acid (cellocedin) is an antibiotic and is active *in vitro* against NF mouse sarcoma.[10] The methylpentynol monoester of phthalic acid (whipizid) is an anthelmintic.[11]

In this chapter, some acetylenic compounds which have been tested as drugs are described, with direct comparisons with olefinic and saturated analogs where possible. The methods of introducing acetylenic and propargylic groups are included in descriptions of some of the drugs, and the introduction of propargylic and propargylidene groups into molecules is described separately.

2. DRUGS CONTAINING ACETYLENIC GROUPS

2.1. Propargylpiperidinols and Their Esters as Antitussives and Analgesics

The partition coefficient of a drug compound between lipids and water is important. It influences the drug's activity by influencing the site of action. Bonding with plasma protein is also important. Many drugs have aromatic rings which are electron rich and which may bond with the receptor proteins. The acetylenic group is electron rich and may also bond with receptor proteins. The acetylenic group in drug molecules allows considerable variation without loss of the protein-bonding property. Prost[12] and co-workers prepared some propargylpiperidinols by reacting piperidones with propargyl bromide under Reformatsky conditions. They etherified, esterified and dehydrated some of the piperidinols (see structure on page 316). They compared the activity of these compounds with their aromatic analogs. Several of the esters showed interesting antitussive, analgesic and local anesthetic activity (Table 8-1). Thus, analgesia and antitussive activity are not always parallel in these products. Compound (b) is especially interesting as a local anesthetic, and compound (a) as an antitussive. Meperidine is both analgetic and antitussive.

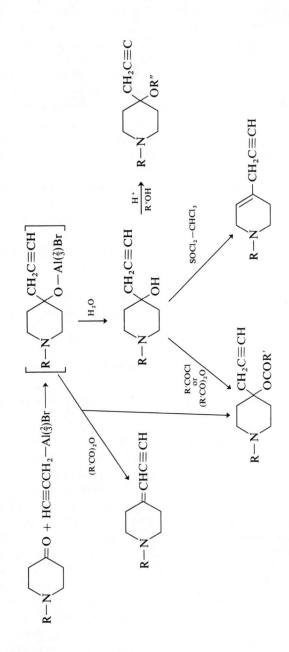

TABLE 8-1

Antitussive, Analgesic and Local Anesthetic Activity of Acetylenic Esters

$$RN \diagup \overset{CH_2C\equiv CH}{\underset{OCOR'}{}}$$

R	R'	Analgesia, Meperidine = 1	Antitussive, Codeine = 1	Local anesthetic, Xylocaine = 1
(a) PhCH$_2$—	Et—	1.3	3	11
(b) Ph(CH$_2$)$_2$—	—CH=CHMe	0	0	22
(c) PhCH$_2$ĊH— (Me)	Et—	1	2	7
(d) Ph(CH$_2$)$_3$—	Et—	1	2	0

2.2. Acetylenic Carbinols and Carbamates as Hypnotics

Lauger and co-workers[13] prepared and tested many acetylenic, ethylenic and some saturated carbinols and carbamates. Some of the compounds were effective hypnotics. The strongest hypnotic effect was exhibited by 1-propargyl-1-cyclohexyl carbamate. This compound was nearly four times as effective as the allyl carbamate and seven times as effective as the propyl carbamate:

Compound	R	Hypnotic Activity Dose (mg/kg), ip	Duration (min)
(cyclohexyl with R and OH)	—CH$_2$C≡CH	250	53 ± 18
	—CH$_2$CH=CH$_2$	250	30 ± 25
(cyclohexyl with R and OCONH$_2$)	—CH$_2$C≡CH	175	225 ± 47
	—CH$_2$CH=CH$_2$	175	58 ± 21
	—CH$_2$CH$_2$CH$_3$	175	34 ± 22

Ethynylcyclohexanol carbamate is also very effective.[5] There seems to be little difference between ethynyl and propargyl derivatives here.

The effect of structure on hypnotic activity is interesting and frequently unpredictable, as data in Table 8-2 show.

TABLE 8-2

The Effect of Structure on Hypnotic Activity of Acetylenic Carbinols[13]

Compound	Hypnotic Activity, 250 mg/kg, ip Duration (min)
▷—C(Me)(OH)CH$_2$CH=CH$_2$	38 ± 2
▷—C(Me)(OH)CH$_2$C≡CH	21
▷—C(Me)(OCONH$_2$)CH$_2$C≡CH	10
▷—C(Me)(OH)CH$_2$C≡CBr	420 ± 49
cyclobutyl C(OH)(CH$_2$C≡CH)	7
cyclohexyl C(OH)(CH$_2$C≡CH)	53
cyclohexyl C(OH)(CH$_2$C≡CH)	23
cyclooctyl C(OH)(CH$_2$C≡CH)	110

McLarmore[14] prepared and evaluated numerous ethynylvinylcarbinols as hypnotics and anticonvulsants. A one-step reaction gave the ethynylvinyl-carbinols: Alkyl β-chloroethyl ketones with 2 moles of lithium acetylide in ammonia reacted by an ethynylation-elimination reaction sequence to form the alkylethynylvinylcarbinols directly. The most active hypnotics in one series were methylethynylvinylcarbinol and ethynylmethylcyclopropylcarbinol. Al-kynylcarbinols without the acetylenic hydrogen were less active. Substitution of chlorine on the β-carbon of the vinyl group had little effect for methylethynyl-vinylcarbinol, but the homologous ethylethynyl-β-chlorovinylcarbinol was twice as active as the vinyl compound. Substitution of halogen for acetylenic hydrogen decreased activity in the β-chlorovinylcarbinols.

2.3. Acetylenic Carbamates as Oncolytic Agents

Dillard, Easton and their co-workers have published many papers related to acetylenic drugs. In 1967, they described some acetylenic oncolytic agents.[15] 1,1-Dialkyl-2-propynyl carbamates show hypnotic activity, but no oncolytic activity. 1,1-Diaryl-2-propynyl carbamates have no hypnotic activity, but have

significant oncolytic activity. In the compounds
$$\begin{array}{c} Ar \\ \diagdown \\ \diagup \quad C \quad \diagdown \\ Ar' \qquad C{\equiv}CR'' \end{array} \begin{array}{c} OCONRR' \\ \diagup \\ \\ \diagdown \end{array}$$
, all

three functions must be present in the molecules which are active. The aromatic groups can be phenyl, p-fluorophenyl or p-tolyl; Ar and Ar' can also be tied together as the 9-fluorenyl group. Both of these groups must be aromatic. The acetylenic group is necessary. An olefinic group lowers the oncolytic activity and increases the toxicity. R″ can be methyl or hydrogen. The carbamate group is also essential. Ethers and esters are ineffective. The best RR′ group is cyclohexyl.

The carbamates were especially active against plasma cell tumor X-5563 and the atypical myelogenous leukemia C-1498. Oral administration required doses double those effective intraperitoneally. Treatment was most effective when started immediately after implantation of the tumor. The toxicity : effective dose ratio was quite favorable.

The best agent 1,1-diphenyl-2-propynyl-N-cyclohexyl carbamate was easily prepared by reacting benzophenone with sodium acetylide in ammonia. The ethynyldiphenylcarbinol reacted with phenyl chlorocarbonate to form
$$\begin{array}{c} C{\equiv}CH \\ \diagup \\ Ph_2C \\ \diagdown \\ OCOPh \end{array}$$
, which reacted with cyclohexylamine to form the carbamate.

The carbamate-forming reaction is the only low-yield step in the entire sequence. The carbamates can cyclize if R or R′ is hydrogen (see structure on page 320). These and other reaction products were inactive as oncolytic agents.

2.4. Propargylic Amines as Anticancer Agents

Propargyl bromide reacts with amino alcohols to form $HOCH_2CH_2\overset{\displaystyle R}{\overset{|}{N}}CH_2C{\equiv}$ CH. Amino alcohols also react with 1,4-dichloro-2-butyne to form the

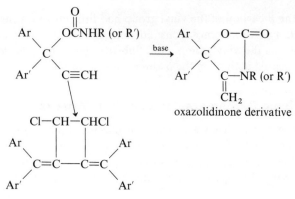

corresponding diols which can be converted to dichlorides. Of the many compounds tested,[16] the order of activity against Yoshida sarcoma was (1) > (2) > (3):

(1) $ClCH_2CH_2NR—CH_2C\equiv CCH_2NR—CH_2CH_2Cl\cdot 2HCl$
(2) $ClCH_2CH_2NR—CH_2C\equiv CH$
(3) $HOCH_2CH_2NR—CH_2C\equiv CCH_2NR—CH_2CH_2OH$

2.5. Propargylic Amines as Hypotensives

Cyclic hindered secondary and tertiary amines are less active hypotensives than their open-chain analogs.[17] The acetylenic amines are frequently more active than the ethylenic and saturated analogs (Table 8-3).

Acetylenic groups decrease the basicity of amines[18,19] (Table 8-4). Propargylanilines are much less basic than propyl- or allylanilines.[20] Is there a correlation between basicity of amines and their hypotensive activity? This has apparently not been investigated, at least with acetylenic amines.

TABLE 8-3
Hypotensive Activity of Tertiary Amines—Effect of Structure[17]

Amine·HCl	Oral dose (mg/kg)	% Blood Pressure Change (mean)	Side Effects
t-BuN—C$+$C≡CH (with Me Me Me groups)	1	−4.5	None
	5	−11.5	
	20	−15.7	
$+$CH=CH$_2$	5	−6	None
	20	−15	Moderate to severe
$+$CH$_2$CH$_3$	1	−7	Moderate
	5	−12	
	20	−11	

TABLE 8-4
The Effect of the Acetylenic Group on the Basicity of Amines

$$HC{\equiv}CCNH{-}\underset{\underset{Me}{|}}{\overset{\overset{Me}{|}}{C}}{-}R$$

$$Me_2\underset{\underset{}{}}{\overset{\overset{NH(t\text{-}Bu)}{|}}{C}}{-}R$$

R	pK$_a$ in Water	R	pK$_a$ in Dimethylformamide
$-C{\equiv}CH$	6.45	$-C{\equiv}CH$	8.2
$-CH{=}CH_2$	8.20	$-CH{=}CH_2$	10.0
$-CH_2CH_3$	9.0	$-CH_2CH_3$	10.6

1-Bromopropargylic amines have about the same potency as the unbrominated analogs in hypertensive rats.[21] Replacing acetylenic hydrogen by Br thus has no effect. The most potent of the many compounds tested[21] is

$$BrC{\equiv}C{-}\underset{\underset{Me}{|}}{\overset{\overset{NH(t\text{-}Bu)}{|}}{C}}Me{\cdot}HCl$$

Biel and DiPierro[22] studied the effect of the acetylenic group in some bis-(ammonium)alkane hypotensives. Methonium hypotensives are poorly absorbed from the gastrointestinal tract, so replacement of ethyl by an acetylenic group should improve the absorption. The distance between the two quaternary nitrogens is critical: The rigid four-carbon rod of the acetylenic group and its two flanking methylene groups allow more precise spacing.

Three kinds of known hypotensives and their acetylenic homologs are:

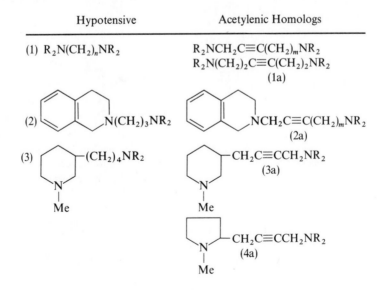

where $n = 4, 5, 6$; $m = 1, 2, 3$. All amines are used as RX salts. The most effective of the 45 compounds tested was (1a), $Et_2NCH_2C{\equiv}CCH_2CH_2NEt_2{\cdot}MeBr$. The dimethiodide of 1,6-bis(morpholino)-2,4-hexadiyne showed no hypotensive effect, but the corresponding 2-hexyne compound was fairly active. The acetylenic bis-(onium) hypotensives are usually better than their olefinic or saturated counterparts. They are more potent, last longer and are absorbed more easily from the gastrointestinal tract. Hydration of the triple bond to a ketone decreases the activity.

The general reaction used to synthesize the amines is:

$$BrCH_2C{\equiv}CH + HNR_2 \longrightarrow R_2NCH_2C{\equiv}CH \xrightarrow[\text{toluene, reflux}]{\text{NaNH}_2,}$$

$$R_2NCH_2C{\equiv}CNa \xrightarrow{\text{Cl(Y)NR}'_2} R_2NCH_2C{\equiv}C(Y)NR'_2$$

When 3-chloro-N-methylpiperidine reacts with sodium t-aminomethyl-acetylide, ring contraction gives a pyrrolidine derivative (4a) instead of a piperidine.

2.6. Oral Contraceptives

Sales of oral contraceptives in the United States average around 100 million dollars annually.[23] All the drugs sold for this use are mixtures of two components, an estrogen and a progestin. All of them contain at least one ethynyl steroid or a derivative (hydration of the triple bond to a ketone). Ethynylestradiol is the estrogen in many preparations. Ethynylpregnones are commonly used as progestins (see reference 24 for the chemistry of steroids).

Estrogens

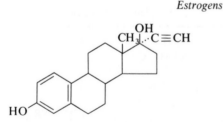

17α-ethynylestradiol (15–20 times as active as estradiol, orally)[25]

Variations Not Now Used (groups attached to the carbons numbered in the above formula)

	1	2	3	4	5	6
(1)	OH	C≡CH	—	C=C	=O	(reference 26)
(2)	OH	C≡CH	Et	C=C	=O	
(3)	OH	C≡CH	Me	—	OH	Me (reference 27)

Progestins

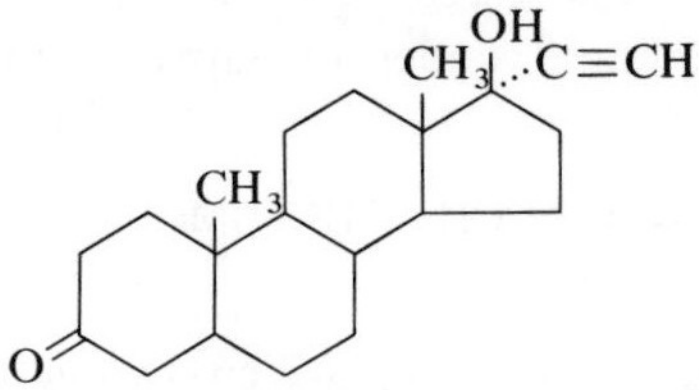

17-hydroxy-19-nor-17α-pregn-5(10)-en-20-yn-3-one

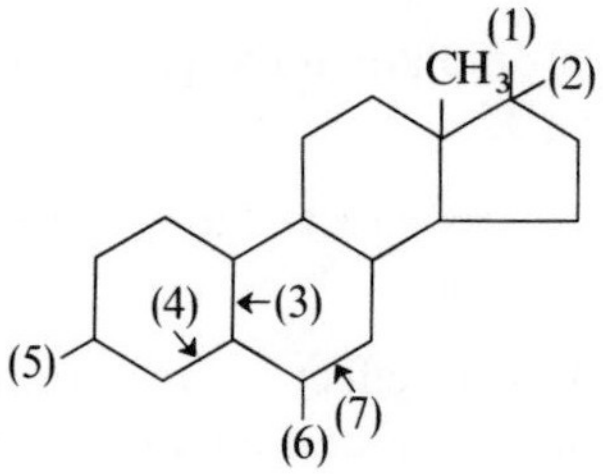

Variations Now Used
(groups attached to the positions as numbered)

	1	2	3	4	5	6	7
(1)	OAc	$C{\equiv}CH$	C—C	C=C	OAc		
(2)	OH	$C{\equiv}CH$	C—C	C=C	=O		
(3)	OAc	$C{\equiv}CH$	C—C	C=C	=O		
(4)	OAc	$C(=O)CH_3$	C—C	C=C	=O	Me	
(5)	OH	$C{\equiv}CCH_3$	C—C	C=C	=O	Me	
(6)	OAc	$C(=O)CH_3$	C—C	C=C	=O	Cl	C=C

2.7. Ethynyl Derivatives of Acylpromazines as Drugs

2-Acylpromazines in dimethylformamide react with sodium acetylide (from acetylene and $NaNH_2$ in DMF) to form:[28]

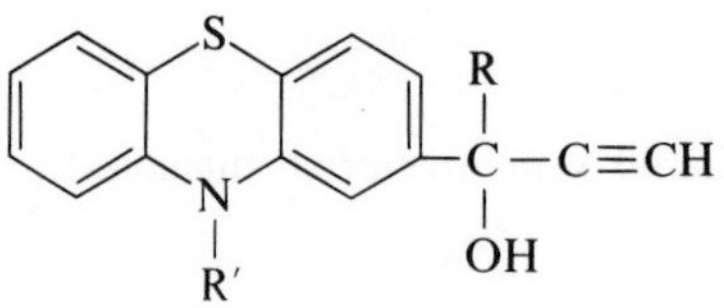

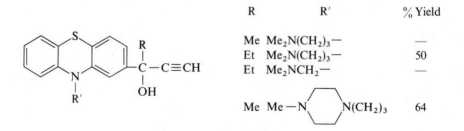

R	R′	% Yield
Me	$Me_2N(CH_2)_3$—	—
Et	$Me_2N(CH_2)_3$—	50
Et	Me_2NCH_2—	—
Me	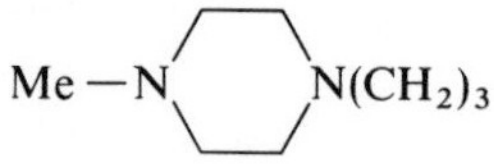	64

The ethynyl products increased hexabarbitol narcosis, induced catatonic depression and loss of equilibrium in the mouse, and decreased or reversed the effects of adrenaline or noradrenaline in the dog.

2.8. Polyacetylenic Antibiotics

Methyl propiolate undergoes Straus coupling[29] under oxidative coupling conditions:[30]

$$2HC{\equiv}CCO_2Me \xrightarrow[\text{slightly acidic}]{Cu_2Cl_2-NH_4Cl} MeO_2CC{\equiv}CCH{=}CHCO_2Me$$
$$(36\%)$$

Oxygen has no effect on the coupling reaction. *trans*-Pent-2-en-4-ynoic acid couples normally, and cross-couples normally with methyl propiolate to form low yields of $HO_2C{\equiv}CC{\equiv}CCH{=}CHCO_2H$ (after hydrolysis). The mono-amide of this acid is the antibiotic diatetryne I.[31] Methyl propiolate and penta-2,4-diyn-1-ol couple to form 5% yield of the alcohol-ester, which with ammonia

gives the antibiotic agrocybin, $H_2N\overset{\overset{\displaystyle O}{\|}}{C}C{\equiv}CC{\equiv}CCH{=}CHCH_2OH$.

2.9. Other Uses of Acetylenic Compounds in Drugs

The physiological effects of other acetylenic compounds are listed in the following summary:

Convulsants

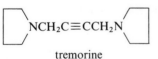

Me(C≡C)₃—CH=CH—

ichthyothereol and its acetate

From *Ichthyothere terminalis*, family Compositae, this is a fish poison and convulsant in mammals.[32]

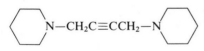

tremorine

Induces Parkinsons' syndrome.[7]

Anticonvulsants

N—CH₂C≡CCH₂—N

Muscle relaxant; tremorine antagonist.[8]

Local anesthetics

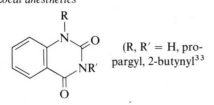

(R, R′ = H, propargyl, 2-butynyl[33]

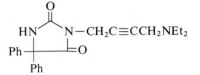

Strong, safe.[34]

Analgesics

N-Propargyloxy-β-(4-phenyl-1,2,5,6-
tetrahydropyridino) propionamide
(reference 35)

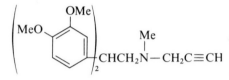

As analgetic as aspirin, also is a CNS
depressant, ganglionic blocker.[36]

MAO Inhibitor

$$\underset{\text{Me}}{\text{PhCH}_2\text{CH}}-\underset{\text{Me}}{\text{NCH}_2\text{C}\equiv\text{CH}}$$

N,α-dimethyl-N-(2-propynyl)phenethyl-
amine

Combines amphetamine effect with pargy-
lin's MAO effect. Lowers blood pressure,
does not increase motility.[37]

Hypotensives

$$\underset{\text{Me}}{\text{PhCH}_2\text{NCH}_2\text{C}\equiv\text{CH}}$$

pargyline

Comparable to guanethidine and methyl-
dopa. Also is an antidepressant.[38]

5-Phenyl-3-methyl-4-pentyn-3-ol-2-one
oxime

Fast, strong action, lasts several hours.[39]

$$\underset{\text{NR}_3\text{R}_4}{\overset{\text{R}_2}{\text{RR}_1\text{CHC}}}-\text{C}\equiv\text{CR}_5 \text{ (reference 40)}$$

$$\underset{\text{R} \quad \text{R}'}{\overset{\text{OH}}{\text{PhC}\equiv\text{CC}}}-\text{C}=\text{NOH} \text{ (reference 41)}$$

$$\underset{}{\overset{\text{OH O}}{\text{Ph}_2\text{C}-\text{COCH}_2\text{C}\equiv\text{CCH}_2\text{NR}_2\cdot\text{HCl}}}$$

Antispasmodics.[42]

Anticholinogenic

$$\underset{\text{R(or Ar)}}{\overset{\text{OH}}{\text{R(or Ar)C}}}-\text{C}\equiv\text{CCH}_2\text{NR}'_2$$

Best is R$'_2$ is pyrrolidino. Ethers have poor
lethal dose: oxotremorine dose ratio.[43]

Ganglionic Blocking Agents

Several prepared starting with propargylic amines:

$$RR'C(NHR'')-C\equiv CH \xrightarrow{\text{hydration}}$$

$$\underset{\text{ketone}}{} \xrightarrow{\text{reduction}} RR'\overset{\overset{NHR''}{|}}{C}-\overset{\overset{H}{|}}{\underset{\underset{OH}{|}}{C}}Me \quad \text{(references 44–46)}$$

CNS Stimulants

Amphetamine

$$PhCH_2\overset{\overset{NH_2}{|}}{C}HC\equiv CH$$

$$PhCH_2\overset{\overset{Me}{|}}{N}CH_2C\equiv CH \text{ (pargyline)}$$

activity ↓

Both of the acetylenes increase the CNS effect of amphetamine—pargyline more strongly.[47]

$$Ph\overset{\overset{Ph}{|}}{C}HCH_2C\equiv CCH_2NEt_2\cdot HCl$$

(reference 48)

Antibacterials

$$Ph\overset{\overset{O}{||}}{C}C\equiv CC\equiv C\overset{\overset{OH}{|}}{C}CMe_2,$$

$$PhCH_2C\equiv CC\equiv CBr,$$

$$Ph\overset{\overset{O}{||}}{C}C\equiv CC\equiv CEt \text{ (reference 49)}$$

Fungicides

PhCH$_2$C≡CC≡CMe
     agropyrene or capillen

Intense fungicidal action, too toxic for therapeutic use.[50]

11-Iodo-10-undecynoic acid

Quickly absorbed through the skin.[51]

Fungistats

Furans containing the $-\overset{\overset{O}{||}}{C}C\equiv CH$ group

Have marked effect on dermatophytes.[52]

Antibiotics

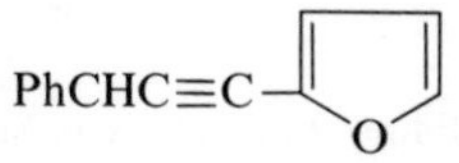

PhCHC≡C—

Carlina oxide

Naturally occurring, too toxic for use with animals.[50]

Mycomycin[53]

HC≡CC≡CCH=C=

OH
|
CHCHCH$_2$CH$_2$CO$_2$H   Occur in fungi as glycosides.[50]
(nemotinic acid and its lactone, nemotin)

Me(C≡C)$_2$CH=C=

OH
|
CHCHCH$_2$CH$_2$CO$_2$H   Occur in fungi as glycosides.[50]
(odyssic acid, and its lactone, odyssin)

HO$_2$CCH=CHC≡CC≡CCN   Hydrolysis to amide destroys antibiotic
         diatretyne II   activity.[50]

3. INTRODUCTION OF ACETYLENIC GROUPS INTO MOLECULES TO BE USED AS DRUGS

The techniques used to introduce acetylenic groups into molecules to be used as drugs generally fall into three classes: (1) ethynylation and alkynylation, (2) dehydrohalogenation and (3) "propargylation," the introduction of propargyl or substituted propargyl groups.

Ethynylation, alkynylation and elimination reactions have been discussed in Chapters 3 and 5.

3.1. Ethynylation and Alkynylation

Another example of ethynylation and alkynylation as a method of introducing acetylenes is given here. Bishop[54] combined the known sedative groupings— trichloromethyl, *t*-acetylenic carbinol and carbamate—in single molecules:

$$O$$
$$\|$$

Cl$_3$CCRR'OH and Cl$_3$CCRR'OCNH$_2$, where one of the R groups is an acetylenic group. He prepared the acetylenic carbinols by reacting trichloromethylcarbonyl compounds with sodium acetylide or with acetylenic or propargylic Grignard reagents. For the reaction of chloral with acetylene, sodium acetylide in ether-tetrahydrofuran gave 52% yield, while the Grignard reagent in tetrahydrofuran gave only 12% yield. The various preparations are summarized in Table 8-5. Several of the products showed strong hypnotic activity in rodents. Succinate esters of the carbinols retained their hypnotic action, but glycinates, acetates and allophanates were inactive. Test data were not reported, and no mention of the effect of carbamate is included in the report.[54]

TABLE 8-5
1,1,1-Trichloromethyl Alcohols, Cl₃C·CRR'·OH

R	R'	Method[a]	% Yield	m.p. (°C) or b.p. (°C, @ mm Hg)
H—	HC≡C—	G	53	77–78, @ 18
		E	12	
H—	CH₂=CH—		22	68–69, @ 12
H—	Et—	B	67	66.5–67, @ 13
Me—	HC≡C—	E	14	73–75, @ 17
H—	HC≡CCH₂—	C	63	49–50
		F	62	
H—	MeC≡C—	G	28	55–57
		E	10	
H—	CH₂=CHCH₂—	D	58	78, @ 15
H—	n-Pr—	B	69	88–89, @ 20
Me—	HC≡CCH₂—	C	12	97–99, @ 15
		F	83	
Et—	CH₂=CH—	A	82	90–91, @ 16
H—	Me₂C=CH—		73	76–77
Me—	CH₂=CHCH₂—	D	16	87–88, @ 13
Et—	Et—	B	71	90–93, @ 16
Me—	n-Pr—	B	82	88, @ 13
H—	Me₂CHCH₂—	B	36	88, @ 10
H—	n-Bu—	B	57	87.5–88, @ 10
n-Pr—	HC≡C—	E	35	48–49, @ 0.5
Et—	HC≡CCH₂—	C	37	64–64.5, @ 0.9
Et—	CH₂=CHCH₂—	A	80	64, @ 1.0
n-Pr—	CH₂=CH—	A	64	53, @ 0.7
n-Pr—	Et—	B	57	66–66.5, @ 1.3
n-Pr—	HC≡CCH₂—	C	81	64, @ 0.5
n-Pr—	CH₂=CHCH₂—	D	24	60–61, @ 0.5
n-Pr—	n-Pr—	B	60	64–66, @ 0.5

[a] A = Lindlar semihydrogenation of the acetylenic compound.
 B = Full hydrogenation over PtO₂.
 C = Propargyl Grignard reagent.
 D = Allyl Grignard reagent.
 E = Acetylene Grignard reagent.
 F = Propargyl aluminum Grignard reagent.
 G = Sodium acetylide or alkynylide in ether-tetrahydrofuran.

3.2. "Propargylation"

Since introduction of triple bonds as propargylic groups is frequently involved in synthesis, a summary of some reactions of propargylic compounds is given to furnish additional leads into the literature. The propargylic halides are common intermediates. Some, such as propargyl bromide, are commercially available. Others must be prepared by the reaction of carbinols with hydrogen halides.

3.2.1. PROPARGYL BROMIDE

The bromine atom is active in many nucleophilic displacement reactions:

Reference

$HC{\equiv}CCH_2Br$ + $P(OEt)_3$ $\longrightarrow$ $(EtO)_2PCH_2C{\equiv}CH$ 55

    + PMH (M = S, O, Se) $\longrightarrow$ $PhMCH_2C{\equiv}CH$ 56

    + anilines, acetanilides $\longrightarrow$ N-propargyl derivatives

                     (20–60%)   57

    + RNH_2 $\longrightarrow$ $HC{\equiv}CCH_2NHR$

                     (70–95%)   22

    + barbituric acids $\longrightarrow$ N,N'-bis(propargyl)

                     derivatives   58

    + succinimide + $EtNH_2$ +

      HCHO $\longrightarrow$ $NCH_2C{\equiv}CCH_2NEt_2$ 59

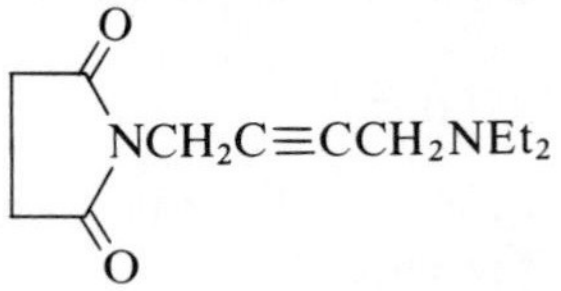

(high specificity, low toxicity, for Parkinson's disease)

3.2.2. INTRODUCTION OF PROPARGYLIDENE GROUPS

$(\diagdown C{=}CHC{\equiv}CH)$:

Two methods can be used: (1) the Wittig reaction and (2) the Reformatsky reaction, which is better:[60]

(1) Wittig reaction:

$$Ph_3P + HBr + HC{\equiv}CCH_2Br \xrightarrow{\text{dioxane}}$$

propargyltriphenylphosphonium bromide $\xrightarrow[\text{RCHO}]{\text{MeCN, excess NH}_3,}$

cis- and trans-$RCH{=}CHC{\equiv}CH$ + Ph_3PO

(2) Reformatsky reaction:

$$RR'C{=}O + BrCH_2C{\equiv}CH \xrightarrow[\text{Al}]{\text{Zn or}} RR'\overset{\text{OH}}{\underset{|}{C}}CH_2C{\equiv}CH \xrightarrow{PBr_3} RR'\overset{\text{Br}}{\underset{|}{C}}CH_2C{\equiv}CH \xrightarrow{-HBr}$$

$RR'C{=}CHC{\equiv}CH$

3.3. Tertiary Propargylic Halides

3.3.1. PREPARATION

These compounds, $HC\equiv C\underset{\underset{R}{|}}{\overset{\overset{R}{|}}{C}}X$, are not commercially available, but can easily be
made. Hennion[61] obtained 70–75% yields of 1-chloro-1-ethynylcyclohexane
from ethynylcyclohexanol and concentrated HCl with cuprous chloride catalyst.
Attempts to use thionyl chloride instead of HCl gave at least five products,
including the 1-allenyl chloride and some dehydration products. For noncyclic
tertiary acetylenic carbinols, $RR'C(OH)C\equiv CH$, good yields are possible with
the HCl-$CaCl_2$ reaction system if neither R nor R' is larger than ethyl. If the R
groups are larger than ethyl, the products are chloroallenes and chlorobut-
adienes. Hennion[62] added copper bronze (or Cu_2Cl_2) catalyst to the HCl-$CaCl_2$
system and obtained 80% yields of tertiary propargylic chlorides. The size of the
R groups had little effect when the catalyst was present.

3.3.2. REACTIONS

Formation of Ethers: The *t*-propargylic chlorides react with ethanol and methanol in the presence of strong bases to form ethers in good yield.[63] The reactions
are second order,[64] and no allenyl ethers form. The *t*-propargylic ethers have
normally reactive ethynyl groups; they alkylate easily with sodamide and alkyl
halides in ammonia, and hydrate[65] to the 2-ketoethers. The Mannich reaction
gives poor yields.

Formation of Amines: Propargylic chlorides react at room temperature with
amines which are strong bases and good nucleophiles to give 50–73% yields of
t–propargylic amines. Cuprous chloride is a good catalyst.[66] The function of the
catalyst may be to accelerate the formation of the tertiary carbonium ion via the
cuprous derivative of the propargylic chloride.

Reactions of t-Propargylic Amines: Grignard reagents form slowly.[67]
Grignards or lithium derivatives react with ketones to form propargylic amino-
carbinols. Sodium derivatives react with alkyl bromides to give alkynylamines,
$RR'\underset{\underset{}{|}}{\overset{\overset{NR''_2}{|}}{C}}{-}C\equiv CR'''$. In contrast to the propargylic ethers, the amines enter the
Mannich reaction to form 1,4-diamines in excellent yield. Oxidative coupling is
easy. The best coupling system is cuprous chloride-ammonium chloride at 50°
and slight oxygen pressure. The amines cross-couple with acetylenic carbinols to
give dipropargylic amino alcohols. The triple bond hydrates normally to form
α-amino ketones. Sodium derivatives react with carbon dioxide to give the
expected aminopropargylic carboxylic acids ($RR'\underset{\underset{}{|}}{\overset{\overset{NR''_2}{|}}{C}}{-}C\equiv CCO_2H$).

3.4. Reactions of *t*-Acetylenic Carbinols

Carboxylic acids esterify *t*-acetylenic carbinols easily in the presence of an arylsulfonyl chloride and pyridine.[68] The hydroxyl group reacts with potassium amide in ammonia to form the potassium alkoxide, which reacts easily with alkyl halides to give 50–80% yields of ethers.[69] Sodium alkoxides of tertiary ethynylvinylcarbinols react with alkysulfonyl chlorides to form sulfonate esters in 50% yield.[70] The hydroxyl group reacts with isocyanates to form urethanes, some of which are claimed to be potential pharmaceuticals:[71]

3.5. Acetylenic α,β-Epoxides as Intermediates

α-Chloroketones react with acetylene to give α-chloro-*t*-acetylenic carbinols. Treatment with alkali gives the α,β-epoxide. The epoxides react with nucleophilic reagents to give α-substituted *t*-acetylenic carbinols:[72]

$$RCH{-}\underset{\underset{O}{\diagdown\diagup}}{C}{-}C{\equiv}CR' + Nuc^-H^+ \longrightarrow RCH{-}\overset{Nuc}{\overset{|}{C}}(R')(OH)C{\equiv}CR''$$

References

1. Bock, H., Dissertation, University of Breslau, 1930.
2. Margolin, S., *et al.*, *Science*, **114**, 384 (1951).
3. Reisch, J., and Walker, H., *Deutsche Apotheker Z.*, **103**, 1139 (1964); *Chem. Abstr.*, **60**, (1964).
4. Leeds, M. W., *et al.*, *Ind. Eng. Chem.*, *Prod. Res. Dev.*, **4**, 236 (1965).
5. Langecker, H., Schumann, H. J., and Junkmann, K., *Naunyn-Schmiedebergs Arch. Exptl. Pathol. Pharmacol.*, **219**, 130 (1953); *Chem. Abstr.*, **47**, 9498 (1953).
6. Keil, W., Muchaweck, R., and Rademacher, E., *Arzneimittel-Forsch.*, **4**, 477 (1954); *Chem. Abstr.*, **49**, 517 (1955).
7. Ehrhart, G., *Med. Chem.*, **3**, 366 (1936).
8. Jenden, D. J., and Cho, A. K., *Biochem. Pharmacol.*, **12**(Suppl), 38 (1963).
9. Jacob, J., *et al.*, *Compt. Rend.*, **235**, 263 (1959).
10. Suzuki, S., *et al.*, *J. Antibiotics (Tokyo)*, Ser A., **11**, 81 (1958).
11. Ried, W., Schmidt, H.-J., and Urschel, A., *Chem. Ber.*, **91**, 2472 (1958).
12. Prost, M., Urbain, M., and Charlier, R., *Helv. Chim. Acta*, **49**, 2370 (1966).
13. Lauger, P., Prost, M., and Charlier, R., *Halv. Chim. Acta*, **42**, 2379 (1959).
14. McLarmore, W. M., *et al.*, *J. Org. Chem.*, **19**, 570 (1954).
15. Easton, N. R., *et al.*, *J. Med. Chem.*, **10**, 40 (1967).
16. Fujiki, S., *Nippon Kagaku Zasshi*, **87**, 189 (1966); *Chem. Abstr.*, **65**, 15215 (1966).
17. Easton, N. R., *et al.*, *J. Med. Chem.*, **9**, 465 (1966).

18. Hennion, G. F., and DiGiovanna, C. V., *J. Org. Chem.*, **30**, 2645 (1965).
19. Hennion, G. F., and Hanzel, R. S., *J. Am. Chem. Soc.*, **82**, 4908 (1960).
20. Wolff, V., and Ramin, D., *Ann. Chem.*, **610**, 67 (1957).
21. Ryan, C. W., *et al.*, *J. Med. Pharm. Chem.*, **5**, 780 (1962); *Chem. Abstr.*, **57**, 3595 (1962).
22. Biel, J. H., and DiPierro, F., *J. Am. Chem. Soc.*, **80**, 4609, 4614 (1958).
23. *Chem. Eng. News*, 26 (Apr. 25, 1966).
24. Fieser, L. F., and Fieser, M., "Steroids," New York, Reinhold Publishing Corp., 1954.
25. Wilson, C. O., and Gisvold, O., "Textbook of Organic Medicinal and Pharmaceutical Chemistry," Sixth ed., p642, Philadelphia, Lippincott, 1962.
26. Buzby, C. C., Jr., *et al.*, *J. Med. Chem.*, **9**, 338 (1966).
27. Dorfman, R. I., Fajkos, J., and Joska, J., *Steroids*, **3**, 675 (1964).
28. Schmitt, J., *et al.*, *Bull. Soc. Chim. France*, 1140 (1961).
29. Straus, F., *Ann. Chem.*, **342**, 190 (1905).
30. Skattebøl, L., *Acta Chem. Scand.*, **13**, 198 (1959).
31. Ashworth, P. J., *et al.*, *J. Chem. Soc.*, 950, 1054 (1958).
32. Durham, L. J., *et al.*, *J. Am. Chem. Soc.*, **87**, 5237 (1965).
33. Danielsson, B., and Skoglund, E., *Acta Pharm. Suecica*, **2**, 167 (1965); *Chem. Abstr.*, **63**, 5643 (1965).
34. Danielsson, B., *et al.*, *Acta Pharm. Suecica*, **2**, 155 (1965); *Chem. Abstr.*, **63**, 5630 (1965).
35. Biel, J. H., and Hopps, H. B. (to Aldrich Chem. Co.), U.S. Patent 3,221,019 (Nov. 30, 1965); *Chem. Abstr.*, **64**, 5053 (1966).
36. Cho, A. K., and Haslett, W. L., *Life Sciences*, **4**, 2411 (1965).
37. Knoll, J., *et al.*, *Arch. Intern. Pharmacodyn.*, **155**, 154 (1965).
38. Oates, J. A., *et al.*, *New Eng. J. Med.*, **273**, 729 (1965).
39. Cascio, G., *et al.*, *Farmaco* (*Pavia*). *Ed. Sci.*, **20**, 336 (1965); *Chem. Abstr.*, **63**, 7524 (1965).
40. Beechan Group, Ltd., Netherlands Appl. 6,511,503 (Mar. 4, 1966); *Chem. Abstr.*, **65**, 3745 (1966).
41. Cascio, G., *et al.*, *Farmaco* (*Pavia*), *Ed. Sci.*, **20**, 336 (1965).
42. Dahlbom, R., Hannson, B., and Mollberg, R., *Acta Chem. Scand.*, **17**, 2354 (1963); *Chem. Abstr.*, **60**, 9191 (1964).
43. Dahlbom, R., *et al.*, *Acta. Pharm. Suecica*, **1**, 237 (1964); *Chem. Abstr.*, **63**, 5595 (1965); *Acta Pharm. Suecica*, **3**, 187 (1966); *Chem. Abstr.*, **65**, 15313 (1966).
44. Easton, N. R., *et al.*, *J. Org. Chem.*, **26**, 3772 (1961).
45. Easton, N. R., and Hennion, G. F., U.S. Patent 3,168,567 (Feb. 2, 1965); *Chem. Abstr.*, **62**, 10335 (1965).
46. Spinks, H., and Young, E. H. P., *Nature*, **181**, 1397 (1958).
47. Burger, A., and Zimmerman, S. E., *J. Med. Chem.*, **9**, 469 (1966).
48. Golikov, S. N., Razumova, M. A., and Selivanova, A. T., *Farmakol. i Toksikol.*, **28**, 20 (1965).
49. Soloviev, V. N., *et al.*, *Antibiotiki*, **10**, 156 (1965).
50. Jones, E. R. H., *Proc. Chem. Soc.*, 199 (1960).
51. Asami, Y., *et al.*, *Rika Gaku Kenkyusho Hokoku*, **41**, 259 (1965); *Chem. Abstr.*, **65**, 11202 (1966).
52. Hillers, S., *et al.*, *Latvijas PSR Zinatnu Akad. Vestis*, 63 (1966); *Chem. Abstr.*, **65**, 1322 (1966).
53. Celmer, W. D., and Solomans, I. A., *J. Am. Chem. Soc.*, **74**, 1870, 2245, 3838 (1952); *ibid.*, **75**, 1372, 3430 (1953).

54. Bishop, D. C., Meacock, S. C. R., and Williamson, W. R. N., *J. Chem. Soc. (C)*, 670 (1966).
55. Kaufman, S. (to Monsanto Chem. Co.), U.S. Patent 2,843,617 (July 15, 1958); *Chem. Abstr.*, **53**, 2090 (1959).
56. Pourcelot, P., *Compt. Rend.*, **260**, 2847 (1965).
57. Wolff, V., *Ann. Chem.*, **578**, 83 (1952).
58. Derzhinskii, A. R., Mavrov, M. V., and Kucherov, V. F., *Izv. Akad. Nauk SSSR, Ser. Khim.*, 1237 (1965); *Chem. Abstr.*, **63**, 14691 (1965).
59. Aktiebolog Astra Apotek. Kem. Fab., Netherlands Appl. 6,508,385 (Jan. 4, 1966); *Chem. Abstr.*, **65**, 3757 (1966).
60. Eiter, K., and Oediger, H., *Ann. Chem.*, **682**, 62 (1965).
61. Hennion, G. F., and Lynch, C. A., Jr., *J. Org. Chem.*, **25**, 1330 (1960).
62. Hennion, G. F., and Boisselle, A. P., *J. Org. Chem.*, **26**, 725 (1961).
63. *Ibid.*, **26**, 2677 (1961).
64. Hennion, G. F., and Maloney, D. E., *J. Am. Chem. Soc.*, **73**, 4735 (1951).
65. Hennion, G. F., and Watson, E. J., *J. Org. Chem.*, **23**, 656 (1958).
66. Hennion, G. F., and Hanzel, R. S., *J. Am. Chem. Soc.*, **82**, 4908 (1960).
67. Hennion, G. F., and Perrino, A. C., *J. Org. Chem.*, **26**, 1073 (1961).
68. Klosa, J., *Angew. Chem.*, **69**, 135 (1957).
69. d'Engenieres, M. D., Miocque, M., and Gautier, J.-A., *Bull. Soc. Chim. France*, 2471 (1964).
70. Azatyan, V. D., Vasilyan, M. V., and Airapetyan, L. N., *Izv. Akad. Nauk Arm. SSR, Khim. Nauki*, **18**, 535 (1965); *Chem. Abstr.*, **64**, 9582 (1966).
71. Armasescu, L., *Farmacia (Bucharest)*, **14**, 85 (1966); *Chem. Abstr.*, **65**, 3777 (1966).
72. Perveev, F. Ya., Golodova, K. G., and Koshmina, N. V., *Vestn. Leningr. Univ., Ser. Fiz. i Khim.*, **20**, 143 (1965); *Chem. Abstr.*, **64**, 9598 (1966).

INDEX